INTERNATIONAL SERIES OF MONOGRAPHS ON

NUCLEAR ENERGY

GENERAL EDITOR: J. V. DUNWORTH

DIVISION XII · CHEMISTRY

Volume 1

SPECTROSCOPY AND PHOTOCHEMISTRY OF URANYL COMPOUNDS

Spectroscopy and Photochemistry of Uranyl Compounds

by

EUGENE RABINOWITCH

Department of Botany
University of Illinois

AND

R. LINN BELFORD

Department of Chemistry
University of Illinois

PERGAMON PRESS

OXFORD · LONDON · EDINBURGH · NEW YORK

PARIS · FRANKFURT

1964

PERGAMON PRESS LTD.
Headington Hill Hall, Oxford
4 and 5 Fitzroy Square, London W.1

PERGAMON PRESS (SCOTLAND) LTD.
2 and 3 Teviot Place, Edinburgh 1

PERGAMON PRESS INC.
122 East 55th Street, New York 22, N.Y.

GAUTHIER-VILLARS ED.
55 Quai des Grands-Augustins, Paris 6

PERGAMON PRESS G.m.b.H.
Kaiserstrasse 75, Frankfurt am Main

Distributed in the Western Hemisphere by
THE MACMILLAN COMPANY · NEW YORK
pursuant to a special arrangement with
Pergamon Press Incorporated

Library of Congress Catalog Card Number 63-10059

Set in 10 on 12 pt. Times New Roman
and printed in Great Britain by
THE KYNOCH PRESS · BIRMINGHAM

CONTENTS

Contents

vii

PREFACE

DURING the wartime development of the atom bomb in the Manhattan Project, the need arose to systematize our knowledge of the chemistry of uranium. When the project ended in 1945, a compendium of uranium chemistry, prepared by the Information Division of the Project, was about to be converted into a handbook. The first volume of this handbook, by J. J. Katz and E. Rabinowitch, appeared in 1951 as volume 5 in Division VIII of the Nuclear Energy Series, published by McGraw-Hill* and Company for the Atomic Energy Commission. This series, intended to cover all scientific research of the Manhattan Project laboratories, was never completed. The published volume of the chemistry of uranium contained a critical survey of work concerning the element uranium and its binary compounds. A second volume was intended to cover oxygen-containing uranium salts and their solutions, in particular the uranyl compounds. A part of this volume, prepared by E. Rabinowitch and dealing with spectroscopy, fluorescence and photochemistry of uranyl compounds, was circulated in the form of four AEC reports.† Later, the Pergamon Press suggested its publication as a monograph. Professor Belford of the University of Illinois agreed to bring the text up to date by including research carried out in the fifteen years since the writing of the original text. He also added a chapter on the electronic structure of the uranyl ion, including his own work in this field.

The authors believe that the volume will satisfy a real need of researchers in the chemistry and physics of the actinide elements. The uranyl ion is probably the best-known chemical entity in the actinide series. It has been studied for over a century and a half. The fluorescence and photochemical sensitivity of uranyl compounds has attracted early attention; hundreds of research papers exist in this field. Yet many basic experimental questions remain unsettled,

* Reprinted by Dover Publications, New York.

† ANL 5122, 5173, 5291 and 5202.

and a theory of the uranyl ion explaining its spectroscopic behaviour is only rudimentary.

Examination of the literature suggests that many now active researchers had not made sufficient use of previously reported work. This shortcoming is inevitable in the time when research is rapidly expanding; it can be somewhat alleviated by a comprehensive guide to past work. Our aim was to provide such a guide. We have endeavored to present the material in such a manner that the book should be continually useful for many years, providing it is kept up to date by the reader by his own literature scanning. To this end, the presentation within each subchapter is largely chronological; the work of each researcher is clearly attributed, and conclusions are frankly labeled as his own. This presentation may make for choppy reading, but it seemed preferable to a "unified" treatment that would convey the false impression of a well-understood and neatly ordered field, and would soon become obsolete.

Undoubtedly there is some pertinent material in the literature which we have not cited. For example, there are many references to absorption spectra of uranyl complexes in the literature on analytical chemistry, and many reports exist dealing with uranyl oxalate actinometry, to which we have not referred. Further, coverage from 1960 to date is sparse.

This book owes much to the monograph "Spectroscopic Properties of Uranium Compounds" by G. H. Dieke and A. B. F. Duncan* which summarized the studies carried out by these researchers at the Johns Hopkins University under the Manhattan Project program during the war.

E. I. RABINOWITCH
R. L. BELFORD

* See Bibliography

CHAPTER 1

SPECTROSCOPY OF URANYL SALTS IN THE SOLID STATE

1. Introduction. Qualitative Interpretation of the Uranyl Spectrum

THE divalent uranyl ion, UO_2^{++}, can be considered as an intermediate product of hydrolysis of the ion $U^{+6}+4OH^- \rightarrow UO_2^{++} +2H_2O$; an intermediate, however, that possesses a remarkably wide range of stability. The absorption and fluorescence bands of most solid or dissolved uranyl salts in the visible and near-ultraviolet belong to this ion, and are therefore similar in their general pattern, except for minor changes in position, width, and intensity of the individual bands caused by the electrical fields of the surrounding anions (in crystals or ionic complexes), or water dipoles (in crystal hydrates or aqueous solutions).

In addition to the absorption and emission bands due to electronic excitation within the uranyl ion, uranyl compounds could have also spectral bands due to excitation of the associated anions (or molecules), or to the transfer of electrons from these anions or molecules to the uranyl ions ("electron affinity," or—more correctly—"electron transfer" spectra). With the exception of salts of colored anions (such as chromate), the electronic bands of the last-named types lie, however, at much shorter waves than the absorption bands due to excitation of low-lying electronic levels within the uranyl ion itself.

In absorption, most solid or dissolved uranyl salts show a regular sequence of broad bands (or rather, band groups, as revealed by their resolution into narrow bands or "lines" at low temperatures) covering the blue, violet, and near-ultraviolet region; in fluorescence, a similar sequence extends from the blue into the green and yellow part of the spectrum. To interpret the spectra in detail demands structural information about the individual salts.

1

1.1. *Structure of Uranyl Crystals*

X-ray diffraction studies have yielded some information regarding the geometry of uranyl salts. No crystal data have yet shown a bent structure for the ion $(O—U—O)^{++}$ [Zachariasen (1954c)]. Instead,

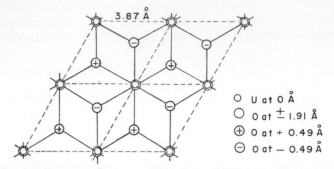

$\bigcirc$ U at 0 Å
$\bigcirc$ O at $\pm$ 1.91 Å
$\oplus$ O at $+$ 0.49 Å
$\ominus$ O at $-$ 0.49 Å

FIG. 1.1. Structure of a layer of $UO_2.O_2$ in $CaUO_4$. After Zachariasen (1948b).

all investigated salts were found to contain a symmetric, linear $(OUO)^{++}$ ion, surrounded by atoms forming secondary U-ligand linkages considerably longer than the primary U—O distance in

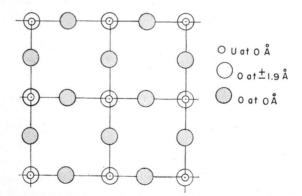

$\bigcirc$ U at 0 Å
$\bigcirc$ O at $\pm$ 1.9 Å
$\bigcirc$ O at 0 Å

FIG. 1.2. Probable structure of a layer of $UO_2.O_2$ in $BaUO_4$. After Zachariasen (1948) and Samson and Sillén (1947).

$(OUO)^{++}$. The first demonstration of this configuration was by Fankuchen (1935); however, he obtained no reliable bond distances.

Zachariasen (1948b) examined $(UO_2)O_2Ca$ and $(UO_2)O_2Sr$. These "orthouranates" consist of sheets containing linear O—U—O groups, directed perpendicular to the sheet plane and having primary U—O bonds of 1.91 ± 0.10 Å, and secondary O atoms at 2.30 Å from the U atoms, arranged as shown in Fig. 1.1. The Ca^{++} or Sr^{++} ions bind the uranate layers together.

Another orthouranate, $BaUO_2O_2$, is not isostructural with the Ca and Sr compounds, and according to the X-ray analysis of Samson and Sillén (1947) each uranyl ion has only four secondary U—O

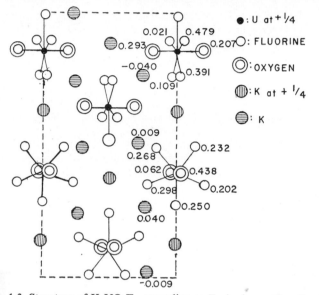

FIG. 1.3. Structure of $K_3UO_2F_5$, according to Zachariasen. Coordinate of some atoms above plane of projection is shown on the diagram. Each UO_2 is surrounded by 5 F, spaced uniformly on the equatorial circle of radius 2.24 ± 03 Å. The shortest K^+—F^- distance is 2.54 Å; the shortest K—O distance is 2.92 Å.

bonds. The structure proposed by Samson and Sillén is shown in Fig. 1.2. According to Frondel and Barnes (1958), there is a $PbUO_2O_2$ isostructural with the Ba compound.

Other uranyl salts are structurally similar to these oxides. Zachariasen (1948a) found that anhydrous UO_2F_2 crystallizes in sheets, each sheet having a structure like the $UO_2O_2^{--}$ layers in calcium uranate (see Fig. 1.1). However, the UO_2F_2 layer is slightly more expanded than the $UO_2O_2^{--}$ layer. Corresponding distances are: U—U = 3.87 Å in the uranate, 4.20 Å in the fluoride; U—O (secondary) = 2.3 Å in the uranate, U—F = 2.5 Å in the fluoride.

The few structural studies of uranyl salts which have been made have revealed a variety of U—O primary bond lengths. Zachariasen (1954a) found that in $K_3UO_2F_5$ crystals, the $UO_2F_5^{-3}$ group is a pentagonal bipyramid with the U—O distance = 1.76 ± 0.03 Å, and the U—F distance = 2.24 ± 0.02 Å. Thus the uranyl ion is considerably shorter in this salt than it is in the orthouranates. More accurate data by Zachariasen (1954b) on a different uranate, $MgUO_2.O_2$, has given the U—O primary distance as 1.91 ± 0.03 Å. This salt contains

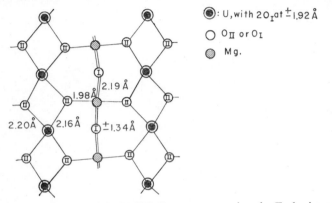

FIG. 1.4. A diagram of the $MgUO_2O_2$ structure as given by Zachariasen (1954b). This seems to be a compound of (OMgO).(OUO), with the oxygens attached to each metal ion forming secondary bonds with another one to give each 4 equatorial ligands.

endless chains of $UO_2.O_2$ groups, with six O atoms from four chains forming octahedra about the Mg^{++} ions. The four secondary U···O bonds are reported as 2.18 ± 0.04 Å (not necessarily all equal). These structures are pictured in Figs. 1.3 and 1.4.

The compounds $RbUO_2(NO_3)_3$ and UO_2CO_3 complete the group of uranyl salts for which we have a fair degree of detailed X-ray structure information. They are similar in that each involves uranyl groups surrounded by a planar arrangement of six NO_3^- or CO_3^{--} oxygens. The nitrate was studied by Hoarde and Stroupe (1949), who placed only the U atoms by intensity considerations, and the rest by a combination of bond-length guesses and symmetry considerations. A similar procedure was followed for the carbonate by

Christ, Clark, and Evans (1955). Their sample was the natural mineral Rutherfordine. However, Cromer and Harper (1955), using a synthesized carbonate sample, augmented the work of Christ *et al.* by an intensity placement of the uranyl oxygens at 1.67 ± 0.09 Å from U. The work of these groups gives a structure as shown in Fig. 1.5, with 6 U—O_{II} distances of about 2.5 Å.

Zachariasen (1954c) has given an interesting rationale for the apparent wide variation in the uranyl bond length among various salts. His discussion is based on variations in "bond strength," but it amounts to a suggestion that the uranyl bond will be longer if its oxygen atoms are shared with other external atoms. It is quite clear that the coordination number of uranium in uranyl can vary at least

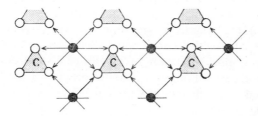

FIG. 1.5. Sketch of the plane of the carbonate groups in uranyl carbonate. Adapted from Christ, Clark and Evans (1955). Carbonate groups shown as shaded triangles; uranium atoms as black circles.

from 4 to 6 (we do not include the uranyl linkages in counting coordination), and very likely coordination with 8 or more ligands can also occur. Moreover, for a given coordination number, the ligand arrangement is not fixed. For example, the six ligand oxygens in $CaUO_2O_2$ (Fig. 1.1) surround the UO_2 in two equilateral triangles, one above and one below the equatorial plane, while the six ligand oxygens of UO_2CO_3 form a (distorted) hexagon in the equatorial plane. This, together with the relative constancy of geometry of the uranyl group itself, suggest that strong directed-valence bonds join the uranyl atoms but that electrostatic forces and packing conditions play the important roles in secondary U–ligand bonds. (This does not, however, imply that directed covalency does not occur in these secondary bonds.) We note in passing that there is no simple correlation between the coordination number of the U and the uranyl bond length.

It seems reasonable to discuss spectra as arising from the uranyl group with specific secondary ligand and lattice interactions.

1.2. *General View of Uranyl Crystal Spectra*

A linear OUO^{++} group has three fundamental vibrations:

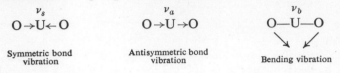

ν_s	ν_a	ν_b
O→U←O	O→U→O	O—U—O
Symmetric bond vibration	Antisymmetric bond vibration	Bending vibration

The bending vibration, ν_b, is degenerate (since it can occur in two mutually perpendicular planes); it should therefore split into two components when the ion is placed into an external field of force (except when this field is directed along the O—U—O axis). The excitation of the symmetric vibration, ν_s, has no dipole moment change associated with it, and should therefore be absent from the infrared absorption spectrum. In the Raman spectrum, inversely, *only* the symmetric vibration, ν_s, should occur. All three vibrations are permitted in combination with changes in electronic structure, i.e. in visible and ultraviolet absorption and emission bands.

These expectations are not confirmed by experience: the frequency 860 cm^{-1}, which should be ν_s in the linear model (cf. p. 28), is represented—albeit weakly—also in the infrared absorption spectrum, and the frequency of ~ 210 cm^{-1}, corresponding to ν_b in the linear model, is present, with moderate intensity, in the Raman spectrum of uranyl salt solutions.

The exclusion rules for the infrared and Raman spectrum are, however, strictly valid only for *free* molecules (or molecular ions), while what is observed in practice are the spectra of uranyl ions in the electric field of anions, other ligands, or solvent dipoles. Under these conditions, "prohibited" transitions are not impossible, although they remain comparatively improbable and can be expected to give rise to lines which are weaker than those due to permitted transitions.

An alternative explanation—that the ion UO$_2^{++}$ is angular—has been advanced, specifically in application to solutions (to avoid contradiction with X-ray data which definitely indicate linear structure in crystals). However, at present it seems most likely that the ion UO$_2^{++}$ remains linear also in the solvated state, but that solvation weakens the exclusion rules for the Raman spectrum so as to bring out the ν_b frequency.

If the three vibrations are assumed to be harmonic, with the elastic force constants f (in the direction of the U—O bond) and d (in the direction perpendicular to this bond), their frequencies must be:

$$\nu_s \text{ (symmetric)} = \sqrt{\left(\frac{f}{m_o}\right)} \tag{1}$$

$$\nu_a \text{ (antisymmetric)} = \sqrt{\left[\frac{f}{m_o}\left(1 + \frac{2m_o}{m_u}\right)\right]} = \nu_s\sqrt{\left(1 + \frac{2m_o}{m_u}\right)} \tag{2}$$

$$\nu_b \text{ (bending)} = \sqrt{\left[\frac{2d}{f}\left(1 + \frac{2m_o}{m_u}\right)\right]} = \nu_a\sqrt{\frac{2d}{f}} \tag{3}$$

where m_o and m_u are the masses of the atoms of oxygen and uranium respectively.

Since $m_u \simeq 15\, m_o$, the antisymmetric vibration frequency must be about 6 per cent higher than the symmetric one. The bending frequency, on the other hand, can be expected to be considerably lower than the other two fundamental frequencies (because of the relation $d \ll f$). We will see below that the values of ν_s and ν_a for uranyl salts (in the stable electronic state) are about 880 and 920 cm^{-1} respectively, while ν_b appears to be of the order of 200 cm^{-1} (although the identification of this vibration is not yet quite certain).

The existence of two fundamental frequencies, ν_s and ν_a, of approximately equal magnitude, could lead to a spectrum of considerable complexity; instead, the absorption spectra (and to an even greater extent, the fluorescence spectra) of uranyl compounds appear to be rather simple, consisting of a single series of approximately equidistant band groups. This indicates that only one type of vibration is so strongly coupled with the electronic transition that several quanta of this vibration (up to 8, as indicated by the number of band groups in the spectrum) can be excited in conjunction with this transition. We will see below that this is the symmetric bond vibration. Of the antisymmetric and the bending vibration, on the other hand, apparently not more than one quantum can be excited in conjunction with the transition from the lowest excited electronic state to the ground state (which gives rise to the fluorescence spectrum at low temperatures). In the reverse transition—from the ground electronic state to the excited electronic state—one or two quanta of the vibrations ν_a^* and ν_b^* can be excited (asterisks denote the excited electronic state). A further complication arises in the absorption spectrum from the fact that apparently not one but several electronic states of the UO_2^{++} ion can be reached by the absorption of visible or near-ultraviolet light, while only the lowest one of these states contributes to fluorescence.

That the one vibration strongly coupled with the electronic transition, must be the symmetric bond vibration, ν_s, follows from the Franck–Condon principle. According to the latter, the electronic transition is so fast that it leaves the nuclei in the positions and with the velocities close to those they had before the transition; if the molecule in the new electronic state cannot have these co-ordinates without a change in the number of vibrational quanta, the acquisition (or loss) of these quanta will follow the electronic transition. In the case of the symmetric bond vibration in the linear O—U—O system, such a change is to be expected, because electronic excitation changes the strength of the U—O bond, and thus also the U—O distance of minimum potential energy.

If, as is likely, the equilibrium distance is wider in the electronically excited state than in the ground state, the oxygen atoms will find themselves, after the emission of a quantum of fluorescent light, too far apart and the system will begin to vibrate like a stretched and released spring.

At first one may think that the same consideration should apply also to the antisymmetric vibration; but while in the case of the symmetric bond vibration, the excess potential energy of the stretched O—U—O system is decreased when two oxygen atoms move simultaneously towards the U atom, no similar approach to equilibrium is possible by the excitation of the antisymmetric vibration, since in it the two oxygen atoms move in the same direction—one toward the uranium atom, and the other away from it. Therefore, in the first approximation (i.e. assuming an elastic force), antisymmetric vibrations should not be excited at all as a consequence of electronic transition; the actually observed excitation of a single quantum of this vibration in fluorescence must be attributed to deviation of the bond from elasticity. This deviation appears to be stronger in the excited electronic state, since two quanta of antisymmetric vibration can be acquired in absorption.

The bending vibration, v_b, is also relatively little affected by the excitation of one of the bonding electrons in the O—U—O system. A much stronger excitation of this vibration could be expected if the uranyl ion were non-linear in the excited electronic state.

To sum up, the (low-temperature) *fluorescence spectrum* of the uranyl ion can be represented by the equation:

$$v_{fl} = v_F - n_s v_s - n_a v_a - n_b v_b - \Sigma\, n_i v_i \qquad (4)$$

where v_F is the pure electronic transition ("resonance transition"), and n_s ($= 0$ to 8) the number of quanta of the symmetric vibration excited simultaneously with the loss of the electronic quantum, hv_f. The coefficients n_a and n_b are either 0 or 1. The term $\Sigma\, n_i v_i$ refers to vibrations of the associated anions (such as NO_3^-), water molecules, or the crystal as a whole, which too can be coupled with the electronic transition—either directly or, more likely, through the intermediary of the fundamental vibrations in the O—U—O system. The low-temperature *absorption spectrum* of the uranyl ion can be similarly represented by the equation:

$$v_{\mathrm{abs}} = v_E + n_s v_s^* + n_a v_a^* + n_b v_b^* + \Sigma\, n_i v_i \qquad (5)$$

where v_E can be equal either to v_F or to the excitation frequency of some higher electronic term of the UO_2^{++} ion. In this case, too, $n_s = 0$ to 8, and n_a and n_b can have the values 0, 1 or 2.

Figures 1.6A and 1.6B are simplified term schemes of the low-temperature fluorescence and absorption spectra of the uranyl ion respectively. Each arrow corresponds to a band group with a common value of n_s. A second electronic level, M, is indicated in Fig. 1.6B in addition to the lowest level, F, in which the low-temperature fluorescence spectrum originates.

The sub-levels due to the vibrational frequencies v_a and v_b are not shown in Fig. 1.6. Because the frequency v_a is $\simeq v_s$, the absorption bands $v_E + n v_s + v_a$ will be located among the bands of the group $v_E + (n+1)v_s$; the fluorescence bands among those of the group $v_F - (n+1)v_s$. Thus, the *empirical* definition of a band group as comprising bands situated close together (and fusing into a single, broad band at higher temperatures), does not quite correspond to the *theoretical* definition, based on equations (4) and (5), according to which a band group is formed by bands having a common value of n_s. Instead, one (or several) components of each theoretical group must be sought within the neighboring empirical group (on the red edge of the main group in fluorescence, and near the violet edge of this group in absorption).

At *low* temperatures only the band group $X_0 \rightleftharpoons F_0$, and at *very low* temperatures only one component of this group, the "resonance" line (involving transition between two levels in which *all* vibrational quantum numbers are zero), can appear in both absorption and

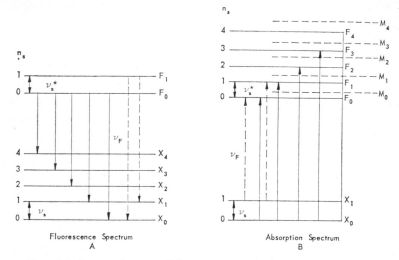

Fig. 1.6. Term schemes of fluorescence and absorption. ν_F is the resonance frequency. Dotted arrows indicate anti-Stokes bands.

fluorescence. At higher temperatures when the strongest "anti-Stokes" band groups ($F_1 \rightleftharpoons X_1$, $F_1 \to X_0$ and $X_1 \to F_0$ in Fig. 1.6) have made their appearance in the spectrum, as many as four band groups of the absorption spectrum can overlap with groups of the fluorescence spectrum (cf. Fig. 1.7). However, since the difference between ν_s and ν_s^* is small, the band groups $F_0 \to X_0$ and $F_1 \to X_1$ may appear as a single group; superficial observation will then suggest that the absorption spectrum and the fluorescence spectrum have *three* bands in common (cf. Table 1.1).

Higher electronic levels, such as M (Fig. 1.6), could also contribute "anti-Stokes" components to the fluorescence spectrum.

At very low temperatures many uranyl bands are as sharp as lines in the iron arc spectrum (cf. Figs. 1.11 and 1.12). This shows that in the uranyl ion, similarly to the ions of the rare earths, electronic transitions are so effectively "shielded" that no low-frequency vibrations (in the solvation sphere, or in the crystalline lattice as a whole) are excited (or lost) when the ion changes its electronic state. Because of the triatomic structure of the group $[OUO]^{++}$, the spectrum of the uranyl ion differs from those of the rare earth ions by the possible co-excitation (or loss) of vibrational quanta in this group; and the complication caused by these quanta becomes greater with increasing temperature, when vibrating UO_2^{++} ions appear in thermal equilibrium with the non-vibrating ones.

However, the broadening of the sharp low-temperature bands of UO_2, and their fusion into broad bands, is observed much earlier and is much more extensive (cf. Figs. 1.11 and 1.12) than could be explained by mere superposition, upon the electronic transition, of the vibrational frequencies of the ion UO_2^{++}. The probable reason is that the electronic transition is coupled also with low-frequency vibrations in the solvation sphere, or intra-ionic vibrations in the salt crystal. In the case of polyatomic anions such as NO_3^-, a coupling occurs also with vibrations within these anions. All these modes of vibration are included in the terms $\Sigma n_i \nu_i$ in equations (4) and (5).

Because of the co-excitation of low-frequency vibrations of the medium, the analysis of the uranyl spectrum (i.e. the determination of the electronic terms and of the fundamental vibrations) must be based on observations at the lowest conveniently obtainable temperature, such as 20°K (liquid hydrogen bath). Even at 77°K (liquid nitrogen bath) the bands are blurred and displaced. At room temperature the peaks of the broad absorption bands often do not indicate, even approximately, the number and position of the strongest individual bands, and therefore do not permit the determination of vibration frequencies with any degree of precision (Figs. 1.11 and 1.12).

As usual, the vibrational frequencies of the ground electronic state must be derived from the *fluorescence* spectrum (Fig. 1.6A), and those of the excited electronic state, from the *absorption* spectrum (Fig. 1.6B).

The interpretation of the fluorescence and absorption spectrum of the uranyl ion, indicated in this introduction, is based on the spectroscopic work of Nichols, Howes and co-workers (1914–19), Dieke and van Heel (1925), Moerman and Kraak (1939), and Freymann and co-workers (1946–48); on infrared studies (cf. Section 3 below) and Raman spectra; but most of all, on the work of Dieke, Duncan, and co-workers, carried out in 1943–44 under the Manhattan District program. In the course of these studies experimental data far superior in precision and detail to the previously available material have been assembled and at least in part

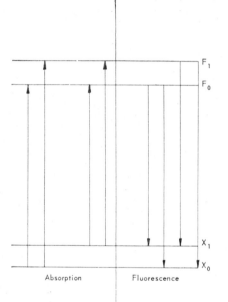

FIG. 1.7. Resonance bands at higher temperatures.

interpreted in terms of the theory of crystal spectra. These experimental and theoretical results are described in detail in Volume 2 of Division III of the National Nuclear Energy Series (Dieke and Duncan, 1949). In the present chapter we will review briefly the earlier investigations in the field of uranyl salt spectroscopy and give a somewhat more detailed summary of the results of Nichols and Howes and, particularly, of Dieke and co-workers.

The interpretation of the 210 cm^{-1} frequency as that of the bending vibration ν_b was contested by Sevchenko and co-workers (1951), mainly on the grounds of its excessive multiplicity (seven components in $UO_2Cs(NO_3)_3$!), and its dependence on crystal structure (in $Cs_2UO_2Cl_4$, Dieke and Duncan interpret as ν_b the frequencies 109 and 118 cm^{-1} instead of the usual 210 cm^{-1}!). Sevchenko also argued that ν_b should exhibit as many overtones as ν_s. Furthermore, the 210 cm^{-1} frequency shows no oxygen-isotope effect, and the polarization of the lines in which this vibration is excited depends on crystal structure. All these characteristics point, according to Sevchenko, to a crystal lattice vibration, rather than to an internal vibration frequency of the UO_2^{2+} ion. However, this interpretation is inconsistent with the lack of influence on the 210 cm^{-1} vibration of the number of water molecules in the series $UO_2(NO_3)_2 \cdot nH_2O$ ($n = 1, 2, 3, 6$) (cf. Section 5). Actually, the bending vibration might well depend strongly upon the lattice crystalline field, as there is a strong electric uranyl-lattice energy which ought to vary considerably with the uranyl angle.

2. Studies of Fluorescence and Absorption Spectra of Solid Uranyl Salts (except those of Dieke and Duncan)

2.1. *Band Measurements and Empirical Classification*

Brewster (1833) was probably the first to observe the green fluorescence of uranyl ions (in so-called Canary glass); Stokes (1852, 1853), the first to systematically study the fluorescence and absorption spectra of uranium compounds. In illuminating a crystal of uranyl nitrate with a beam of blue light (white light filtered through a copper salt solution) and observing in a spectroscope the light emerging from the crystal, Stokes noted "a most remarkable spectrum" consisting of "nothing but bands, arranged at regular intervals." He saw that the bands formed two distinct systems—a system of *emission bands*, beginning in the blue part of the visible spectrum and extending into the region of lower refractability (i.e. towards the longer waves), and a system of *absorption bands*, beginning in the same region but extending in the opposite direction towards the shorter waves into the violet and ultraviolet.

E. Becquerel (1872) counted eight bright bands in the fluorescence spectrum of solid uranyl nitrate and stated that the spectra of other uranyl salts are similar, but that the bands occupy somewhat different positions for different compounds.

Morton and Bolton (1873) mapped the fluorescence and absorption spectra of 87 solid uranium compounds, including 17 double uranyl acetates. They noted the above-mentioned overlapping of the first few bands in the absorption and the fluorescence band systems (cf. Fig. 1.8, strips 1 and 3) and found indications of a "fine structure" of some of the fluorescence bands (particularly in the spectra of the double chlorides, strip 2). Morton and Bolton also described changes in the uranyl spectrum which occur when anhydrous salts are hydrated or dissolved in water or other solvents.

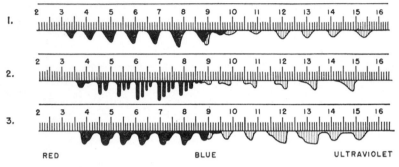

FIG. 1.8. Representative absorption and fluorescence band systems of solid uranyl salts (after Morton and Bolton, 1873), showing overlapping of the two systems and fine structure of some bands.

       1. uranyl nitrate.
       2. potassium uranyl chloride.
       3. calcium uranyl phosphate.

(From Nichols and Howes, 1919, p. 8.)
       Black: Fluorescence bands. Shaded: Absorption bands.

H. Becquerel, J. Becquerel, and Kamerlingh Onnes (1909, 1910) noted the transformation which the fluorescence and absorption spectra of solid uranyl salts underwent upon cooling to liquid air temperature ($-185°C$): some bands disappeared, while others split into a number of narrow, sharp components. They found that some of the sharp low-temperature fluorescence bands coincide almost exactly with the (also sharp) low-temperature bands in the overlapping absorption band groups; these they designated as "reversible" bands (we now call them "resonance bands"). A further sharpening of the bands was observed by them at the temperature of liquid nitrogen.

Nichols, Howes and co-workers carried out in 1915–19 a very extensive study of uranyl salt spectra.

They noted that the broad absorption regions (or band groups) observed in most uranyl compounds at $+20°C$ have approximately constant differences on the frequency scale. This they found to be true of both absorption and fluorescence spectrum, but the characteristic frequency intervals were different—about 820 cm^{-1} in the fluorescence spectrum and about 660 cm^{-1} in the absorption spectrum. Nichols and Howes noticed, however, that the interval

TABLE 1.1. ABSORPTION AND FLUORESCENCE BANDS OF
POTASSIUM URANYL SULFATE AT $+20°C$
After Nichols and Howes (1919)

Absorption			Fluorescence		
λ mμ	ν (cm^{-1})	$\Delta\nu$	λ mμ	ν (cm^{-1})	$\Delta\nu$
435.0	22,989				
447.2	22,361	628			
461.4	21,673	688			
476.0	21,008	665	476.5	20,986	
492.0	20,325	683	492.0	20,325	661
512.7	19,505	820	513.0	19,493	832
			536.0	18,657	836
			560.6	17,838	819
			588.1	17,004	834
			619.0	16,155	849

between the second and the first band on the short-wave end of the fluorescence system was that characteristic of the absorption sequence, while the interval between the last and the penultimate band on the long-wave end of the absorption system was that generally encountered in the fluorescence sequence. Table 1.1 shows, for example, the wavelengths of the peaks of the fluorescence and absorption bands of $K_2UO_2(SO_4)_2.2H_2O$ at $+20°C$; we note the (approximately) constant frequency intervals in each band system, the overlapping of three absorption and fluorescence bands, and the occurrence in the absorption system of a $\Delta\nu$-value (820 cm^{-1}) characteristic of the fluorescence spectrum, and in the fluorescence system, of a $\Delta\nu$ value (661 cm^{-1}) characteristic of the absorption spectrum. All these features are understandable on the basis of Fig. 1.6. They indicate that both systems are due to the same electronic transition (20,325 cm^{-1}) coupled with acquisition of vibrational quanta of about 660 cm^{-1} in the excited electronic state, and of about 820 cm^{-1} in the ground state. The last absorption band group and the first fluorescence band group must originate in the first vibrational level of the excited and the ground state respectively (anti-Stokes bands, dotted arrows in Fig. 1.6). This explains why these band groups are relatively weak at room temperature and disappear at low temperature when practically no vibrating molecules exist in thermal equilibrium.

Band groups which do not fade out at low temperatures are split into sharp components. Nichols and Howes noted that the narrow bands or lines which result from this splitting form identical or almost identical patterns in the several groups. (A typical pattern is shown in Fig. 1.15.) The lines could therefore be arranged into series, each series containing one line from each group. Table 1.2 is a typical example of such empirical analysis. The lines belonging to a given series are separated by approximately the same frequency interval as the peaks of the broad bands at room temperature, but the constancy of the intervals is much improved at low temperature, especially if weak and uncertain components are left out. (Compare the $\Delta\nu$ values in Table 1.1 with those in Table 1.2, particularly in the strongest series, E, D, and F.) This too is understandable, since the positions of the crests of the broad unresolved room temperature bands are more or less accidental, being determined by the summation of several overlapping band components.

The explanation of the origin of the band series, hundreds of which were listed by Nichols and Howes, could not be given by them. As described in Section 1, we know now that each of Nichols and Howes' series consists of bands which have in common not only the electronic transition, but also all vibrational changes other than that of the symmetric bond vibration.

Boardman (1922) plotted the fluorescence intensity of various uranyl salts as a function of the wavelength of the exciting light, and obtained a curve for which the main peaks coincided with the strongest known absorption bands; this coincidence justified considering the (less prominent) excitation peaks, noticeable in the short-wave region, as indicating the location of additional absorption

TABLE 1.2. SERIES IN THE FLUORESCENCE SPECTRUM OF URANYL
NITRATE HEXAHYDRATE [$UO_2(NO_3)_2.6H_2O$] AT $-180°C$
After Nichols and Howes (1919)

Series	Intensity *	ν, (cm⁻¹)	Δν, (cm⁻¹)	Series	Intensity *	ν, (cm⁻¹)	Δν, (cm⁻¹)
A	v.d.	17,601		F	m.	16,313	
	v.d.	18,460	859		d.	17,184	871
	d.	19,301	841		m.	18,036	852
	m.	20,182	881		m.	18,896	860
					m.	19,764	868
B	v.d.	16,895			d.	20,619	855
	d.	17,750	855				
	m.	18,611	861	G	d.	18,104	
	m.	19,471	860		d.	18,973	869
	str.	20,345	874		v.d.	19,831	858
C	d.	16,990		H	v.d.	16,497	
	d.	17,851	861		v.d.	17,374	877
	d.	18,690	839		d.	18,220	846
	v.d.	19,562	872		m.	19,067	847
	m.	20,415	853		m.	19,934	867
D	v.d.	15,349		I	v.d.	18,260	
	d.	16,210	861		v.d.	19,117	857
	m.	17,068	858				
	str.	17,925	857	J	d.	16,655	
	str.	18,778	853		m.	17,518	
	str.	19,636	858		d.	18,378	
	d.	20,500	864		m.	19,231	
E	v.d.	15,401					
	d.	16,292	891				
	m.	17,150	858				
	str.	18,000	850				
	str.	18,861	861				
	str.	19,725	864				
	str.	20,585	860				

* Str., strong; m., medium; d., dim; v.d., very dim.

bands, unknown from direct observation. Several new bands in the
long-wave end of the absorption spectrum could be identified in the
same way. By this procedure, the absorption spectrum of the uranyl
ion, previously known between 380 mμ and 490 mμ, was extended
from 320 mμ to 560 mμ. Tables were given by Boardman for the
so-identified absorption bands of cesium uranyl double chloride

(18,120–27,300 cm⁻¹), of barium uranyl double acetate (18,050–31,480 cm⁻¹), and of uranyl acetate (17,880–31,560 cm⁻¹).

Samojlov (1948) measured lines in the absorption and fluorescence spectra of several uranyl salts in liquid helium (4.2°K). He noted that cooling from 90°K (liquid air) to 4.2°K causes further narrowing and splitting of lines and that corresponding lines shift 5–12 cm⁻¹ towards shorter waves.

2.2. *Term Analysis*

The first step in the analysis of the uranyl spectrum in the light of Bohr's theory of spectra was made by Dieke and van Heel (1925). They pointed out that the different spacing of the fluorescence and absorption bands (Table 1.1) indicates a difference in the vibrational frequency of the UO_2^{++} group before and after the electronic excitation. The lower frequency in the electronically excited ion (600–700 cm⁻¹ vs. 800–850 cm⁻¹ in the non-excited ion) indicates looser binding. The approximate constancy of spacing of the several band groups indicates that the binding is almost elastic (and vibration therefore almost harmonic) in the excited as well as in the ground state.

Moerman and Kraak (1939) pointed out that the strongest absorption band of UO_2^{++} corresponds to the transition from the non-vibrating ground state to the excited electronic state with one vibrational quantum and saw in this relationship a confirmation of the assumption that the U—O distance is larger in the excited state. They also noted the absence of this band in fluorescence at −180°C, and its weak occurrence in fluorescence at room temperature; they saw in this an indication that thermal equilibrium in respect to vibrational energy is established, in the excited electronic state, before any appreciable proportion of absorbed photons has been re-emitted as fluorescence (cf. below).

Freymann, Guilmart, and Freymann (1946, 1947, 1948) undertook a more detailed classification of the uranyl ion lines (as shown by uranyl acetate crystals at low temperatures) using, in addition to the symmetric vibration frequency, 860 cm⁻¹, also two other frequencies derived from the Raman effect measurements—930 and 210 cm⁻¹; only one vibrational frequency, 720 cm⁻¹, was utilized in the excited electronic state. Forty-seven fluorescence lines and 40 absorption lines could be interpreted by means of these frequencies, with the additional assumption that the main vibration frequency has a satellite at a distance of 30 cm^{-1}. This frequency was tentatively interpreted as that of a crystal vibration.

Similar analysis was also found possible in the spectra of uranyl nitrate, chloride, and fluoride.

The Raman frequency, 150 cm^{-1}, was interpreted by Freymann *et al.*, not as an independent frequency, but as the difference between the frequencies 860 and 720 cm^{-1}.

Freymann and co-workers did not know of the earlier Manhattan project work of Dieke and Duncan, first published in 1949, which had carried the term analysis of the spectrum of solid uranyl salts into much more detail. This work will be summarized in Section 4.

2.3. *Fluorescence Spectrum in relation to Exciting Light*

When Nichols and Howes (1919) set out to investigate the uranyl spectrum, the first question they asked was whether the fluorescence spectrum is the same whatever the exciting light. The answer was yes: excitation by light of various wavelengths always produced the same complete pattern of fluorescence bands, with approximately the same relative intensities. (The observed slight variations in the relative intensity of the resonance bands could be attributed to the re-absorption of these bands, which is more effective the deeper the exciting light penetrates into the crystal, i.e. the weaker it is absorbed.)

Van Heel (1925) described monochromatic excitation of fluorescence in autunite (calcium uranyl phosphate) and in a potassium uranyl sulfate crystal at $-183°C$. He noted that fluorescence was strongly excited by light belonging to the absorption bands, including the "resonance frequency" (where absorption and fluorescence bands coincide), but was not excited at all by light belonging to the other fluorescence bands. This result is obvious, since no fluorescence is possible without absorption.

The question whether the fluorescence spectrum of uranyl salt crystals is independent of the wavelength of the exciting light was again taken up by Levshin and Sheremetjev (1947). Spectrophotograms covering all the eight fluorescence bands of uranyl sulfate that appear at room temperature were scanned with excitation either by the mercury line 435 mμ or by a group of lines in the ultraviolet (254–366 mμ, mainly > 311 mμ). The relative intensities of the bands, as well as the shapes of the individual bands, were found to be exactly the same in both cases. This experiment was made with identical results at the beginning of the fluorescence decay, immediately after flash excitation, and 2.7×10^{-4} sec later.

Levshin and Sheremetjev also prepared spectrophotograms of the uranyl sulfate trihydrate fluorescence at $+100°C$ and $-185°C$. At 100°C the spectrum was characterized (compared to its appearance at room temperature) by general broadening and slight decrease in the intensity of all bands, except for those below 490 mμ. There the first anti-Stokes band, present even at room temperature, was enhanced by heating, and a second and perhaps a third anti-Stokes band appeared further in the violet.

Cooling to $-185°C$ had the opposite effect—sharpening (and splitting) of the seven main bands and disappearance of the anti-Stokes band. This transformation will be described in more detail in Section 4.

All these results are easily understood. As indicated in Fig. 1.6B, individual absorption bands lead to the excitation of a different number of vibrational quanta. However, the period of a molecular vibration (order of magnitude 10^{-13} to 10^{-12} sec) is short compared to the natural lifetime of the excited electronic state (about 10^{-8} sec for uranyl ions). In the condensed state each vibration offers a chance of exchange of kinetic energy with the medium. Therefore, the equilibration of the vibrational energy of the electronically excited molecule with the thermal agitation energy of the medium occurs long before a significant proportion of the photons had been re-emitted as fluorescence. The fluorescence spectrum therefore has an intensity distribution determined entirely by the temperature of the medium and bearing no relation to the wavelength of the exciting light.

3. Infrared Spectrum of Uranyl Salt Crystals

An important contribution to the understanding of the uranyl spectrum came from the study of infrared and Raman spectra.

Coblentz (1918) noted absorption bands at 0.92 μ and 1.55 μ in uranium glass. Dreisch (1927) observed the same bands and stated that they are doublets (0.83–0.92 μ and 1.44–1.55 μ respectively). However, he found them only in uranium *glass*; no absorption was seen in the infrared up to 2 μ in uranyl nitrate *solution*, in water or in 96 per cent alcohol. Dreisch concluded that these bands do not belong to the uranyl ion but originate in some other component of uranium glass.

Conn and Wu (1938) studied in more detail the infrared absorption spectrum of solid uranyl salts and found a weak band at 11.6 μ (860 cm^{-1}) and an intense band at 10.8 μ (930 cm^{-1}). The presence of a band corresponding to a frequency found in Raman spectrum

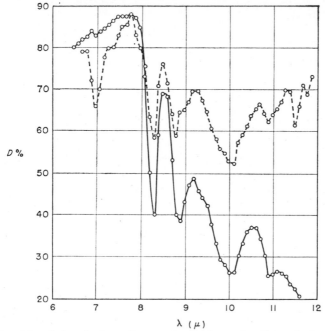

Fig. 1.9a. Infrared absorption spectrum of uranyl sulfate trihydrate. After Sevchenko and Stepanov (1949).

of concentrated uranyl salt solutions (210 cm^{-1}) could not be checked because it was out of range of the instrument.

Lecomte and Freymann (1941) added to the two solid salts studied in the infrared by Conn and Wu eighteen others, including sulfate, double sulfates, double carbonates, nitrate, phthalate, salicylate, etc. They noted absorption bands belonging to UO_2^{++} ions, as well as bands apparently belonging to the associated anions. Intense UO_2^{++} absorption bands were found with peaks at 10.87 μ (920 cm^{-1}) and 11.76 μ (850 cm^{-1}), and a weak band at about

1120 cm⁻¹. The last one was not previously noted; it may represent
the combination of two of the frequencies identified by Conn and
Wu: $210+930 = 1140$ cm⁻¹.

Lecomte and Freymann suggested that the 920 cm⁻¹ band could
be used for the identification of the uranyl ion in compounds in
which its presence is uncertain. For example, this frequency does

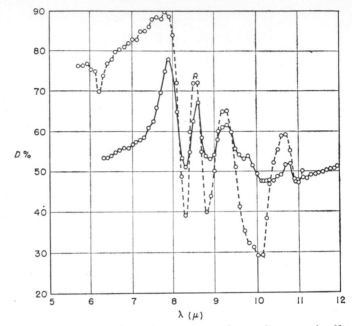

FIG. 1.9b. Infrared absorption spectrum of potassium uranyl sulfate
dihydrate. After Sevchenko and Stepanov (1949).

not appear in the absorption spectrum of uranyl trioxide. (Instead,
the latter shows bands at 890, 1020, and 1090 cm⁻¹; the same frequencies, somewhat displaced, appear also in the spectrum of
sodium uranate and in the product obtained from uranyl salt
solution by precipitation with ammonia; the latter thus proves to
be an ammonium uranate.) The 920 cm⁻¹ frequency was present
(rather unexpectedly!) in the absorption spectrum of $UO_3.2H_2O$
(but *not* in that of $UO_3.H_2O$ or of $UO_4.2H_2O$).

Sevchenko and Stepanov (1949) investigated the infrared absorption spectra of uranyl sulfate, potassium uranyl sulfate, uranyl

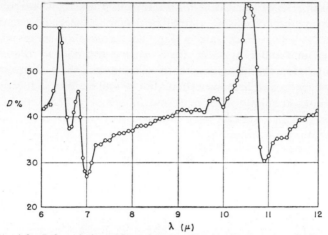

FIG. 1.9c. Infrared absorption spectrum of uranyl acetate hexahydrate.
After Sevchenko and Stepanov (1949).

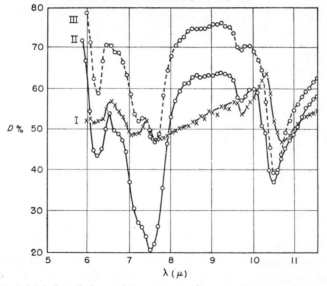

FIG. 1.9d. Infrared absorption spectrum of uranyl nitrate hexahydrate.
After Sevchenko and Stepanov (1949).

acetate, and uranyl nitrate (fine crystal powders pressed between
fluorite plates) up to 15 μ. Figs. 1.9a, b, c, and d show the transmission curves of these four salts. (The three curves in the nitrate

spectrum refer to successive measurements of the same preparation at one day intervals; changes may be due to adsorption of moisture on the powder.) Each salt in Fig. 1.9 has five or more infrared absorption bands; none of them were attributed to the anion. Table 1.3 gives the frequencies of those bands and their interpretation by Sevchenko and Stepanov. In addition, one unclassified frequency was found in sulfate (873 cm^{-1}) and in acetate (877 cm^{-1}), but not in nitrate. Later workers have observed that some of the bands are due to anion vibrations.

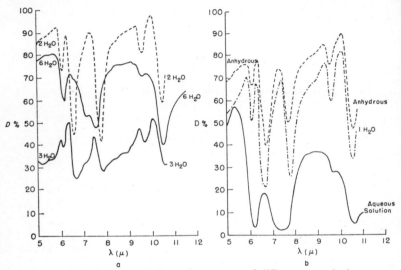

FIG. 1.10a & b. Infrared absorption spectra of different uranyl nitrate hydrates. After Sevchenko and Stepanov (1949).

The frequency 990 cm^{-1} in sulfate is stronger than all the others which is peculiar for a high overtone such as $5\nu_b$. No other explanation of this line has been given.

Asterisks indicate vibrations prohibited for linear molecules. The authors interpreted their occurrence as indication that the UO_2^{++} ion is bent in simple and double sulfates, but almost linear in acetate and nitrate hexahydrates. (The line 1515 could be $\nu_a + 3\nu_b$ rather than $\nu_s + 3\nu_b$; cf., however, pp. 6,29.)

Sevchenko and Stepanov (1949) also studied the effect of hydration on the frequency and intensity of infrared absorption bands of uranyl

TABLE 1.3. INFRARED FREQUENCIES OF URANYL SALTS
Sevchenko and Stepanov (1949)

Interpretation	Frequency calc. (cm⁻¹)	Frequencies found in			
		$UO_2SO_4 \cdot 3H_2O$	$K_2UO_2(SO_4)_2 \cdot 2H_2O$	$UO_2(CH_3COO)_2 \cdot 6H_2O$	$UO_2(NO_3)_2 \cdot 6H_2O$
ν_s*	(830)	836	not measured	not measured	not measured
ν_b	(200)	not measured	not measured	not measured	not measured
ν_a	(920)	913	909	918	935
$5\nu_b$	1000	990	990	1000	...
$\nu_s + \nu_b$	1030	...	1036	...	1031
$\nu_a + \nu_b$	1120	1130	1130	...	...
$6\nu_b$	1200	1204	1204	...	...
$\nu_s + 2\nu_b$	1230	...	...	...	...
$\nu_a + 2\nu_b$	1320	...	...	...	1316
$7\nu_b$	1400	1429	...	1429	1390
$\nu_s + 3\nu_b$	1430	...	...	1515	1515
$\nu_a + 3\nu_b$	1520	873	...	877	...
?	...		...		...

* Prohibited for linear model.

sulfate and uranyl nitrate. In sulfate the band at 9.65 μ ($\nu_s + \nu_b$), missing in the simple trihydrate (but present in complex sulfate), appears strongly in the spectrum of the dehydrated salt. The bands at 10.1, 8.2 and 7.0 μ (interpreted in Table 1.3 as high overtones of ν_b, strong in crystalline trihydrate—cf. Fig. 1.9a—and intense also in trihydrate dehydrated in vacuum at 300°C) are weak or absent in the synthetic anhydrous salt.

The hydrated salts did not show the known strong H_2O band at 6 μ. This would indicate that the binding of water molecules to uranyl ions is so strong as to alter deeply their structure, apparently reducing the dipole of the 6 μ vibration to zero. However, much doubt is cast on this feature of the spectrum by the later work of Gatehouse and Comyns (see below).

TABLE 1.4. INFRARED ABSORPTION BANDS OF URANYL NITRATE
Sevchenko and Stepanov (1949)

Band	Crystals, $n H_2O$, $n =$					Aqueous solution
	0	1	2	3	6	
ν_a	10.6	10.6	10.55	10.6	10.7	10.6
$\nu_s + \nu_b$	9.6	9.7	9.7	9.7	9.7	9.7
$\nu_a + 2\nu_b$	7.8	7.6–7.8	7.8	7.9	7.6	7.6
$7\nu_b$	...	...	...	7.2	7.2	7.2
$\nu_a + 3\nu_b$	6.7	6.7	6.6	6.7	6.6	...

In nitrate, too, the 7.2 μ band disappears upon dehydration ($n \leqslant 2$). The positions of the other bands are practically independent of hydration (Table 1.4), showing that the force constants in the ground electronic state are not changed significantly by the removal of water molecules (however, the relative intensities of the bands vary strongly with the degree of hydration). The differences in the positions of visible absorption and fluorescence bands of the several hydrates (described in Section 5.3) must then be attributed to the effect of water molecules on the electronically excited uranyl ion.

The infrared analysis of Sevchenko and Stepanov, was followed (and largely replaced) by careful studies of the uranyl nitrate spectrum by Burger and Moore (1950) and Tridot (1955), and still more recently by the measurements and interpretations of Gatehouse and Comyns (1958). The latter have contributed the most definitive infrared study of solid uranyl nitrates available at this writing.

Another recent study was carried out on uranyl sodium acetate and the transuranyl sodium acetates by Jones (1955). Jones was

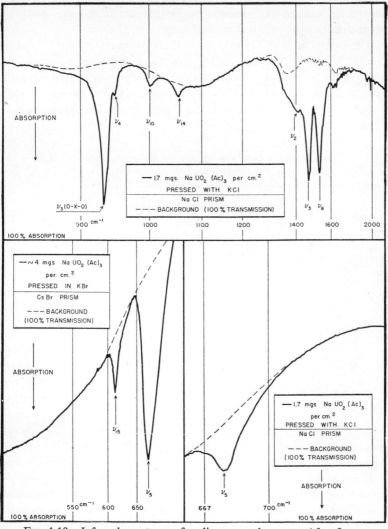

FIG. 1.10c. Infrared spectrum of sodium uranyl acetate. After Jones (1955).

apparently unaware of the earlier Russian work. His spectrum of $NaUO_2(CH_3COO)_3$ is reproduced in Fig. 1.10c. In this spectrum, and in the similar spectra of the corresponding compounds having Np, Am, Pu instead of U, Jones recognized the characteristic frequencies of the acetate ion and assigned the remaining bands to uranyl or transuranyl vibrations. His assignments are given in Table 1.4a.

TABLE 1.4a. VIBRATIONAL FREQUENCIES OF SODIUM ACETATE AND
THE SODIUM ACETATE COMPLEXES OF U(VI), Np(VI), Pu(VI), AND Am(VI)
After Jones (1955)

	Type of vibration	NaAc* cm^{-1}	$NaUO_2.$ $(Ac)_3$ cm^{-1}	$NaNpO_2.$ $(Ac)_3$ cm^{-1}	$NaPuO_2.$ $(Ac)_3$ cm^{-1}	$NaAmO_2.$ $(Ac)_3$ cm^{-1}
ν_1	C—H stretching	2933	2933	2935	2927	. . .
ν_2	CH_3 deformation	1425	1413	1410	1415	. . .
ν_3	C—O stretching	1408	1472	1472	1470	1467
ν_4	C—C stretching	924	948	948	948	948
ν_5	CO_2 deformation	645	678	677	677	675
ν_6	torsion about C—C bond	. . .	. . .	. . .	. . .	. . .
ν_7	C—H stretching	2999	2978	2980	2980	. . .
ν_8	C—O stretching	1578	1537	1536	1540	1541
ν_9	CH_2 deformation	1440	(1450?)	. . .	. . .	. . .
ν_{10}	CH_3 rocking	1012	1004	1004	1004	. . .
ν_{11}	CO_2 rocking	465	. . .	. . .	. . .	. . .
ν_{12}	C—H stretching	2999	2978	2980	2980	. . .
ν_{13}	CH_3 deformation	1488	(1480?)	. . .	. . .	. . .
ν_{14}	CH_3 rocking	1045	1055	1054	1054	1052
ν_{15}	CO_2 rocking	615	612	610	609	. . .
ν_s	(O—X—O)	. . .	856†	844†	818†	749†
ν_a	(O—X—O)	. . .	931	934	930	914
$\nu_s+\nu_a$	(XO_2 group)	. . .	1781†	1770†	1739†	. . .

* The acetate frequency assignments are those of Jones and McLaren (1954).
† These absorption bands were observed only on very thick samples and are not shown in Fig. 1.10c.

These assignments are very reasonable, and their establishment upsets the assignments made previously by Sevchenko and Stepanov (Table 1.3 and Fig. 1.9c). The Russian workers had assigned all bands to OUO^{++} frequencies and their combinations, whereas it is now recognized that many of the bands in the infrared spectrum of uranyl salts are caused by the anions. Although the compounds studied by the two groups of workers are not identical, they are very similar and should display spectra having generally corresponding bands and permitting a common interpretation. On this basis we venture to reassign the bands of $UO_2(CH_3COO)_2.6H_2O$ as follows: 918 cm^{-1}, ν_a; 1000 cm^{-1}, CH$_3$ rock, ν_{10}; ~1046 cm^{-1}, CH$_3$ rock, ν_{14}; 1429 cm^{-1}, CO stretch, ν_3; 1515 cm^{-1}, CO stretch, ν_8.

Jones carried out the study of sodium uranyl acetate in order to compare the force constants of =U=O, =Np=O, =Pu=O, =Am=O bond stretching and to relate these to distances and

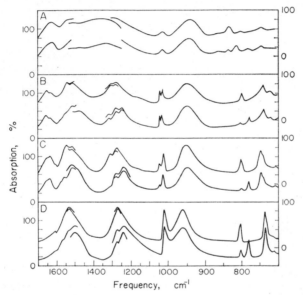

Fig. 1.10d. Infrared absorption spectra of uranyl nitrates. After Gatehouse and Comyns (1958).

atomic configurations. He analyzed the O—X—O vibrations by a model involving an X=O stretching force constant and an interaction force constant between the two bonds. On this basis he found $k_{X=O}$ to be 0.715 Mdyn/cm, 0.698 Mdyn/cm, 0.675 Mdyn/cm, and 0.612 Mdyn/cm for X=U, Np, Pu, and Am respectively. Further references to this work can be found in Chapter 2, Section 5.

Gatehouse and Comyns (1958) made a study of the infrared spectra of uranyl nitrate (hexa-, tri-, and di-hydrated) both with

normal isotopic composition and with enrichment to 80 per cent in
^{15}N. They studied $RbUO_2(NO_3)_3$ in the same way. Their spectra of
mineral oil suspensions of the powders are displayed in Fig. 1.10d.
These spectra were analyzed into fundamentals, overtones, and
combinations of the uranyl vibrations (A, $\sim$ 860 cm^{-1}, sym. stretch;
B, $\sim$ 930 cm^{-1}, asym. stretch; C, $\sim$ 210 cm^{-1}, bend) and the nitrate
or nitrato vibrations. For $UO_2(NO_3)_2.6H_2O$ the nitrate group
nomenclature was used (ν_1, A_1', sym. stretch; ν_2, A_2'', out-of-plane
pyramid motion; ν_3, E', doubly degenerate planar stretch; ν_4, E',
doubly degenerate ONO in-plane bend). For the di- and tri-hydrates

TABLE 1.4b. ASSIGNMENTS OF GATEHOUSE AND COMYNS (1958)
FOR THE INFRARED SPECTRUM OF $UO_2(NO_3)_2.6H_2O$

		^{14}N (obs.)	^{14}N (calc.)	^{15}N (obs.)	^{15}N (calc.)
	ν_1	1030		1031	
	ν_2	803		784	782*
NO_3^-	ν_3	835		814	813*
	ν_3	1366		1339	1333–7†
	ν_4	748		747	744–6†
UO_2^{++}	A	(865)		(866)	
	B	941		943	
H_2O	a	1629		1629	
	b	3270, 3470, 3650			
$A+B$		1802	1806	1799	1809
$\nu_2+\nu_3$		2146	2169	2101	2123
$3\nu_2$		2494	2505	2451	2442
$2\nu_2+B$		(2551)	2547	(2513)	2511

* Calculated from the ^{14}N frequency.
† Calculated by a model attributed to M. H. L. Pryce; appear to agree well
with the fluorescence studies reported by Dieke and Duncan.

and the rubidium salt, their analysis employed nomenclature for a
nitrato group, ONO_2^- (ν_2, A_1, NO stretch; ν_1, A_1, sym. NO_2 stretch;
ν_4, B_1, asym. NO_2 stretch; ν_3, A_1, sym. NO_2 bend; ν_5, B_1, asym NO_2
bend; ν_6, B_2, out-of-plane pyramid motion).

The assignments of Gatehouse and Comyns are, for the hexahydrate, as shown in Table 1.4b.

For $UO_2(NO_3)_2(H_2O)_2$, $UO_2(NO_3)_2(H_2O)_3$, and $RbUO_2(NO_3)_3$,
Gatehouse and Comyns assumed fairly analogous hexa-coordinate
structures; they argued for the following groupings:

$$\bigtriangledown_U^{\bigtriangledown} \text{ for } RbUO_2(NO_3)_3; \qquad \bigtriangledown_U^{\bigtriangledown}_{H_2O \ \ OH_2} ; \qquad \bigtriangledown_U^{\bigtriangledown}_{\bigtriangledown} \begin{matrix} OH_2 \\ OH_2 \\ OH_2 \end{matrix}$$

Their suggested assignments are given in Table 1.4c.

Although some of the specific assignments of Gatehouse and Comyns may be yet upset, it is clear that the assumption of Sevchenko and Stepanov that only uranyl frequencies appear in the spectrum is incorrect and that the newer assignments represent a substantial improvement over the earlier ones.

Caldow, Van Cleave, and Eager (1960) reported infrared absorption spectra of KBr obtained with pressed disks containing hydrates of uranyl salts (nitrate and sodium zinc acetate), and also reportedly anhydrous uranyl acetate. Their preparation technique involved freeze-drying of aqueous solutions of the uranyl salts and KBr. Their spectra reflected the presence of several uranyl salts in the pressed powders. For example, the appearance of the spectra depended upon the ratio of acetate to bromide in the freeze-dried solutions of $UO_2Ac_2 + KBr$ (see Fig. 1.10e).

The same workers studied also the dependence of absorption intensity (for the 933 cm^{-1} UO_2^{2+} asymmetric stretch frequency) upon concentration of UO_2^{2+} in the nitrate-bromide disks. They found the Beer–Lambert law to hold very well.

Infrared spectra of uranyl chelates and complexes have been reported by many workers. Most of the reports on record are of spectra taken incidental to preparation or other physical studies. In only a few instances have detailed assignments been given or theoretical implications discussed.

Sacconi, Caroti, and Paoletti (1958) studied the infrared absorption (600–3600 cm^{-1}) of uranyl β-diketone chelates and some of their solvates, all in mineral oil or fluorocarbon mulls. These spectra are reproduced in Fig. 1.10f. Belford, Martell, and Calvin (1960) reported infrared absorption (600–3600 cm^{-1}) of five uranyl chelates; the samples were studied as mineral oil mulls. The frequencies appear in Table 1.4d. Comyns, Gatehouse, and Wait (1958) reported studies of three crystalline forms of uranyl acetylacetonate monohydrate and one form of anhydrous uranyl acetylacetonate, including their infrared spectra, Table 1.4e.

Picking out the uranyl frequencies causing the many bands in a

TABLE 1.4c. ASSIGNMENTS OF GATEHOUSE AND COMYNS (1958) FOR INFRARED SPECTRA OF $RbUO_2(NO_3)_3$, $UO_2(NO_3)_2(H_2O)_2$, AND $UO_2(NO_3)_2(H_2O)_3$, WITH DIEKE AND DUNCAN'S VALUES FROM THE FLUORESCENCE SPECTRUM OF $CsUO_2(NO_3)_3$

Assignment	$RbUO_2(NO_3)_3$				$UO_2(NO_3)_2 \cdot 2H_2O$				$UO_2(NO_3)_2 \cdot 3H_2O$				$CsUO_2(NO_3)_3$†	
	^{14}N obs.	^{14}N calc.	^{15}N obs.	^{15}N calc.	^{14}N obs.	^{14}N calc.	^{15}N obs.	^{15}N calc.	^{14}N obs.	^{14}N calc.	^{15}N obs.	^{15}N calc.	^{14}N	^{15}N
ν_5	711 sh		711		706		707		720		721		708, 713	708, 712
ν_3	736		736		743 sh, 748		741 sh, 748		743, 747 sh		740, 746 sh		739, 749	738, 748
ν_6	803		782		801		781		800		779		805	784
B	960		960		951		951		950		951		956	956
ν_2	1023		1019		1026, 1044		1025, 1045		1029, 1043		1033, 1046		1021, 1025	1020, 1024
ν_1	1276		1244		1280, 1311		1241, 1280		1284, 1308		1246, 1279		1277	split
ν_4	1536		1499		1515, 1547		1488 sh, 1519		1517, 1545		1471, 1515		1504, 1519	1471, 1480
ν_2 (H_2O)					1637, 1650		1637, 1650		1631, 1656		1634, 1658			
H_2O					3270, 3360, 3560, 3690 sh		—		3240, 3420, 3630, 3670 sh		—			
$2\nu_5$	1429	1422	1424	1422			1488	1486						
$2\nu_3$	1473	1472	1466	1472			1558	1562			1553	1558		
$2\nu_6$	1608	1606	1570	1564	1608	1602								
$\nu_2 + \nu_5$	1727	1734	1733	1730	1733	1732	1733	1732	1739	1749	1739	1754		

Assignment	$RbUO_2(NO_3)_3$				$UO_2(NO_3)_2\cdot2H_2O$				$UO_2(NO_3)_2\cdot3H_2O$				$CsUO_2(NO_3)_3$†	
	^{14}N obs.	^{14}N calc.	^{15}N obs.	^{15}N calc.	^{14}N obs.	^{14}N calc.	^{15}N obs.	^{15}N calc.	^{14}N obs.	^{14}N calc.	^{15}N obs.	^{15}N calc.	^{14}N	^{15}N
$\nu_2+\nu_3$	1761	1759	1764	1755	1783	1787	1783	1786	1779	1772	1770	1773		
$\nu_2+\nu_3$									1795	1790	1799	1792		
$A+B$	1845	1840*	1845	1840*	1828	1831*	1832	1831*	1828	1824§	1835	1825§		
$2B$					1898	1902	1898	1902						
?														
$\nu_1+\nu_5$	1990	1987	1957	1955	2008	{2017	1972	{1987	1934		1942	1967		
$\nu_1+\nu_3$	2008	2009	1976	1980		{2023		{1982	2004	2004	1969			
$\nu_1+\nu_6$											2024	2025		
$2\nu_2$	2070	{2046	2038	2053‡	2079	2088	2079	2090	2092	{2084	2101	2092		
$A+B+C$		{2053‡	2066							{2086				
$2B+C$									2114	2113‡	2119	2115‡		
$2\nu_5+A$	2299	2299	2268	{2263	2309	2292*	2299	2294*						
$\nu_1+\nu_2$	2326	2339		{2281										
$\nu_4+\nu_6$									2331	2337	2315	2312		
?											2347			
?											2457			
?											2538			
$2\nu_1$	2545	2552	2494	2488	2571	2553	2519	2513						
$2\nu_6+B$	2571	2566	2538	2524	2591	2591	2571	2564						
$\nu_2+\nu_4$														
$A+B+\nu_3$									2558	2567§	2564	2565§		

* Assuming $A = 880$ cm^{-1}.
† Calc. for $CsUO_2(NO_3)_3$, using frequencies in the fluorescence spectrum.
‡ Assuming $C = 213$ cm^{-1}.
§ Assuming $A = 874$ cm^{-1}, as in the fluorescence spectrum. Figures in braces are alternative assignments.

rich spectrum—such as that shown by β-diketone compounds—is somewhat difficult, especially since detailed isotopic substitution work has not been done, and since these frequencies in a strong chelate surely are different from those in simple inorganic salts. However, Sacconi, Caroti, and Paoletti attempted an assignment, placing ν_a at 910–925 cm^{-1} for the acetylacetonates, $\sim$ 910 cm^{-1} for the benzoylacetonates, and 910–913 cm^{-1} for the benzoylaceto-phenonates. They attributed the band of low intensity, at $\sim$ 829 cm^{-1} in the acetylacetonate complexes, to ν_s of the uranyl group. In each

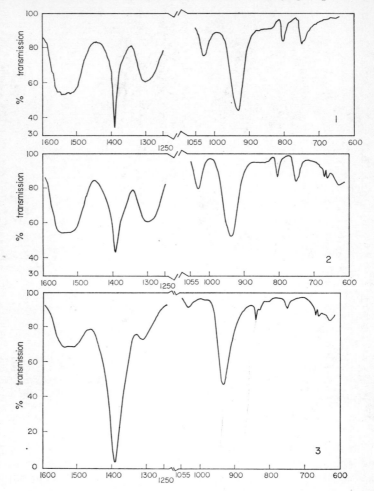

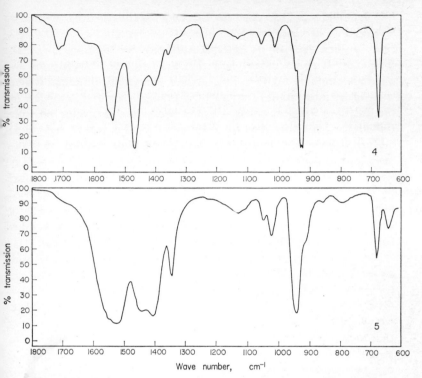

Fig. 1.10e. Infrared spectra of KBr pressed disks containing uranyl salts, demonstrating anion exchange or altered coordination of uranyl ions in preparation of the disks.

Curve 1: $UO_2(NO_3)_2.6H_2O + KBr$ (mixed mechanically).

Curve 2: $UO_2(NO_3)_2. 2H_2O + KBr$ (mixed mechanically).

Curve 3: $UO_2(NO_3)_2.2H_2O + KBr$ (mixed by freeze-drying aqueous solution at $-80°C$). The 830–842 pair, absent in Curve 2, is attributed to KNO_3.

Curve 4: $UO_2(OAc)_2 + KBr$ (mixed by freeze-drying; U : K :: 0.1 : 1.0).

Curve 5: $UO_2(OAc)_2 + KBr$ (mixed by freeze-drying; U : K :: 1000 : 1 in preparation. Extra KBr was mixed in mechanically to make the overall proportions equal to those of Curve 4). The difference between Curves 4 and 5 is attributed to coordination of Br^- to uranyl in the preparation of Curve 4.

Taken from Caldow, Van Cleave, and Eager (1960).

of the anhydrous compounds, uranyl benzoylacetonate (UO_2Bzac_2) and uranyl benzoyl-benzophenonate (UO_2Dbzm_2) they observed a pair of bands of about equal intensity—915 and 887 cm^{-1} for

UO_2Bzac_2, 920 and 886 cm^{-1} for UO_2Dbzm_2. The pair was attributed to ν_a and ν_s; however, the high intensity of the band at $\sim$ 886–887 cm^{-1} argues against its interpretation as the symmetric-stretch frequency. It seems more likely that the two bands are caused by different kinds of OUO^{++} ions at two chemically different lattice sites, or by interaction of a pair of uranyl ions, or by interaction of the uranyl ν_a frequency with a ligand band. It is also quite possible that all the bands ascribed to UO_2^{++} vibrations, in reality, belong to perturbed ligands. Comyns, Gatehouse and Wait assumed that the most intense band in the region 900–950 cm^{-1} is the UO_2^{++} frequency ν_a. For all stable forms of UO_2Acac_2 and $UO_2Acac_2.H_2O$ studied by them, this strong band occurred at 917–925 cm^{-1} (921 $\pm$ 4). For form 3 the most intense peak lay at 905 cm^{-1}; the authors thought some common explanation was needed for this unusually low value for a ν_a frequency and for the unusual red color of the crystal.

The assignments mentioned in the preceding paragraph, as well as some cited by other authors, were made principally by analogy to a few inorganic uranyl salts, which have been shown to have OUO^{++} stretching bands in about the same locations. However, we would be better advised to make assignments without assuming that these bands shift very little, if at all, from compound to compound. Fortunately, a simple method—O^{18} isotope substitution—can be used with relatively few assumptions and will clearly distinguish between UO_2^{++} stretching and bending vibration modes and any ligand vibrations (cf. Equations (1)–(3)). Since O^{18} is now

TABLE 1.4d. INFRARED SPECTRA OF NUJOL MULLS OF
COMPOUNDS OF URANYL ION WITH CHELATING AGENTS
After Belford, Martell and Calvin (1960)

I	I-UO$_2$*	II	II-UO$_2$†	III	III-UO$_2^{\ddagger}$	IV	V
3550							
		3360	3360		3530		
	3100	(3120)	3200	3120	(3170)	3160	3160
2960		2980		2950			
						(2700)	(2700)
(2620)				(2580)			
				2420			
(2350)	(2340)	(2350)	(2280)			2340	2340
				(2200)			
				2000			
		1775		1790			
		1745		1765			

Table 1.4d (*continued*)

I	I-OU₂*	II	II-OU₂†	III	III-OU₂‡	IV	V
(1725)		(1713)					
1708		1680		1680	1650		
1620			1623	1625	(1620)		
	1580		1600			1575	1578
			1555		1568		1550
	1530		1534		1540	1530	
			1514				1520
		(1475)			1460		(1495)
		1455		1450			
1425		(1430)					
1365		1375	1368				
		1350		(1350)			
						1335	1330
1305			1300			(1315)	
						1287	
1252	1268	1282	1280	1270	1258	1270	1270
1252		1230	1233	1220	1210	1214	1215
	1195	1200	1192			(1195)	(1190)
							1175
	(1150)	1160	1150	1160	1145	(1150)	(1160)
			1140		1108	1112	1138
		1095		1085			1080
	1020	1030	1025		1035	1020	1016
		(990)			995	990	975
	(945)		955		945	950	955
	923		928		925	923	923
		900	912	913		910	906
			860			858	(850)
	815	822	837	819		830	827
			800		810	805	
780					775	780	785
				743	745		763
		730	727		(723)	720	725
		700					
							675
		665		655	660		650

* Probably a monohydrate.   † Monohydrate (or dihydrate, possibly).
‡ Tetrahydrate.

I = Acetylacetone.   II = Trifluoroacetylacetone.   III = Hexafluoroacetylacetone.
IV = Reaction product of UO_2^{++} and bis-acetylacetoneethylenediimine, orange crystals. V = Reaction product of UO_2^{++} and bi-acetylacetonetrimethylenediimine, orange crystals.

available in 90–100 per cent purity, we urge that future infrared studies of complex uranyl compounds include comparative studies of the $O^{16}UO^{16++}$ and the $O^{18}UO^{18++}$ compounds. The shifts should be dramatic, ca. 55–60 cm⁻¹ for ν_a, 40–50 cm⁻¹ for ν_s, and ca. 10 cm⁻¹ for ν_b.

TABLE 1.4e. INFRARED ABSORPTION FREQUENCIES OF
URANYL AND THORIUM ACETYLACETONES
After Comyns, Gatehouse, and Wait (1958)

Uranyl acetylacetone							Thorium acetyl-acetone
Form 1 hydrate	Form 2 hydrate	Form 3 hydrate	Form 3 trans.	Form 1 anhyd.	Form 2 anhyd.	Form 3 anhyd.	
		761					765
		(774)					
780		781		777	778	778	779
793	799		799				792
	805		805				805
814				816	816	816	
		825					
	835	830	836	837	838	837	
					(903)		
	912	918	910	(912)	(910)	914	923
917	*925*	*905*	*924*	*924*	*925*	*926*	
(943)		(942)	(947)				943
1012	1014	1017	1014	1012	1014	1019	1018
	1024		1022	1022	1024	1024	
(1032)	(1031)		(1032)				
		1176	1171	1172		1172	
1195	1198	1190	1200	1200	1200	1200	1193
1271	1272	1272	1276	1264	1264	1264	1267
		(1280)		1279	1277	1279	
1361	1348	(1370)	1348	1350	1351	1351	1401
(1431)	1427	1431	1433	(1437)	(1437)	1435	
1524	1531	1534	1531	1531	1529	1529	1531
1572	1572	1580	1577	1575	1570	1567	1585
1577							
				1592	(1590)	(1590)	
(1650)	(1637)	1647	1639				
3205	(3090)	3205	×				
(3320)	3255	3362	×				
	3580		×				

Units, cm^{-1}. Approximate positions of shoulders are given in parentheses. Regions marked × were not examined with the lithium fluoride prism. "Form 3 trans." denotes a sample of the form 3 monohydrate which had spontaneously transformed into a yellow form at room temperature.

NOTES

Form 1 was stable, occurring in orthorhombic and monoclinic modifications by recrystallization from dichloroethane. It appeared as yellow crystals.

Form 2 was a stable, monoclinic yellow crystal obtained by spontaneous transition of Form 3 or by crystallization from an aqueous solution of uranyl nitrate and acetylacetone.

Form 3 was an unstable, orthorhombic red needle obtained from the original aqueous solution.

Frequencies printed in italic type are assigned to $\nu_a(UO_2^{++})$ by Comyns Gatehouse, and Wait.

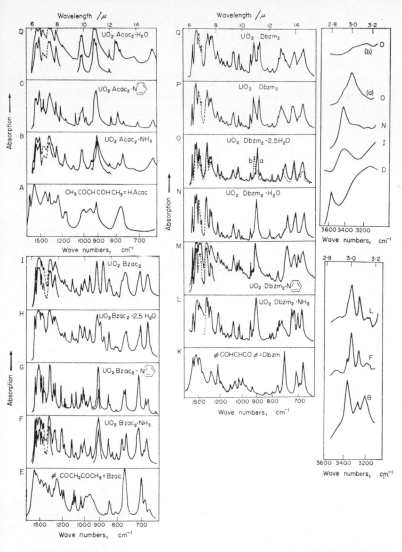

FIG. 1.10f. Infrared absorption spectra of some uranyl β-diketones and their addition compounds. All were mulls in mineral oil. Sample *P* was made by drying a hydrate; *Q*, by benzene crystallization. After Sacconi, Caroti, and Paoletti (1958).

4. Analysis of Uranyl Spectrum by Dieke and Co-workers

As mentioned above, an investigation of the absorption and fluorescence spectra of a number of uranyl salts was undertaken in 1942–44, first at Columbia University and later at the Johns Hopkins

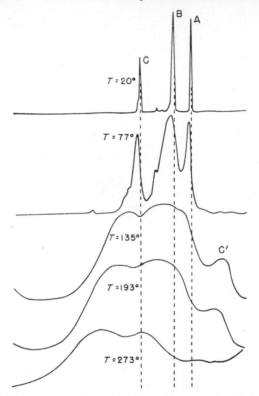

FIG. 1.11. Temperature changes in the structure of the third group in the fluorescence spectrum of $CsUO_2(NO_3)_3$. After Dieke, Duncan, *et al.*

University under the Manhattan project. Remarkably sharp photographs and precise measurements of the fluorescence and absorption bands were obtained in this work; the intensities and the shapes of the individual bands were determined by photoelectric spectrophotometry. These investigations have been reported by Dieke and co-workers (Dieke and Duncan, 1949).

We will present here the general results of this study; some additional data on individual compounds will be given in Section 5.

4.1. *Temperature Effect*

The transformation of uranyl spectra at low temperatures, discovered by the Becquerels and Kamerlingh Onnes (cf. Section 2.1)

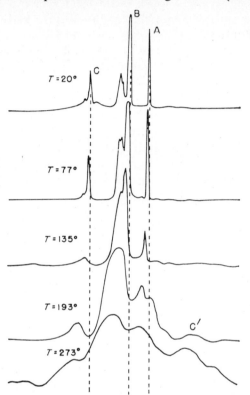

FIG. 1.12. Temperature changes in the structure of the third group in the fluorescence spectrum of cesium uranyl chloride. After Dieke, Duncan *et al.*

and observed on many salts by Nichols and Howes (cf. p. 6 and Fig. 1.20) and Levshin and Sheremetjev (p. 20), was studied by Dieke and co-workers by photoelectric spectrophotometry. The results are illustrated by Figs. 1.11 and 1.12. Figure 1.11 shows a group in the fluorescence spectrum of a crystal of cesium uranyl nitrate, $CsUO_2(NO_3)_3$, at five temperatures from 20° to 273°K. The three bands, *A*, *B*, and *C* appear as sharp as atomic lines at 20°K. At 77°K they are considerably broadened and displaced by about 10 cm^{-1} towards the longer waves; at 135°K they are fused into a single, three-peaked band. A new "anti-Stokes" band, *C'*, appears at that temperature at the short wave side of band *A*. At 193° and 273°K all one sees is a single broad band with two flat peaks, of which one is situated about 100 cm^{-1} toward the longer waves from the original line *C* and the other about the same distance from the center of gravity of the lines *B* and *A*. The peak *C'* has all but disappeared at room temperature, while increased absorption has appeared at still shorter waves.

Figure 1.12 shows a similar transformation of a band group in the fluorescence spectrum of a uranyl double chloride. As mentioned before on p. 14 (Fig. 1.8), the "fine structure" is visible, in this case, even at room temperature.

The explanation of the temperature effect already was indicated in Section 1. At room temperature fluorescence originates in various vibrational levels of the excited electronic state, including not only those of the individual ion UO_2^{++} but also those of the associated anions, water molecules, and of the crystal lattice as a whole. As the temperature is lowered, the bands originating in levels involving excitation of the high-frequency fundamental vibrations, ν_a and ν_s (anti-Stokes bands), are the first to disappear; at still lower temperatures the somewhat slower vibrations involving the frequency ν_b and the still slower lattice vibrations also are "frozen" until the non-vibrating electronic state becomes the only initial level of emission; the remaining fluorescence bands are then those leading from this level to the non-vibrating ground level and to the few vibrational levels of the ground state that can combine with the vibrationless upper level according to the Franck–Condon rule.

Measurements of uranyl salt spectra at the temperature of liquid helium (4.2°K) by Samojlov (1948) have been described in Section 2.

4.2. *Analysis of Uranyl Spectrum: Electronic States*

The four last columns in Table 1.7 contain the frequencies corresponding to the excitation of the several upper electronic states, derived by Dieke and co-workers from the absorption spectra of uranyl salts. In Fig. 1.13 the lower half shows schematically the arrangement of vibrational states over the ground electronic state, while the upper half indicates the arrangement of four excited electronic states; only the sequence of v_a quanta and a single v_b doublet is shown for excited states.

In addition to the superposition of transitions leading to several electronic states, the complexity of the absorption spectrum (as compared to the fluorescence spectrum) may be due to a non-vanishing orbital momentum of some excited states (Π, Δ, etc.), to stronger interaction between the excited ion and the associated anions or molecules and, possibly, to a non-linear configuration of the excited ion. Despite this complexity, Dieke and co-workers found it possible to order the most important absorption bands into a system similar to that used in the interpretation of the fluorescence spectrum, i.e. to interpret them as combinations of an electronic transition with the excitation of vibrations of the types v_s, v_a, or v_b. Studies of isotopic effects have helped in this identification. The influence of polarization on absorption helps to separate bands corresponding to the several electronic transitions (since the component of a given electric dipole oscillation in a given plane in the crystal is determined primarily by the two electronic states whose combination produces this oscillation).

4.3. *Analysis of Uranyl Spectrum: Dichroism, the "Yellow" and the "White" Absorption Spectrum*

Howes and co-workers (1915, 1916, 1919, pp. 102–31) noted that crystals of uranyl double chlorides are dichroic. When a beam of white, linearly polarized light passes through them in appropriate crystallographic direction, they appear of different color, depending on the angle between the plane of polarization and the crystallographic axis. This means that in these crystals certain electromagnetic vibrations (or, in the language of quantum theory, oscillations of the virtual dipole associated with certain electronic transitions) occur preferentially in a definite crystallographic direction. The spectral bands which correspond to these vibrations are absorbed most strongly when the electric vector of the incident light vibrates in this direction. Inversely, the emission of the corresponding band in fluorescence will occur preferentially in the direction normal to the plane in which the corresponding oscillation occurs, and the fluorescence light will be polarized more or less strongly, depending on the direction of observation.

Nichols and Howes mounted triclinic crystals of hydrated uranyl double chlorides of sodium, ammonium, or rubidium so that the light beam fell in the direction of the *c*-axis; in the case of the (anhydrous) cesium uranyl chloride, the light was directed parallel to the *b*-axis. Under these conditions two different absorption spectra could be obtained for light beams polarized in two mutually perpendicular planes. The crystals appeared greenish-yellow in one

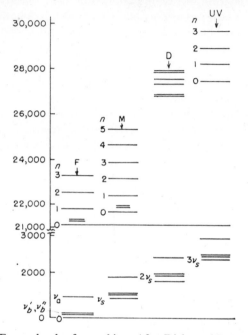

Fig. 1.13. Energy levels of uranyl ion. After Dieke and Duncan (1949).

case ("green spectrum") and yellowish-white in the other ("white spectrum").

Similarly, the *fluorescence spectrum* could be divided into two spectra ("green" and "white") depending on the polarization of its bands. The fluorescence bands of the uranyl double chlorides at $+20°C$ can often be considered as unresolved doublets (cf. p. 56); polarization experiments indicated that one component of the doublet often belongs to the "green" and the other to the "white" spectrum. The relation between the two types of bands in the *absorption spectrum* appeared less simple, but here, too, many bands proved to be doublets, consisting of one "green" and one "white" component. As the temperature was lowered to $-185°C$, the two systems changed in sharpness and relative intensity.

Similar observations were made by Dieke and co-workers. They, too, noted that in properly oriented single crystals of uranyl double chlorides or nitrates the absorption spectra were different for light beams polarized in two mutually perpendicular planes. By using a calcite rhomb between crystal and spectrograph slit, the absorption spectrum could be divided into two spectra—one for the ordinary and one for the extraordinary beam. Crystals of uranyl double chlorides or nitrates are thin plates with the axis of optical asymmetry (which probably coincides with the O—U—O axis in the UO_2^{++} ion) in the plane of the plate. The two light beams fell normally on the face of the plate and were polarized perpendicular and parallel to the optical axis, respectively. Most of the absorption bands could be observed at low temperatures only in one of the two polarized beams. A few appeared in both, but with different relative intensities and with slightly different wave lengths. This strong dichroism made the crystals appear differently colored in the two transmitted beams. When the transmitted light was polarized parallel to the optical axis, little absorption occurred in the blue and the crystals appeared whitish ("white spectrum"). Blue light polarized normally to the optical axis was absorbed much more strongly than blue light polarized parallel to the axis, and in the so-polarized beam the crystals appeared yellow ("yellow spectrum," equivalent to Nichols and Howes' "green spectrum").

The differences in polarization must be taken as indicating a further multiplicity of excited electronic states in addition to that derived from the existence of the "fluorescent," "magnetic," and "ultraviolet" series (see below).

4.4. *Analysis of Uranyl Spectrum: Vibrational Frequencies ν_s, ν_a, and ν_b*

The main reason for identifying the frequency 810–880 cm^{-1} with the symmetric bond frequency ν_s was given before (p. 7): it is its strong coupling with electronic transitions, revealed by the excitation of several (up to 8) quanta of this vibration in electronic absorption and fluorescence bands.

Attribution of the higher frequency ($\nu \simeq 900 \text{ cm}^{-1}$) to the anti-symmetric bond vibration also seems certain. It is supported by the analysis of the isotope effect and by the frequency values. According to Equation (2), the ratio ν_s/ν_a should be 1.065; the observed ratios of the two frequencies are $956/884 = 1.081$ for cesium uranyl nitrate and $916/836 = 1.096$ for cesium uranyl chloride.

An argument *against* this interpretation is that symmetry considerations make simultaneous excitation of ν_s and ν_a appear impossible; but, as mentioned once before, exclusion rules of this type apply strictly to free gaseous emitters or absorbers. (For other arguments and an alternative interpretation of the 210 cm^{-1} frequency see p. 12.)

In some compounds, such as $CsUO_2(NO_3)_3$, there is only one strong band in addition to those accounted for by ν_s and ν_a, and its interpretation as $\nu_s + \nu_b$ appears natural. However, this band has three components, and the frequency ν_b must thus be triple, while theoretically one would expect only a doublet (p. 6).

The frequencies ν_s, ν_a, and ν_b vary somewhat from compound to compound. Already Nichols and Howes knew that the intervals in the fluorescence band series of uranyl compounds (which we now know to be equal to the symmetric bond vibration frequency, ν_s) are not quite constant. Further examples of such variations were given by Pant (1944, 1945). The highest ν_s frequencies (up to 888 cm^{-1}), indicating the strongest U—O bond, were observed in simple and double uranyl nitrates; lower values (830–860 cm^{-1}) were found in chloride, acetate, and sulfate, and the lowest one (804–815 cm^{-1}) was found in carbonate and phosphate.

Exact determinations of ν_s values at low temperatures for a number of uranyl compounds were made by Dieke and co-workers. They were able to determine the antisymmetric frequencies, ν_a, and the changes which ν_s and ν_a undergo with increasing intensity of vibration.

Table 1.6 contains the values of ν_a derived from the fluorescence series $\nu_F - n\nu_s - \nu_a$. The decline of the values in the vertical asymmetric vibration is the result of a growing number of quanta of the symmetric vibration.

In the second and third column of Table 1.7, the vibrational frequencies ν_s and ν_a of the ground state are given for a larger variety of solid uranyl salts.

TABLE 1.5. SYMMETRIC VIBRATION FREQUENCIES (IN cm⁻¹) OF THE GROUND STATE OF THE UO_2^{++} ION After Dieke and Duncan (1949)

Interpretation	Double nitrates, $XUO_2(NO_3)_3$				Uranyl nitrate, $UO_2(NO_3)_2$		Double chlorides, $X_2UO_2Cl_4$	
	Cs	Rb	K	NH_4	$3H_2O$	$6H_2O$	Cs_2	K_2
ν_s	883.98	887.89	875.46	885.67	873.98	863.85	836.10	831.83
$(2\nu_s - \nu_s)$	879.76	883.12	871.38	885.01	870.79	862.58	832.85	833.41
$(3\nu_s - 2\nu_s)$	878.60	882.16	869.56	...	...	...	830.51	...
$(4\nu_s - 3\nu_s)$	876.32	879.79	867.13	...	...	...	828.14	...

TABLE 1.6. ASYMMETRIC BOND VIBRATION FREQUENCIES (IN cm⁻¹) OF THE GROUND STATE OF THE UO_2^{++} ION After Dieke and Duncan (1949)

Interpretation	Double nitrates, $XUO_2(NO_3)_3$				Uranyl nitrate, $UO_2(NO_3)_2$		Double chlorides, $X_2UO_2Cl_4$		
							Cs_2	K_2	
	Cs	Rb	K	NH_4	$3H_2O$	$6H_2O$		20°K	70°K
$(\nu_s + \nu_a) - \nu_s$	956.20	962.07	949.91	959.41	948.12	940.99	906.26	903.18	902.89
$(2\nu_s + \nu_a) - 2\nu_s$	951.82	955.64	944.34	956.43	941.47	935.95	909.74	901.75	902.04
$(3\nu_s + \nu_a) - 3\nu_s$	948.22	951.91	940.49	951.56	936.32	931.38	904.82	...	...
$(4\nu_s + \nu_a) - 4\nu_s$	942.71	946.25	935.09	...	930.11	938.50	899.03	...	...

TABLE 1.7. SPECTROSCOPIC CONSTANTS OF SOLID URANYL SALTS AT 20°K
After Dieke and Duncan (1949)

Compound	ν_s	ν_a	ν_E			
			Fluorescence series	Magnetic series	Difference series	Ultraviolet series
Nitrates						
$UO_2(NO_3)_2.3H_2O$	874.0	948.1	20,778.7			
$UO_2(NO_3)_2.6H_2O$	863.9	941.0	20,578.3	21,480	23,219	27,196
$CsUO_2(NO_3)_3$	884.0	956.2	21,089.6	21,693.2		26,832
Impurity in above	876.0	949.8	20,947.5			
$RbUO_2(NO_3)_3$	887.9	962.1	21,199.4	21,796.8	23,801	26,959
$KUO_2(NO_3)_3$	875.5	949.9	21,183.0	21,873		
$NH_4UO_2(NO_3)_3$	885.7	959.4	21,097.7			
$Rb_2UO_2(NO_3)_4$	861.3	937.7	20,817.8			
$K_2UO_2(NO_3)_4$	870.3	949.5	20,807.8			
Chlorides						
$Cs_2UO_2Cl_4$	836.1	916.3	20,096.3	22,245.4	22,975	26,185
Impurity in above	827.9	891.2	19,958.3			
Impurity in above	827.7	904.6	19,728.2			
Impurity in above	827.1	905.2	19,521.4			
$Rb_2UO_2Cl_4.2H_2O$	831.8	903.2	19,961.2	22,279.5		
$K_2UO_2Cl_4.2H_2O$	831.6	902.9	19,969.9			
Sulfates						
$Cs_2UO_2(SO_4)_2.3H_2O$	860.5	923.1	20,593.6			
$Rb_2UO_2(SO_4)_2$	838.2		20,390.2			
$K_2UO_2(SO_4)_2$	827		20,389		22,680	27,702
$(NH_4)_2UO_2(SO_4)_2$	840		20,358		22,544	27,635
Acetates						
$CsUO_2(CH_3COO)_3$	842.2	920.0	20,992.1			
$RbUO_2(CH_3COO)_3$	852.1	924.0	21,049.4	21,800		
$NaUO_2(CH_3COO)_3$	855.2	927.2	21,135.0	21,912	23,820	27,140
$NH_4UO_2(CH_3COO)_3$	847		21,056	21,811	23,740	26,876
$MgUO_2(CH_3COO)_4$			20,996	21,725	23,636	27,568
$PbUO_2(CH_3COO)_4$	853		20,958			
Carbonate						
$K_2UO_2(CO_3)_2$	808	856	20,943			27,775

Table 1.5 shows the frequencies ν_s derived from the successive members of the fluorescence series, $\nu_F - n\nu_s$, in the fluorescence spectrum of several UO_2^{++} salts. The decline of ν_s with increasing

excitation of the symmetric vibration, shown in vertical columns of Table 1.5, indicates the extent of deviation of the O—U—O system from harmonic conditions.

4.5. *Zeeman Effect*

Dieke and Duncan (1949, p. 73) could observe no Zeeman splitting in the fluorescence spectrum of solid uranyl salts: The same was true of the *absorption spectrum* of certain of them; a Zeeman effect appeared, however, in some of the absorption lines of others. There the lines subject to Zeeman splitting formed a separate series which was designated as "magnetic series" (symbol M). The name was used also for an analogous series of lines in compounds in which no Zeeman effect was noticeable, (cf. Table 1.7). For the Zeeman effect to appear, the O—U—O direction in the crystal must be a symmetry axis; in this case, the angular momentum around this axis is quantized (quantum number λ), and except for the states for which $\lambda = 0$ (Σ states), all other spin singlet states ($\Pi, \Delta \ldots$) are doubly degenerate in the absence of a magnetic field (since the λ vector can have two opposite directions). This degeneracy is removed by the application of a magnetic field parallel to the axis of symmetry. The lines in which λ is the same for both terms must remain single in the magnetic field and polarized parallel to the field. The lines for which $\Delta\lambda = \pm 1$ must split into two components which are circularly polarized but appear linearly polarized (normally to the field) when viewed at right angles to the magnetic vector.

These theoretical expectations were confirmed by observations, mainly in the absorption spectrum of $CsUO_2(NO_3)_3$. The crystals of this salt have a threefold axis of symmetry parallel to the U—O direction. When a single crystal of this salt is placed in the magnetic field with the symmetry axis parallel to the field vector, many lines are split into doublets. No splitting is observed when the optical axis is normal to the field. The magnitude of the observed splitting (about 2 cm^{-1} in a field of 24 kG) corresponds, within the limits of error, to the theoretical value (which is 0.0935 cm^{-1}, per kG).

The fact that of the several electronic transitions involved in the absorption spectrum only one is affected by the magnetic field suggests, but does not prove, that all the other observed series—except the M series—are due to $\Sigma \rightarrow \Sigma$ transitions. (That the ground state is a $^1\Sigma$ state follows from the absence of large permanent paramagnetism at low temperatures; the lines showing no Zeeman splitting are expected to lead to excited states of the same type.) The upper electronic state of the magnetic series would then be a Π state. But there is room for other interpretations (see Chapter 5).

If absorption were due to a multipole (rather than a weak dipole) transition (cf. p. 54), lines with $\Delta\lambda \geqslant 2$ (e.g. $\Delta \to \Sigma$ transitions) could appear; these could give rise to more complex Zeeman patterns. The fact that only doublets have so far been observed in the magnetic field indicates that the uranyl spectrum contains only lines with $\Delta\lambda = 0$ or 1, and this in turn argues for the attribution of this spectrum to a weak dipole transition.

The crystals of $RbUO_2(NO_3)_3$, with a structure similar to that of the cesium uranyl double nitrate, show a similar magnetic splitting, and one may expect the same behavior from other uniaxial uranyl salts. In *biaxial* crystals, on the other hand, no degeneracy in respect to the O—U—O axis exists, even in states with a non-vanishing momentum around this axis, since the asymmetry of the internal electric field is enough to cause a separation. In agreement with this, no magnetic splitting is observed in the absorption spectra of biaxial crystals, such as $CsUO_2Cl_4$ and $K_2UO_2(SO_4)_2$.

4.6. *Isotope Effect*

The isotope effect was studied by Dieke, Duncan, and co-workers by preparing uranyl salts enriched in U^{235}, N^{15}, O^{17}, O^{18}, and H^2. The substitution of uranyl or oxygen isotopes affects the vibrational frequencies in the UO_2^{++} ion itself; the substitution of nitrogen or hydrogen isotopes, only vibrations involving the nitrate anion or the associated water molecules (in hydrated salts). The occurrence of spectral shifts caused by nitrogen and hydrogen isotope substitutions thus permits the identification of lines involving excitation of vibrations in crystal elements other than the uranyl ion itself. For a detailed discussion of these effects, we refer to the monograph of Dieke and Duncan; here we will present only a brief summary of observations concerning the effect of the U^{235}—U^{238} and O^{16}—O^{18} substitution.

Assuming simple elastic force between the uranium atom and the oxygen atoms in UO_2^{++}, the effect of isotopic substitutions on vibrational frequencies can be calculated theoretically (from equations (1) to (3) and the somewhat more complex equation for the asymmetric molecule $O^{18}UO^{16}$).

Table 1.8 shows the expected ratios of frequencies for the six isotopic molecules. For the bending vibration (ν_b) these ratios are expressed in terms of the parameter $c = \sqrt{(2d/f)}$, where d and f are the elastic constants of the U—O bond vibration and the bending vibration respectively (cf. p. 7).

TABLE 1.8. CALCULATED OXYGEN- AND URANIUM-ISOTOPE EFFECTS
$(c = \sqrt{(2d/f)})$

		Ratios of analogous frequencies		
		O^{16}—O^{16}	O^{16}—O^{18}	O^{18}—O^{18}
ν_s	U^{238}	1.00000	0.96149	0.94281
	U^{235}	1.00000	0.96159	0.94281
ν_a	U^{238}	1.06511	1.04827	1.01160
	U^{235}	1.06591	1.04900	1.01245
ν_b	U^{238}	$1.06511c$	$1.03870c$	$1.01160c$
	U^{235}	$1.06591c$	$1.03953c$	$1.01245c$

TABLE 1.9. EXPECTED ISOTOPIC SHIFTS IN cm^{-1} FOR
SUBSTITUTION U^{238}—U^{235}

	O^{16}—O^{16}	O^{16}—O^{18}	O^{18}—O^{18}
ν_s	0	0.09	0
ν_a	0.71	0.64	0.75
ν_b	0.17	0.17	0.18

For the symmetric vibration in the molecule $O^{16}UO^{16}$, in which the uranium atom remains at rest, the effect of the substitution of U^{235} is nil. It becomes finite but is still very small, for the similar vibration in the asymmetric molecule, $O^{18}UO^{16}$. The largest uranium-isotope effect can be expected in the asymmetric vibration, ν_a.

The effect of substituting O^{18} for O^{16} is considerably larger than that of the uranium substitution (cf. Tables 1.9 and 1.10).

Shifts of about 0.7 cm^{-1} have been observed by Dieke *et al.* in many lines of the (low-temperature) fluorescence spectrum of $CsUO_2(NO_3)_3$ when U^{235} was substituted for U^{238}. These lines must involve the excitation of a quantum of the antisymmetric vibration, ν_a. Absence of shifts of 1.4 or 2.1 cm^{-1} indicates that only one quantum of asymmetric vibration is excited in coupling with the

TABLE 1.10. EXPECTED OXYGEN ISOTOPE EFFECTS IN cm^{-1}

	O^{16}—O^{16} frequency	O^{16}—O^{18} shift	O^{18}—O^{18} shift
ν_s	860	33.1	50.2
ν_a	940	14.9	47.3
ν_b	220	5.5	11.1

electronic transition. In the fluorescence spectrum of $Cs_2UO_2Cl_4$, in addition to isotopic shifts of 0.6–0.8 cm^{-1}, shifts of ~ 0.3 cm^{-1} and of 1.1–1.3 cm^{-1} also have been noted.

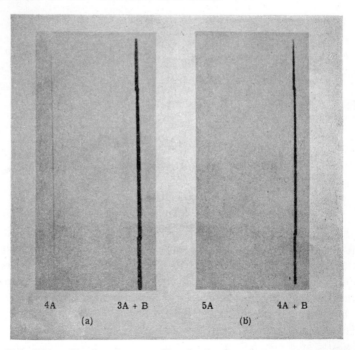

4A   3A + B   5A   4A + B

(a)   (b)

FIG. 1.14a. Uranium-isotope effect in the fluorescence spectrum of $CsUO_2(NO_3)_3$. Middle, enriched sample; top and bottom, ordinary sample.

Figure 1.14a shows a typical uranium isotope effect in the fluorescence spectrum of cesium uranyl nitrate. The "U^{235}" specimen was an enriched sample containing 79 per cent U^{235}.

In the *absorption* spectrum of $Cs_2UO_2Cl_4$, the calculated shift of the v_a^* frequency (731 cm^{-1}) is 0.6 cm^{-1}. Experimentally, shifts up to 1.62 cm^{-1} have been noted. Three quanta of asymmetric vibration, v_a^*, must be acquired in lines showing this strong shift (expected shift for 3 v_a^* is 1.8 cm^{-1}). Lines in which *two* v_a^* quanta are acquired show an isotopic shift of 1.3–1.4 cm^{-1} (expected, 1.2 cm^{-1}). Observed shifts which are *smaller* than 0.6 cm^{-1} may be due to lines whose terms are perturbed by the proximity of terms containing v_a^* vibrations.

Only small uranium isotope shifts, attributable to perturbation effects, have been observed in the absorption spectrum of $CsUO_2(NO_3)_3$, indicating that v_a^* vibration quanta are not involved in any of the measured lines (cf. p. 64).

The results of O^{18} *substitution* (1.36 per cent O^{18}) are, as expected, far more pronounced. For example, isotope shifts up to 166 cm^{-1} have been observed in the fluorescence spectrum of $CsUO_3(NO_3)_3$. Such a shift is to be expected, according to Table 1.10, for the excitation of five quanta of symmetric vibrations, v_s, in the asymmetric molecule $O^{18}UO^{16}$. The observed shifts for the excitation of single vibrations are as follows:

In nitrate	In chloride	*Expected* (*Table* 1.10)
31.4	29.7	33.1 cm^{-1}
13.7	16.3	14.9 cm^{-1}

Agreement with the simple model is as good as could reasonably be expected.

4.7. *Intensity Studies: Lifetime of Excited State*

Absolute intensity measurements of a number of absorption bands were made by Dieke *et al.* at 77°K rather than at 20°K, because it was easier to measure the contours of broader bands. Measurements were made with a 1.5 mm thick crystal of $CsUO_2(NO_3)_3$.

Values of the order of 3.7×10^{-8} (resonance band at 4740.36 Å); 8.2×10^{-8} (4698.91 Å) and 1.36×10^{-8} (4608.45 Å) were obtained for the "electronic strength," f, of some of the strongest bands. A summation over all the bands belonging to the same electronic transition (e.g. all bands of the fluorescent series) could not change the magnitude of these values by more than one unit ($\Sigma f \simeq 10^{-7}$). This is a value expected theoretically for *quadrupole* (rather than dipole) radiations. It may be, however, that we deal here with a very weak (forbidden) dipole transition; this alternative is supported by Vavilov and Levshin's interpretation of experiments on de-polarization of uranyl fluorescence.

An f number of 10^{-7} means that the natural lifetime of the excited electronic state is of the order of 10^{-1} sec. This value can be compared with the experimentally determined lifetime of fluorescence of uranyl salts. According to Chapter 3, the latter is much shorter (about 5×10^{-4} sec). Dieke saw here no contradiction, pointing out that only an upper limit for the actual duration of fluorescence is given by the natural lifetime of the excited state. However, the reduction of natural lifetime by a factor of 200 (from 10^{-1} to 5×10^{-4} sec) must mean a corresponding reduction in the yield of fluorescence (from 100 per cent to 0.5 per cent), while the actual yield of uranyl fluorescence in solution was estimated—albeit by a very rough and indirect method—as close to 100 per cent! The discrepancy with Dieke's results remained to be explained. The extinction curve on non-hydrolyzed uranyl ions in solutions indicates a peak absorption coefficient of the order of 10. Assuming a band width of 100 mμ, or about 5000 cm^{-1}, with an average absorption coefficient of $\alpha \simeq 1$, this corresponds to a mean lifetime of the order of 10^{-4} sec in agreement with the fluorescence measurements.

Another interesting result of the intensity measurements relates to the *width* of the fluorescence bands. At very low temperature, the lines belonging to impurities were often found to be sharper than those of the UO_2^{++} ions themselves; among the latter the lines of the first group were generally sharper than those belonging to the second and the subsequent groups. A plausible and significant explanation of this phenomenon is that the band is broadened by electronic resonance between neighboring UO_2^{++} ions (a resonance which cannot develop in the case of impurities irregularly scattered in the lattice). Excitation of the symmetric vibration, ν_s, appears to enhance this resonance. The resonance broadening implies the occurrence of excitation energy transfers between neighboring UO_2^{++} ions in the lattice. A quantitative analysis leading to an estimate of the frequency of these exchanges would be of interest for the

understanding of photochemical reactions and fluorescence phenomena in uranyl salts.

5. Additional Spectroscopic Data on some Uranyl Salts

5.1. *Fluorides*

Pant and Sakhwalkar (1944) made a study of the fluorescence
spectrum of solid, hydrated uranyl fluoride at $-185°C$. They
assumed that the simplest vibrational structure of any uranyl salt
can be expected in fluoride. They arrived at Table 1.11 for the main
fluorescence bands (italic indicates intensity).

Using three normal frequencies (863, 242, and 928 cm^{-1}) for the
ground state and a single frequency (150 cm^{-1}) for the excited state,
a term diagram could be constructed accounting for all bands in
Table 1.11 within ± 10 cm^{-1}. The $B1$ band (20,082 cm^{-1}) is the
resonance band. Some combinations in the table are prohibited,
but as mentioned before, the exclusion rules are not strict. Excitation
with short waves ($\nu_{exc} > 27,000$ cm^{-1}) produced no lines with
$\nu > 20,234$ cm^{-1}; this means that all vibrational quanta of the
excited state, except one, are lost before the emission of fluorescence
(the remaining quantum gives rise to the "anti-Stokes" band series
in the first row of the table).

TABLE 1.11. FREQUENCIES (IN cm^{-1}) OF FLUORESCENCE BANDS
OF UO_2F_2 AT $-185°C$

Series	Group					$\Delta\nu$ (cm^{-1})
	1	2	3	4	5	
A	20,234	19,366	18,504	17,641	...	864
B	*20,082*	*19,217*	*18,353*	17,492	16,640	863
C	...	19,150	18,289	*17,427*	16,577	862
D	...	19,124	18,263	17,404	...	861
E	...	18,970	...	...	...	...

Dieke and Duncan (1949) reported that the sample of UO_2F_2
they prepared showed only faint fluorescence with no resolution
into lines even at 20°K. The contrast between this finding and that
of Pant may have been due to differences in water content of the
sample. A table is given by Dieke and Duncan for the absorption

spectrum of the double fluoride, $K_3UO_2F_5$, at 20°K. Similarly to the $CsUO_2(NO_3)_3$ spectrum it has a double resonance line, *two* double lines in the $\nu_F + \nu_a$ group, *three* double lines in the $\nu_F + 2\nu_a$ group, etc. The reason for such a splitting, suggested in the case of nitrate (resonance with an NO_3^- frequency), could not be valid for the fluoride; perhaps, in this case, there is a resonance between the frequencies ν_s and ν_a. According to the same observers, the fluorescence spectrum of $Cs_2UO_2F_4$ shows almost no evidence of the asymmetric frequency, ν_a.

5.2. *Chlorides*

According to Dieke and Duncan (1949), the fluorescence spectrum of the simple uranyl chloride, UO_2Cl_2, varies strongly with the sample used. A very pure, supposedly anhydrous, sample showed no fluorescence at all; samples containing water fluoresced more or less strongly, often with a strong continuous background.

Compared to the spectra of the double chlorides (cf. below), that of UO_2Cl_2 (hydrated) is shifted towards the violet, and the asymmetric vibration, ν_a, occurs with much lower intensity.

The fluorescence spectra of uranyl *double chlorides* have been studied by Nichols and Howes, as well as by Dieke and co-workers. Nichols and Howes investigated four double chlorides: $UO_2Cl_2 \cdot 2KCl \cdot 2H_2O$, $UO_2Cl_2 \cdot 2RbCl \cdot 2H_2O$, $UO_2Cl_2 \cdot 2NH_4Cl \cdot 2H_2O$, and $UO_2Cl_2 \cdot 2CsCl$.

All four crystallize in triclinic plates. Their fluorescence bands are partially resolved into components even at room temperature (cf. Figs. 1.8 and 1.12). Five components could be distinguished at $+20°C$ in six groups and two components in the seventh ("anti-Stokes") band in the ammonium salt; an additional (eighth) band group, also consisting of five components, was discernible at the long-wave end of the spectrum.

Nichols and Howes noted that the groups as a whole were shifted towards the shorter waves with increasing atomic weight of the alkali, ammonium falling between potassium and rubidium in accordance with the general optical properties of this ion. For example, the two strongest bands of the spectrum were found in positions listed in Table 1.12.

As the temperature was lowered from $+20°C$ to $-185°C$, the bands first split into doublets; then one component of each doublet increased in brightness while the other became indistinct or disappeared altogether. The bands observed at $+20°C$ often could be considered as unresolved doublets, the stronger component being the one which is comparatively weak at lower temperatures. One component of the doublet usually belonged to the "white" and one to the "green" spectrum (p. 43).

TABLE 1.12. STRONGEST FLUORESCENCE BANDS OF DOUBLE
CHLORIDES, $UO_2X_2Cl_4.2H_2O$, AT 20°C

	K	NH_4	Rb	Cs
λ	503.9	503.1	502.7	502.4 mμ
λ	525.9	525.0	524.8	523.4 mμ

TABLE 1.13. CHLORIDE SPECTRA STUDIED BY DIEKE AND CO-WORKERS
After Dieke and Duncan (1949)

Compound	Spectrum	$T°$ abs.	Region, (cm^{-1})	No. of lines
$Cs_2UO_2Cl_4$	Fluorescence	20°K	20,102–15,057	170
$Cs_2UO_2Cl_4$	Absorption	20°K	20,092–24,837	682
$K_2UO_2Cl_4.2H_2O$	Fluorescence	20°K	19,967–16,568	22
$K_2UO_2Cl_4.2H_2O$	Fluorescence	77°K	20,059–17,376	27
$K_2UO_2Cl_4.2H_2O$	Absorption	20°K	19,978–28,098	457
$((CH_3)_4N)_2UO_2Cl_4$	Fluorescence	77°K	20,142–16,578	38
$((CH_3)_4N)_2UO_2Cl_4$	Absorption	20°K	20,053–27,413	91

The *absorption spectra* of the double chlorides also are better resolved at room temperature than those of most other uranyl salts. By using several large crystals in series, Howes (1918) (cf. Nichols and Howes (1919, p. 73)) was able to measure absorption bands of the ammonium salt from 18,025 to 27,568 cm^{-1} at 20°C and from 19,459 to 26,575 cm^{-1} at $-185°C$.

With declining temperature the absorption bands were found to shift, generally towards the violet, and split into numerous components.

Dieke and co-workers studied the fluorescence and absorption spectra of several double chlorides. Dieke and Duncan (1949) listed the lines of the spectra indicated in Table 1.13.

The number of lines in the fluorescence spectrum of $Cs_2UO_2Cl_4$ is considerably smaller than in the cesium uranyl nitrate spectrum, undoubtedly because of the absence of a polyatomic group such as NO_3^-.

The electronic transitions ν_F and the vibrational frequencies ν_s and ν_a, derived from the analysis of the spectra listed in Table 1.13, were given in Table 1.7 for $Cs_2UO_2Cl_4$, $RbUO_2Cl_4 \cdot 2H_2O$, and $K_2UO_2Cl_4 \cdot 2H_2O$. The transition ν_M was identified in the cesium and rubidium salts, the transitions ν_D and ν_{UV} in the cesium salt only.

The fluorescence spectra of the (triclinic) dihydrates of $Rb_2UO_2Cl_4$ and $K_2UO_2Cl_4$ resemble each other closer than they do the spectrum of the anhydrous (but probably also triclinic) cesium salt. The vibrational frequencies of all double chlorides are lower than those of the double nitrates. The asymmetric vibrations are strongly excited in all chlorides. In these compounds both the frequencies ν_s and ν_a are narrow doublets, with a separation of about 2 cm^{-1}.

The resonance line has a weak violet satellite in the rubidium and potassium double chloride (but not in the anhydrous cesium salt).

According to Dieke and Duncan (1949), the *absorption spectrum* of the uranyl chlorides appears at the first sight more complex than that of the nitrates [680 bands between 4975 and 4025 Å in $Cs_2UO_2Cl_4$, as against 615 bands between 4740 and 3360 Å in $CsUO_2(NO_3)_3$], but its basic structure is simpler. However, only the first groups (4976–4483 Å) have been analyzed by Dieke. The resonance band (of the fluorescence series) occurs in the "white" spectrum only and lies at 4974.91 Å. Other lines correspond to combinations of this transition with vibrational frequencies of the excited state, identified as $\nu_b^{*\prime}$, $\nu_b^{*\prime\prime}$ (232.61, 237.11 cm^{-1}), ν_s^{*} (713.7 cm^{-1}) and $\nu_a^{*\prime}$, $\nu_a^{*\prime\prime}$, $\nu_a^{*\prime\prime\prime}$ (731.1, 732.4, 734.6 cm^{-1}). The bending vibration is thus double, and the asymmetric bond vibration, triple. In contrast to the conditions in the fluorescence spectrum, several quanta of these vibrations can be excited simultaneously with the absorption of an electronic quantum. In addition to these fairly well identified fundamental UO_2^{++} vibration frequencies, the absorption spectra of the double chlorides show several other repeatedly occurring frequencies, among them 106.86, 116.30, 310.19, 507.89, 510.78, and 538.51 cm^{-1}; some bands correspond to combinations of two or three of these frequencies with the electronic transition. Some of these may belong to separate electronic transitions (as indicated by differences in polarization, described on p. 45), others to vibrations of unknown nature.

Only a few bands in each absorption group are clearly identifiable with corresponding bands in the fluorescence spectrum. The numerical values of their frequencies are slightly higher in fluorescence. (This shift indicates somewhat stiffer binding in the ground state.) Their planes of polarization are the same in absorption and fluorescence.

The fluorescent series has been followed in the cesium salts down to about 4500 Å; from this region down to 3100 Å a number of bands were identified as belonging to the "magnetic" series (p. 49); the lines of these series are wide doublets ($\Delta\nu = 53.6$ cm^{-1}) even in the absence of a magnetic field. Each of the two components is in turn a narrow doublet ($\Delta\nu \simeq 2$ cm^{-1}). Of the two splittings, the wider one can be attributed to internal field asymmetry, while the cause of the smaller one remains unknown. (The smaller interval is of the same order of magnitude as the splitting produced in other uranyl salts by the magnetic fields used in the Zeeman effect study; if this interval—rather than the larger one—were caused by field asymmetry, it should have been possible to obtain a Zeeman effect in this compound, which was not the case.) In this series, too, a second group is situated at a distance of about 708 cm^{-1} from the first group, corresponding to the excitation of one quantum of symmetric vibration combined with the electronic excitation ν_M.

In the fluorescence spectrum of tetramethyl ammonium uranyl chloride [(CH$_3$)$_4$N]$_2$UO$_2$Cl$_4$ at 77°K, each group was found to contain six lines, twice the number found in other chlorides; however, all the lower frequency doublet components disappeared at 20°K.

The *absorption spectrum* of uranyl double chlorides was studied by Dieke and co-workers in considerable detail with anhydrous Cs$_2$UO$_2$Cl$_4$. The separation of this spectrum into a "yellow" and a "white" spectrum was described on p. 45. Some lines appeared in both components, but with different intensities. The "yellow" spectrum contained many more lines than the white one, particularly < 4500 Å. This biaxial crystal forms thin plates; the light beam fell normally to the large face, and the polarization of the "white" component probably corresponded to the O—U—O direction in the plane of the plate (since a similar spectrum was obtained in uniaxial, double nitrate crystals, when light was polarized in the direction of the optical axis, which is the O—U—O direction).

The absorption spectrum continues into the ultraviolet; electron transitions similar to those observed in the same region in cesium uranyl nitrate contribute to this part of the spectrum.

Samojlov (1948) made measurements in liquid helium (4.2°K) of 33 absorption lines ($\lambda < 486.7$ mμ) and 18 fluorescence lines (486.8—540.9 mμ) of UO_2Cl_2.

5.3. *Uranyl Nitrate and Double Nitrates*

Nichols and Howes studied the spectra of uranyl nitrate, $UO_2(NO_3)_2$, at $-180°C$, with different numbers of water molecules.

The rhombic hexahydrate (large single plates) exhibited 55 *fluorescence* bands, 48 of which could be arranged in ten series (cf. Table 1.2) with a constant difference of 860 cm^{-1}. The *absorption* spectrum consisted of a number of similar series, but the constant differences (731, 717, 703, 690 cm^{-1}) varied more widely than in the fluorescence spectrum.

The triclinic *trihydrate* in the form of large single crystals exhibited 63 fluorescence bands, of which 55 formed 12 series with $\Delta\nu = 865$–875 cm^{-1}. In the *absorption* spectrum of the trihydrate, 28 bands were measured, 37 of which were arranged in 9 series with $\Delta\nu = 710$–738 cm^{-1}.

The *dihydrate* could be obtained only as a powder (by drying the trihydrate at 100°C). It showed 74 fluorescence bands, 60 of which could be ordered in 12 series with $\Delta\nu = 876$–883 cm^{-1}. The absorption spectrum had to be obtained by reflection, a less satisfactory method than transmission measurement on single crystals, and only 4 series could be identified.

"*Anhydrous*" nitrate was obtained by reacting UO_2 with N_2O_5; but the products may have contained some water, although certainly $< 2H_2O$. The spectra of such preparations were variable; if free nitric acid was left, bands remained diffuse even at $-180°C$. The fluorescence spectrum of the pure anhydrous nitrate apparently contains, at $-185°C$, only 3 sharp and strong bands.

Figure 1.14b shows the structure of a band group in the fluorescence spectra of $UO_2(NO_3)_2.6H_2O$, $3H_2O$, $2H_2O$ and "anhydrous" nitrate, respectively.

The $\Delta\nu$ in the fluorescence spectrum was found to increase with progressive dehydration from 860 cm^{-1} in hexahydrate to 868 cm^{-1} in trihydrate, 881 cm^{-1} in dihydrate, and 885 cm^{-1} in the "anhydrous" salt (compare Dieke's values for hexahydrate and trihydrate in Table 1.7). This means that the frequency of the higher, i.e. bond vibration in the linear ion O=U=O becomes symmetric the bond becomes stiffer, when the number of water molecules decreases.

No similar systematic shift with hydration was noticeable in the

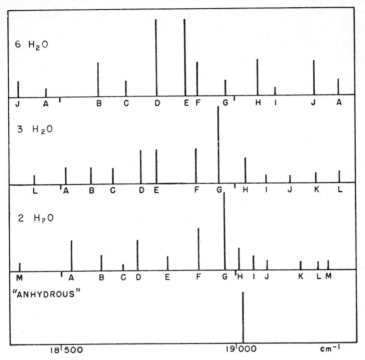

Fig. 1.14b. Comparison of a band group in the low-temperature spectra of different uranyl nitrate hydrates. The spectrum of the hexahydrate contains 7 such groups; that of the trihydrate, 6; the dihydrate, 5; and the anhydrous salt, 3. From Nichols and Howes (1919, p. 128).

absorption spectrum (i.e. in the vibrational quanta of the excited state of the uranyl ion).

The structure of the individual band groups changes with hydration as deeply as with a change in the anion. Nichols and Howes surmised that in both cases the main factor is different *crystal symmetry* rather than different chemical composition. The importance of crystal symmetry is indicated also by the spectra of *double nitrates* (Howes and Wilber, 1917). The bands of the two monoclinic double nitrates $(NH_4)_2UO_2(NO_3)_4.2H_2O$ and $K_2UO_2(NO_3)_4$ had almost identical positions, while the bands of $NH_4UO_2(NO_3)_3$ (trigonal) and $KUO_2(NO_3)_3$ (rhombic) were shifted toward higher frequencies (Fig. 1.15).

The structure of the band groups is similar in all four double nitrates (Fig. 1.15), but different from that in simple uranyl nitrate (Fig. 1.14b).

Dieke, Duncan, and co-workers studied extensively both simple and double uranyl nitrates. The pure electronic transitions and the

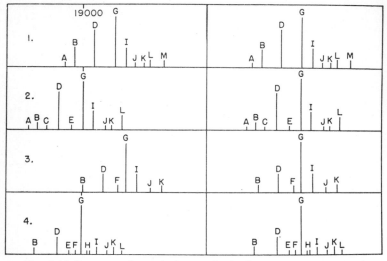

FIG. 1.15. Structure of a typical group in the fluorescence spectrum of double uranyl nitrates at −180°C.
1, $KUO_2(NO_3)_3$: trigonal.   3, $NH_4UO_2(NO_3)_3$: rhombic.
2, $K_2UO_2(NO_3)_4$: monoclinic.   4, $(NH_4)_2UO_2(NO_3)_4$: monoclinic.
The bands occupy their natural positions in the left-hand panel, but have their strongest bands in vertical alignment in the right-hand panel. From Nichols and Howes (1919, p. 138).

vibrational frequencies ν_s and ν_a of the ground states are shown for eight such compounds in Table 1.7. Dieke and Duncan's monograph (1949) contains tables of the spectra listed in Table 1.14.

The $CsUO_2(NO_3)_3$ tables contain fluorescence bands between 4740 and 6419 Å. Of these, the strongest ones can be interpreted (cf. Table 1.15) as combinations of the resonance frequency ν_F with vibrational frequencies ν_s, ν_a, and ν_b. The remaining bands must be

TABLE 1.14. URANYL NITRATE SPECTRA
Studied by Dieke and Duncan (1949)

Compound	T° abs.	Spectrum	Region (cm^{-1})	No. of lines
$CsUO_2(NO_3)_3$	20°K	Fluorescence	21,090–15,575	236
$CsUO_2(NO_3)_3$	20°K	Absorption	21,090–28,748	617
$RbUO_2(NO_3)_3$	20°K	Absorption	21,198–29,049	145
$RbUO_2(NO_3)_3$	77°K	Absorption	21,195–27,549	30
$RbUO_2(NO_3)_3$	20°K	Fluorescence	21,199–16,728	48
$RbUO_2(NO_3)_3$	77°K	Fluorescence	21,192–16,720	39
$KUO_2(NO_3)_3$	77°K	Fluorescence	21,168–18,993	13
$KUO_2(NO_3)_3$	20°K	Absorption	20,168–23,928	13
$UO_2(NO_3)_2.6H_2O$	20°K	Fluorescence	20,624–16,214	50
$UO_2(NO_3)_2.6H_2O$	77°K	Fluorescence	20,622–16,200	45

TABLE 1.15. STRONGEST FLUORESCENCE BANDS OF $CsUO_2(NO_3)_3$ AT 20°K
After Dieke and Duncan (1949)*

ν (cm^{-1})	λ (Å)	$\nu = \nu_F - n\nu_s - x$		Intensity (photoelectric)
		n	x	
20,880.56	4787.81	0	ν_b'	...
20,876.41	4788.76	0	ν_b''	103
20,867.49	4790.81	0	ν_b'''	...
20,205.58	4947.75	1	...	471
20,133.36	4965.50	0	ν_a	902
19,994.08	5000.09	1	$\nu_b' + \nu_b''$	232
19,983.05	5002.85	1	ν_b'''	...
19,325.92	5172.96	2	...	355
19,253.76	5192.35	1	ν_a	1000
19,112.89	5230.62	2	$\nu_b' + \nu_b''$	213
18,447.32	5419.34	3	...	123
18,377.70	5439.87	2	ν_a	468
18,328.67	5454.42	?	?	144
17,504.61	5711.20	3	ν_a	146

* $\nu_F = 21,089.6$ cm^{-1}; $\nu_s = 884.0$ cm^{-1}; $\nu_a = 956.2$ cm^{-1}; $\nu_b' = 209.00$ cm^{-1}; $\nu_b'' = 213.5$ cm^{-1}; $\nu_b''' = 222.07$ cm^{-1}.

attributed to vibrations in which particles other than the UO_2^{++} ion also take part.

In the nitrate absorption spectrum of $CsUO_2(NO_3)_3$ single crystal, Dieke and Duncan listed 615 bands between 4740 and 3360 Å. The "∥ spectrum" was in this case much simpler than the "⊥ spectrum."

In addition to the fluorescent and the magnetic series, a third "ultraviolet" series could be recognized in this spectrum. The resonance band of the fluorescent series lies at 4740.36 Å, and occurs with both polarizations; the magnetic series begins at 4608 Å. The ultraviolet series begins at 3726 Å in the ⊥, and at 3721 Å in the ∥ spectrum.

In each series of the nitrate absorption spectrum, groups of bands are recognizable which are separated by the v_s frequency; however, *two* such frequencies seem to be involved, v_s' and v_s'', giving a progressively increasing number of combinations (v_s' or v_s'' in the first group, $2v_s'$, $2v_s''$ or $v_s'+v_s''$ in the second group, and so on). The values of the two frequencies in the lowest state are $v_s' = 734.1$ and $v_s'' = 766.3$ cm^{-1}. One could ask, why not identify the second vibration with v_a—an interpretation which seems supported by the numerical values? The answer is that such an interpretation is incompatible with the observed isotopic effects. The v_s'-v_s'' split must be therefore attributed to resonance between the symmetric bond vibration in the UO_2^{2+} ion and a crystal vibration of closely similar frequency; some NO_3^- vibrations are known to exist in this region.

The changes in the uranyl nitrate spectrum with decreasing hydration also were studied by Levshin and Sheremetjev (1947) at room temperature and by Sevchenko (1949) at low temperature. They noted that with dehydration the total intensity of fluorescence decreased, frequencies and relative intensities of the lines changed. Sevchenko and co-workers (1951) prepared 6-, 3-, 2- and 1-hydrates with water content within 0.2 per cent of the stoichiometric values and measured their fluorescence spectra at −185°C; many more lines were determined than was done by Nichols and Howes.

The lines found for hydrates with $n < 3$ were quite different from those given by Nichols and Howes. The effect of deuterium substitution was strong in the higher hydrates (Table 1.16).

Table 1.17 shows the effect of H_2O and D_2O on the energy levels (in the first group, at −185°C). v_s values decrease with increasing hydration. Two explanations are possible: The lattice forces may decrease with n, or the vibrating masses may increase (if one assumes that water molecules can participate in vibrations of the UO_2^{++} ion).

Table 1.18, taken from Sevchenko and Stepanov (1951), proves the constancy of structure in groups I to IV. The multiplicity of small frequencies seems indicative of crystal vibrations rather than

TABLE 1.16. URANYL NITRATE SPECTRA MEASUREMENTS
By Sevchenko *et al.* (1951)

Compound	No. of lines	Range, (cm⁻¹)
$UO_2(NO_3)_2.6H_2O$	78	20,670–15,385
$UO_2(NO_3)_2.6D_2O$	58	20,684–15,370
$UO_2(NO_3)_2.3H_2O$	100	20,903–15,303
$UO_2(NO_3)_2.3D_2O$	43	20,777–15,375
$UO_2(NO_3)_2.2H_2O$	32	20,973–16,327
$UO_2(NO_3)_2.2D_2O$	8	20,775–15,405
$UO_2(NO_3)_2.H_2O$	36	20,818–15,405
$UO_2(NO_3)_2.D_2O$	14	20,219–16,969
$UO_2(NO_3)_2.$ . . .	33	20,805–16,270

of vibrations in the uranyl ion. The hydration number n affects ν_s and ν_a but not the third main frequency, ν_b, supporting its interpretation as a lattice vibration rather than as a bending vibration of the uranyl ion (cf. Section 1).

TABLE 1.17. ELECTRONIC (E) AND VIBRATIONAL (ν) LEVELS OF
$UO_2(NO_3)_2.nH_2O$ AND $UO_2(NO_3)_2.n'D_2O$ AT $-185°C$
After Sevchenko *et al.* (1951)

	anh.	H_2O	D_2O	$2H_2O$	$3H_2O$	$3D_2O$	$6H_2O$	$6D_2O$
E	20,802	20,802	. . .	20,776	20,776	20,776	20,588	20,596
ν'_s	882	882	. . .	874	874	874	865	865
ν''_s	878	878	(Weak)	871	871	874	863	863
ν'''_s	875	875	. . .	868	868	868	861	861

Luminescence of polycrystalline coordination compounds of uranyl nitrate with different ligands X were studied by Kobyshev and Suglobov (1958) [$X = 2H_2O$, $3H_2O$, $6H_2O$, ?NH_3, $2C_5H_5N$, $2C_2H_5OC_2H_5$, $2C_4H_9OC_4H_9$, $2(C_2H_4Cl)_2O$, $2O(CH_2)_2O(CH_2)_2\overline{}$, ?$C_2H_5OH$, $2CH_3CN$, $2C_6H_5NO_2$, $2CH_3NO_2$, $2NO_2$, $2(H_2O)$.

$2(C_2H_5OC_2H_5)$, $2(H_2O).2(NO_2)$.] Their work was thought to show that coordination with "Lewis base" molecules is necessary for uranyl ion in a nitrate to show the characteristic structured fluorescence. They reported that at $90°K$ all the coordination compounds except uranyl nitrate amines showed a sharply or moderately sharp structured, fairly intense fluorescence, while anhydrous uranyl acetate showed only a weak, broad, featureless fluorescence.

Kobyshev and Suglobov also noted that the fluorescence maxima regularly shifted to lower frequencies with increasing basicity of the molecules in the solvation or coordination sphere. This effect is shown in the following table:

Added molecule	$\bar{v}_{max}/cm^{-1}$
NH_3	18,850
C_5H_5N	18,970
C_2H_5OH	19,150
$C_2H_5OC_2H_5$	19,850
Dioxane	19,800
$(CH_3)_2CO$	19,800
CH_3CN	18,950
$C_6H_5NO_2$	19,800
CH_3NO_2	20,000
NO_2	20,270

This correlation is somewhat difficult to interpret at present because of the lack of knowledge about the precise structures of the complexes. The observation is in agreement with the red shifts of the absorption bands which Belford, Martell, and Calvin (1960) found upon increasing the basicity of the ligand in the series $(CF_3COCHCOCF_3)_2UO_2.4H_2O$, $(CF_3COCHCOCH_3)_2UO_2.2H_2O$, $(CH_3COCHCOCH_3)_2UO_2$—all in $CHCl_3$ solution. Unfortunately, Kobyshev and Suglobov did not report their interesting observations in sufficient detail to allow using their results as critical tests of theoretical predictions.

5.4. *Uranyl Acetate and Double Acetates*

Nichols and Howes (1919) reported data on uranyl acetate, UO_2Ac_2 (powder), uranyl acetate dihydrate, $UO_2Ac_2.2H_2O$ (crystals), and a series of double acetates, as well as one triple acetate.

		3H$_2$O				6D$_2$O					
Group I		Group II		Group III		Group II		Group III		Group IV	
1	$v_a - v$	1	$v_a' - v$	1	$v_a'' - v$	1	$v_a' - v$	1	$v_a'' - v$	1	$v_a''' - v$
1	−127	4	−122	5	−119						
1	−106			1	−91						
2	−69	1	−67								
2	−38	1	−44	4	−42						
8	0	10	0	10	2	10	0	10	0	10	0
1	42										
2	69										
3	119					1	136				
3	159	6	159	5	152						
2	176					2	177				
2	204										
1	233										
3	249	2	244	2	247	3	251	3	250	1	249
5	271	4	271	3	273						
3	303	4	304	4	306						
1	313										
8	352	5	350	4	349						
6	383	2	389								
4	421					1	414	1	413		
4	449	5	441	8	442	1	444	1	450		
5	517	5	518	5	519	3	483	1	490	1	496
		1	565			1	547				
3	601	1	609	3	600	1	592	1	597		
				3	627						
1	656										
2	676	3	686	1	684	2	667	1	670		
1	723	1	727								

v = 19,902 − v
871 − v = 19,031 − v
871 − 868 − v = 18,163 − v

20,596 − 865 − v

20,596 − 865 − 863 − v

20,596 − 865 − 863 − 861 − v

ways gives intensity.

The change of the fluorescence spectrum at $-180°C$ upon hydration is illustrated by Fig. 1.16.

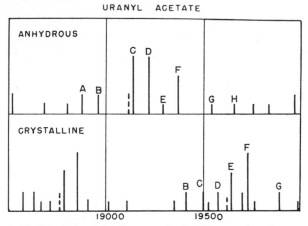

URANYL ACETATE

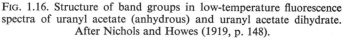

FIG. 1.16. Structure of band groups in low-temperature fluorescence spectra of uranyl acetate (anhydrous) and uranyl acetate dihydrate. After Nichols and Howes (1919, p. 148).

The frequency intervals in the fluorescence spectrum of the two simple acetates are similar: 859.6 and 857.2 cm^{-1} ($-185°C$) respectively. In the *double acetates* the intervals are smaller—mostly

TABLE 1.19. VIBRATION FREQUENCIES $\Delta\nu_s$ IN DOUBLE URANYL ACETATES
Nichols and Howes (1919)

Double acetate of uranyl and:	$\Delta\nu_s$, cm^{-1}	
	Fluorescence	Absorption
Li (3H$_2$O)	845.0	702.7
Na	852.2	704.6
Mg (7H$_2$O)	851.9	706.0
NH$_4$	844.0	701.9
K	845.7	691.8
Ca (8H$_2$O)	838.8	705.4
Mn (6H$_2$O)	851.9	712.5
Zn (7H$_2$O)	845.1	707.7
Rb	848.6	707.8
Sr (6H$_2$O)	847.4	701.1
Ag	847.4	700.1
Ba (6H$_2$O)	850.8	713.6
Pb (4H$_2$O)	851.2	712.1

under 850 cm^{-1}—showing a looser U—O binding (cf. Table 1.19).

The fluorescence spectra of the double acetates of lithium, potassium, calcium, and strontium show close similarity at $-180°C$, each group containing four main, almost equidistant, narrow bands (Fig. 1.17). The spectra of the double acetates of sodium, magnesium, zinc, silver, and lead are much more complex. The composition of

DOUBLE ACETATES

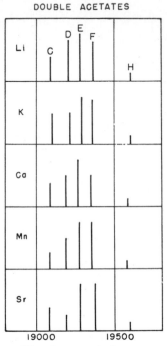

FIG. 1.17. Structure of band groups in low-temperature fluorescence spectra of double acetates of uranyl. After Nichols and Howes (1919, p.150).

these salts was: XUO_2Ac_3 for monovalent cations; $X(UO_2)_2Ac_6$ for Mg, Ca, Zn, Sr, Ba; and XUO_2Ac_4 for Mn and Pb.

The *absorption spectra* of the two simple acetates and of the double acetates of magnesium, manganese, and lead overlapped the fluorescence spectrum considerably; those of the other double acetates ended at about $\nu = 21,800$ cm^{-1}, just where the fluorescence series began. The ν_s (abs.), similarly to $\Delta\nu_s$ (fluor.), was found to be higher for the simple uranyl acetate than for most double acetates (Table 1.19), indicating a tighter U—O bond in both the excited and the ground state.

Table 1.7 shows ν_s and ν_a values at 20°K for the six double acetates studied by Dieke and co-workers and also the electronic terms ν_F, ν_M, ν_D, and ν_U. Tabulations are given in Dieke and Duncan's monograph of the acetate spectra listed in Table 1.20.

In the *fluorescence* spectrum of all acetates, Dieke and co-workers found a conspicuous frequency of about $610\ cm^{-1}$, which was represented in each group. It does not occur in any other uranyl compound and must therefore be due to a vibration of the acetate group. Asymmetric vibration lines are present in the spectra of all acetates, and are even stronger than the ν_s lines; the ν_b lines have a complex structure in most acetates. In $CsUO_2Ac_3$ the resonance line is double; the ν_a and ν_b lines in higher groups are double or triple. $NaUO_2Ac_3$ is cubic and shows no double refraction; its resonance line is single and its ν_a line is double in the first group, but apparently single in other groups.

TABLE 1.20. URANYL ACETATE SPECTRA
Measured by Dieke and Duncan (1949)

Compound	Spectrum	$T°$ abs.	Region (cm^{-1})	No. of lines
$RbUO_2Ac_3$	Fluorescence	20°K	21,047–16,336	70
$RbUO_2Ac_3$	Fluorescence	77°K	21,048–16,751	45
$RbUO_2Ac_3$	Absorption	20°K	20,881–22,860	32
$NaUO_2Ac_3$	Fluorescence	20°K	21,131–17,663	39
$NaUO_2Ac_3$	Fluorescence	77°K	21,250–16,378	61
$NaUO_2Ac_3$	Absorption	20°K	21,136–29,388	102
$NaUO_2Ac_3$	Absorption	77°K	21,129–31,008	107
$NH_4UO_2Ac_3$	Fluorescence	20°K	21,051–16,747	65
$NH_4UO_2Ac_3$	Fluorescence	77°K	21,052–16,737	43
$NH_4UO_2Ac_3$	Absorption	20°K	21,056–27,740	82
$NH_4UO_2Ac_3$	Absorption	77°K	21,062–28,570	58
$MgUO_2Ac_4$	Absorption	20°K	20,079–28,300	70
$PbUO_2Ac_4.2H_2O$	Fluorescence	20°K	20,958–16,222	67
$PbUO_2Ac_4.2H_2O$	Fluorescence	77°K	20,949–16,201	60

The *absorption* spectrum of sodium uranyl acetates, too, is entirely unpolarized as expected for a cubic crystal. The fluorescence series is weak with narrow single lines; the ν_a frequency seems to be present. In the ammonium salt the resonance line is a narrow doublet. The fluorescence series is sharp and the magnetic series lines are very broad; because of this, no Zeeman effect could be observed.

Samojlov (1948) found, on the other hand, that the fluorescence of a single crystal of $NaUO_2Ac_3$ at the temperature of liquid air was circularly polarized. Polarization disappeared in crystal powder; this was ascribed to mutual compensation of *l*- and *d*-crystals. The fluorescence lines of uranyl acetate anhydrate showed linear (or a very narrow elliptical) polarization.

In sodium uranyl acetate Samojlov noted a doubling of all fluorescence bands after cooling from 90°K to 4.2°K (liquid helium) and found from these doublets a repetition of the frequency intervals 164 and 608 cm^{-1}.

Samojlov measured absorption and fluorescence lines of uranyl acetates in liquid helium (Table 1.21).

TABLE 1.21. SAMOJLOV'S MEASUREMENTS (1948) OF URANYL
ACETATE SPECTRUM AT 4.2°K

Compound	Spectrum	No. of lines	Region (Å)
$UO_2Ac_2.2H_2O$	Absorption	34	4556–4854
$UO_2Ac_2.2H_2O$	Fluorescence	89	4854–5395
UO_2NaAc_3	Absorption	58	4296–4730
UO_2NaAc_3	Fluorescence	133	4729–5692

5.5. *Sulfates*

Nichols and Howes (1919) studied $UO_2SO_4.3H_2O$ and several double sulfates. They found their spectra to be more complex and varied than those of nitrates or acetates. All fluorescence band groups are, however, characterized by a pair of strong bands shifted toward shorter waves with increasing molecular weight of the second cation, as shown in Fig. 1.18, although less regularly than in the case of nitrates. The spectrum of the simple sulfate resembles that of the double salts more closely than in the case of nitrate or acetate.

Tables were given by Nichols and Howes for the bands, at the temperature of liquid air, of the compounds listed in Table 1.22 (cf. Dieke and Duncan's values of ν_s and ν_a at 20°K for Cs, Rb, K, and NH_4 double sulfates in Table 1.7).

Of the eight broad fluorescence bands of uranyl sulfate visible at room temperature, the first and the eighth disappear in liquid air; the others are resolved into sharp components.

Dieke and Duncan (1949) gave tables of the spectra listed in Table 1.23.

In rubidium double sulfate the resonance line is a narrow doublet; in the potassium salt it is triple.

SULFATES

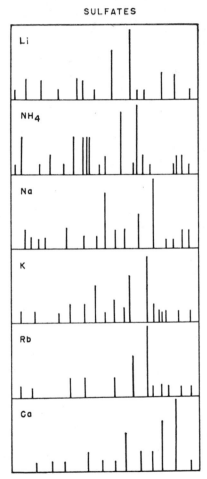

Fig. 1.18. Structure of low-temperature fluorescence band groups of simple and double uranyl sulfates, $X_2UO_2SO_4.2H_2O$. After Nichols and Howes (1919, p. 169).

Lines involving the excitation of the asymmetric bond vibration, ν_a, are relatively weak or absent in the fluorescence spectra of uranyl double sulfates of cesium, rubidium, potassium and ammonium. The ν_b vibration has a peculiar structure not encountered in all the other salts studied. In the rubidium salts, for example, the ν_b group consists of eight very sharp lines, 65–106 cm^{-1} away from the resonance line. If the identification of these frequencies as belonging to the bending vibration is correct, the frequency of this vibration is here much lower than usual (about 210 cm^{-1}).

TABLE 1.22. BANDS OF URANYL SULFATE AT −180°C

	ν_s (cm^{-1})	
	Fluorescence	Absorption
$UO_2SO_4.3H_2O$	852	696
$(NH_4)_2UO_2(SO_4)_2.2H_2O$	837	703
$Na_2UO_2(SO_4)_2.3H_2O*$	843	713
$K_2UO_2(SO_4)_2.2H_2O$	830	703
$Rb_2UO_2(SO_4)_2.2H_2O$	832	698
$Cs_2UO_2(SO_4)_2.3H_2O*$	857	704

* Water content as given by Dieke and Duncan (1949).

$Tl_2UO_2(SO_4)_2$ showed no fluorescence at all at 77°K.

Levshin and Sheremetjev (1947) noted that recrystallization of a uranyl sulfate trihydrate preparation changed the fluorescence spectrum (at room temperature); the usually observed double-peaked bands vanished and single-peaked bands, similar to those of other uranyl salts, appeared instead. The single peaks are shifted by 3–4 mμ towards the violet compared to the main components and

TABLE 1.23. URANYL SULFATE SPECTRA MEASURED BY DIEKE *et al.*
Dieke and Duncan (1949)

Compound	Spectrum	$T°$ abs.	Region (cm^{-1})	No. of lines
$K_2UO_2(SO_4)_2.2H_2O$	Fluorescence	77°K	20,454–16,161	66
$K_2UO_2(SO_4)_2.2H_2O$	Absorption	20°K	20,381–23,822	93
$(NH_4)_2UO_2(SO_4)_2.2H_2O$	Fluorescence	77°K	20,425–16,100	48
$(NH_4)_2UO_2(SO_4)_2.2H_2O$	Absorption	20°K	20,357–27,379	43

2–5 mμ towards the red of the weaker components of the doublet bands.

Photometric curves were obtained for the single and double bands in the trihydrate spectra and also for the spectra of the dihydrate and the monohydrate, obtained by dehydration of the two trihydrate preparations. The intensity of fluorescence was found to decrease strongly with dehydration in both cases but particularly in that of the doublet spectrum. Waterfree preparations of uranyl sulfate are non-fluorescent. The number and position of the bands of the doublet spectrum remain unchanged by drying down to one water molecule (a result that contradicts the observations of Nichols and Howes); in the singlet spectrum desiccation causes the appearance of a doublet structure.

The two types of fluorescence spectra of uranyl sulfate were again studied by Gordon (1950). He observed the fluorescence spectra at $-180°C$ using crystals of uranyl sulfate obtained by slow crystallization and by rapid crystallization, respectively. The analysis indicated the presence of three molecules of water in both preparations, but the slowly formed larger crystals (type I) lost 2.5 molecules of water by drying at 80°C, while the rapidly formed, smaller crystals (type II) lost only approximately 1.5 molecules. Table 1.24 shows the positions of the bands in the two preparations; the spectrum of a frozen uranyl sulfate solution is shown for comparison and appears to be similar to that of crystals II. The spectra of the usual laboratory preparations of uranyl sulfate correspond to the superposition of the spectra of forms I and II; at room temperature the bands are double-peaked, one peak corresponding to the singlet bands of form I and the other to the center of gravity of the doublet bands of form II. Levshin and Sheremetjev (cf. above) must have obtained by recrystallization a preparation of Gordon's type I.

TABLE 1.24. FLUORESCENCE BANDS OF UO_2SO_4 AT $-180°C$
After Gordon (1950)

Preparation	Band maxima (cm^{-1})				
$UO_2SO_4 \cdot 3H_2O$ (I)	. . .	19,675	18,825	17,975	17,125
$UO_2SO_4 \cdot 3H_2O$ (II)	20,340	19,475;	18,615;	17,750;	. . .
		19,395	18,530	17,665	
$UO_2SO_4(3M)$ frozen	20,310	19,460	18,610	17,750	16,900

The *absorption spectrum* of $K_2UO_2(SO_4)_2.2H_2O$ was measured by Dieke *et al.* in polarized light at 20°K. The resonance line is double with a weaker violet component with both polarizations. Throughout the spectrum the lines are slightly shifted in the ∥ spectrum in respect to those in the ⊥ spectrum. The M series is diffuse, if at all present; the D series dominates the middle of the spectrum, beginning at 4335 Å. There is a series of sharp lines in the ultraviolet, but the structure there is highly complex. Continuous absorption begins at 3450 Å.

Samojlov (1948) made wavelength measurements summarized in Table 1.25a.

Fluorescence spectra of several samples of uranyl sulfate were redetermined by Pant (1952a) particularly to find out whether the source of material (presumably linked to possible impurities) had any effect on the A series of bands. Five samples of the hydrate were obtained from five different sources (including one freshly prepared in Pant's laboratory), and two samples of (presumably) anhydrous material were prepared in different ways.

TABLE 1.25a. URANYL SULFATE SPECTRUM MEASUREMENTS AT 4.2°K
Samojlov (1948)

Compound	Spectrum	Region (Å)	No. of lines
$UO_2SO_4.3H_2O$	Absorption	4597–4917	46
$UO_2SO_4.3H_2O$	Fluorescence	4918–5453	36
$UO_2K_2(SO_4)_2.2H_2O$	Fluorescence	4943–5603	38

The hydrated commercial samples were reported (by Pant, 1952a) to give identical spectra. The laboratory sample of hydrate was reported to give the same fluorescence spectra except for a smaller relative intensity of the first band group. Pant attributed this difference to the larger size of the laboratory-prepared crystals, his postulate being that reabsorption of the A_o band would be stronger in the larger crystals. (Surprisingly, he did not report measurements on his own crystals after grinding!) The dehydrated samples gave identical spectra consisting of six groups of bands, each group about 260 cm⁻¹ higher than the corresponding group in the B series of the hydrate spectrum. This shift is smaller than the 400 cm⁻¹

blue shift reported by Nichols and Howes. However, Nichols and Howes' method of dehydration was different.

Pant's recorded $UO_2SO_4 \cdot 3H_2O$ fluorescence lines are tabulated in Table 1.25b. Some discrepancies between these values for the A

TABLE 1.25b. FLUORESCENCE BANDS OF URANYL SULFATE AT
LIQUID AIR TEMPERATURE
As measured by Pant (1952a), and Nichols and Howes (1919)

Int.	Desig.	ν_{vac} (Pant)	(N. & H.) $1/\lambda$	Int.	Desig.	ν_{vac} (Pant)	(N. & H.) $1/\lambda$
		Group I					
0	A_0	20,566	20,648 } 499			Group III	
		dif.		5	A	18,855	18,864 } 859
1		20,380	20,387	0		18,772	792 } 707 } 667
3		20,351 29	358				
8	B_0	20,323 28	339				
4		20,293 30	300				
3		20,263 30	272	10	B	18,611	624
1	C	20,228	239	6	C	18,523	538
4	D	20,168*	182		{ D?		
1	E_1	20,128	143	1	{ or	18,411	439
2		20,098 30	105		{ E_1		
5	E	20,068 30	088; 076	4	E	18,350	379 } 349
3		20,036 32	040				
0		20,006 30	—	0	F	18,259	256
1	F	19,980*	19,985	0	F'	18,160	165
1		19,943*	944				
0	F'	19,871*	892				
0	G	19,786*	786			Group IV	
0	G	18,927	18,939				
				2	A	18,006	18,070 } 18,013
		Group II		0		17,922	17,941 } 857
5	A	19,707	19,720 } 644 } 518				
				7	B	17,763	761
10	B	19,467†	475	4	C	17,676	677
7	C	19,366‡	392	2	D	17,589	588
3	D	19,312	298	1	E	17,502	494
1	E_1	19,259		0	F	17,424	422
5	E	19,205	219				
1	F	19,122	19,127 095				
1	F'	19,022	026				

* Broad. † Diffuse. ‡ Sharper.

series and Nichols and Howes' values are to be noted. Otherwise the agreement is good. Pant apparently did not know of Gordon's work. It appears that all of Pant's trihydrate samples showed the bands characteristic of both of Gordon's crystal forms I and II (compare Table 1.24 with 1.25b). Further, the largest of Pant's crystals, synthesized in his laboratory, showed weaker fluorescence at the high-frequency end of the spectrum; the largest of Gordon's crystals, sample I, showed weak fluorescence (or none at all) at the high-frequency end. All of this makes it possible that Pant did not succeed in establishing that the fluorescence spectrum reported by him belongs to one type of trihydrate crystals rather than to a mixture. On the other hand, Pant reported that he carefully examined the trihydrate spectra for signs of fluorescence from possible anhydrous impurity and that no such contamination could be discovered. However, by exposing the anhydrous sulfate to moist air, he could obtain partial hydration; the resulting material had fluorescence lines of his anhydrous spectra superimposed on those of the trihydrate spectra.

The temperature effect on the fluorescence spectrum of uranyl sulfate trihydrate was studied by Pant (1952b). He observed frequencies and intensities of a commercially prepared sample between 77°K and 525°K. (Uranyl sulfate was chosen because of its thermal stability: Pant reported the fluorescence spectrum did not change during 2 hr at 200°C.) Some of the observed lines are given in Table 1.25c, with Pant's designations. In general, the bands shift to the red with increased temperature.

Comparing the A and B series at liquid air and dry ice–alcohol temperatures, Pant argued that they belong to two different electronic transitions rather than to vibrational structure or to a mixture of chemical species. He felt that if their difference represented a vibrational frequency ($\sim$ 240–243 cm^{-1}), the A and B bands would have shifted by the same amount between 77°K and 201°K. Instead, the A bands shifted by -23 cm^{-1}; the B bands, by -16 cm^{-1}. He thought that the relative constancy of the large vibrational frequency ($20{,}566 - 19{,}707 = 859$, $20{,}543 - 19{,}684 = 859$ at 77°K; $20{,}323 - 19{,}467 = 856$, $20{,}307 - 19{,}451 = 856$ at 201°K) was evidence of the vibrational frequencies, being generally not much affected by temperature changes within the range 77–200°K. This argument is not convincing. More interesting is Pant's observation that the A_o

TABLE 1.25c. SOME FLUORESCENCE LINES OF $UO_2SO_4 \cdot 3H_2O$ AT SEVERAL TEMPERATURES
Data from Pant (1952b)

T (°K)	Designation	Band group I			Band group II			Band group III			Band group IV	
		A_0	B_0	C	A	B	C	A	B	C	A	B
77	$\bar{\nu}$ (cm^{-1})	20,566	20,323	20,228	19,707	19,467	19,366	18,855	18,611	18,523		
	Rel. int.	0	8	1	5	10	7	5	10	6		
	$\bar{\nu}_{201} - \bar{\nu}_{77}$	23	16	(16)	23	16	(11)	24	17	(14)		
201	$\bar{\nu}$ (cm^{-1})	20,543	20,307	20,212	19,684	19,451	19,355	18,831	18,594	18,509		
	Rel. int.	3	8	1	6	10	5	5	9	6		
	$\bar{\nu}_{308} - \bar{\nu}_{77}$	(106)	(79)		(92)	(75)		(100)	(71)			
308	$\bar{\nu}$ (cm^{-1})	20,460	20,244	E 19,976	19,615	19,392	E 19,134	18,755	18,560	E 18,304	A 17,899	B 17,595
	Rel. int.	5	9	3	6	10	4	5	9	2	2	5
	$\bar{\nu}_{473} - \bar{\nu}_{77}$	(138)	(95)		(158)	(115)		(183)	(128)			
473*	$\bar{\nu}$ (cm^{-1})	20,428	20,228	19,962	19,549	19,352	19,100	18,672	18,483		17,821	17,624
	Rel. int.	5	9	3	6	10	3	4	7		1	3

* Since uranyl sulfate begins to lose water of hydration above 388°K, data for 473°K are not strictly comparable with the previous data.

band becomes relatively more intense at high temperature. This fact might imply that the A series originates in a vibrationally excited upper state which becomes more highly populated at the higher temperatures. However, Pant points out that the relative intensity increase is much less than the increase in the Boltzmann factor, $\exp(-ch\bar{\nu}/kT)$, with $\bar{\nu} = 240\ \mathrm{cm^{-1}}$. He concluded that the *relative* transition probabilities of the A and B bands change with temperature; he believed this to be good evidence that the two series belong to two different electronic transitions.

Considering the possibility that the A and B series belong to different chemical (or physical) forms of uranyl sulfate coexisting in his crystals, Pant claimed that the increase in the relative intensity

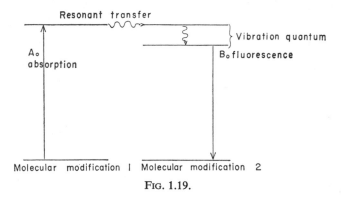

FIG. 1.19.

of the A bands would mean an increase in the relative quantity of the modification giving rise to them. However, one must realize that two different crystal or molecular modifications would not have the same temperature dependence of fluorescence intensity, in any case. A more germane point is that Pant studied the fluorescence of an individual crystal from his sample—the smallest that he could find—and that this crystal showed the same series with the same relative intensities.

Pant suggested an interesting and simple experiment which might test the hypothesis that both the A and B series of the $UO_2SO_4 \cdot 3H_2O$ fluorescence belong to the same species. He proposed a study of the fluorescence spectra excited by radiation corresponding to the A and B bands, respectively. Presumably, absorption of A_0 radiation would lead to A *and* B fluorescence only if the molecules which absorbed the A_o line could provide a B spectrum. However, it would be necessary, if A_o absorption yielded A and B fluorescence, to investigate whether resonance energy transfer were responsible, as in Fig. 1.19.

5.6. Carbonates

Dieke and Duncan (1949) tabulated the spectra summarized in Table 1.26. By a microscopic method the absorption spectra of potassium and of guanidonium uranyl carbonate were obtained with small crystals. In both materials the M series appeared between the second and the third group of the F series. An intricate structure was found in the M series of both salts and in the F series of the guanidonium salt. It was also noted in the fluorescence spectrum of the potassium salt.

TABLE 1.26. URANYL CARBONATE SPECTRA
Tabulated by Dieke and Duncan (1949)

Compound	Spectrum	$T°$ abs.	Region (cm⁻¹)	No. of lines
$K_2UO_2(CO_3)_2$	Fluorescence	20°K	20,921–16,605	65
$K_2UO_2(CO_3)_2$	Fluorescence	77°K	20,933–17,393	57
$K_2UO_2(CO_3)_2$	Absorption	77°K	20,943–28,483	55
$(CN_3H_6)_2UO_2CO_3.xH_2O^*$	Absorption	77°K	20,757–27,699	75

*Guanidonium uranyl carbonate.

5.7. Phosphates

Only diffuse bands were found by Nichols and Howes in the fluorescence spectrum of glassy uranyl phosphate containing excess phosphoric acid even at liquid air temperatures, while sharp bands could be observed with crystalline double phosphates (Fig. 1.20).

The three crystalline preparations free of phosphoric acid exhibited, at $-180°C$, identical systems of narrow fluorescence bands with $\Delta\nu = 804$–815 cm⁻¹ (a lower vibration frequency than found in all other uranyl salts). Preparations 4 and 5 showed both narrow and diffuse bands, the latter with $\Delta\nu - 825$ cm⁻¹; preparations 6 and 7 had only diffuse bands with $\Delta\nu = 851$ and 870 cm⁻¹ respectively.

Howes and Wilber (1916) concluded from these experiments that the occurrence of sharp spectral bands at liquid air temperature depends on crystalline structure. We understand now why this must be so, since the spectrum of ions in crystals is the result of broadening and splitting of the bands of free ions in the electric field of the adjoining ions (or dipoles). In a crystalline structure the field is the same for all ions of a given type, and this produces splitting into more or less sharp components; in the glassy, i.e. undercooled,

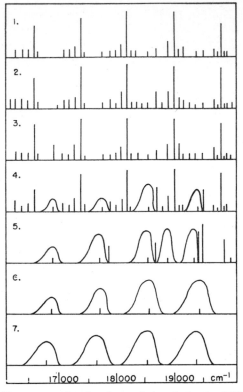

FIG. 1.20. Fluorescence bands of uranyl phosphate at $-180°C$. 1, 2, 3: without excess H_3PO_4; 4, 5, 6, 7: with increasing proportion of free H_3PO_4. After Nichols and Howes.

1. $4UO_2HPO_4.3\frac{1}{2}H_2O + 1Na_2HPO_4$
2. $2UO_2HPO_4.3\frac{1}{2}H_2O + 1Na_2HPO_4$
3. $1UO_2HPO_4.3\frac{1}{2}H_2O + 1Na_2HPO_4$
4. $2UO_2HPO_4.3\frac{1}{2}H_2O + 1Na_2HPO_4 + 1H_3PO_4$
5. $UO_2HPO_4.3\frac{1}{2}H_2O + 2Na_2HPO_4 + 1H_3PO_4*$
6. $UO_2HPO_4.3\frac{1}{2}H_2O + 1Na_2HPO_4 + 2H_3PO_4†$
7. $UO_2HPO_4.3\frac{1}{2}H_2O + excess H_3PO_4‡$

* Much free sodium phosphate.   † Syrupy at $20°$; vitreous at $-180°$.
‡ Vitreous at all temperatures.

liquid state, on the other hand, random distribution and orientation of ions and molecules lead to variations in the strength and direction of electric forces, and this results in diffuse broadening of the spectral lines rather than in their splitting into well-defined components.

5.8. *Frozen Uranyl Salt Solutions*

Nichols and Howes also studied the absorption and fluorescence spectra of frozen UO_2^{++} salt solutions in water and alcohol. The results are, as one could expect, rather confusing, since the spectra are produced by a variety of crystal hydrates. What hydrate (or hydrates) will be present in any given case will depend not only on temperature but also on the rate of cooling (or heating). The spectrum of each solvate, as well as that of the free ion UO_2^{++}, changes with temperature in its own characteristic way as described above for crystalline salts. Despite this complexity spectroscopic observations could perhaps be used to identify different crystalline solvates of uranyl salts and to determine the limits of their stability and the rates of their transformation. Therefore, a brief summary of the findings of Nichols and co-workers is given here.

Nichols and Merritt (1914) and Howes (1915) first investigated the spectra of uranyl salt solutions of different concentrations (from 1M to 1×10^{-3}M) as a function of temperature (cf. also Nichols and Howes (1919), pp. 180–205). The solutions were frozen and cooled to the desired temperature by inserting test tubes into a massive copper block (cooled with liquid air) with openings provided for the incident and the fluorescent light.

The investigated systems included UO_2SO_4 in water or sulfuric acid; $UO_2K_2(SO_4)$ in water or sulfuric acid; UO_2Cl_2 in water; and $UO_2(NO_3)_2$ in water, nitric acid, or alcohol.

Upon cooling, a general increase in the intensity of the whole fluorescence spectrum was noted; two or more bands, not visible at room temperature, became visible at low temperature. The band peaks were shifted gradually, over a total range of the order of 1 mμ. Usually, the shift was towards the shorter waves; sometimes it was first towards the shorter and then back towards the longer waves.

Bands became narrower as the temperature decreased; often they were resolved into two or more components. The spectra were sometimes quite different, depending on whether the cooling was sudden or gradual (Fig. 1.21).

The observed changes must have been due to two superimposed phenomena: (1) decrease in thermal vibrations in the ions and in the medium surrounding the ions, and (2) crystallization and re-crystallization. Cessation of thermal agitation would affect the spectrum even if the uranyl ions (and their balancing anions) remained scattered at random in the ice mass, as they may be upon sudden freezing. The arrangement of solvent molecules around each frozen-in uranyl cation may undergo discontinuous changes as the temperature is lowered. In addition to structures which are disorderly in respect to cations and anions but more or less orderly in respect to the

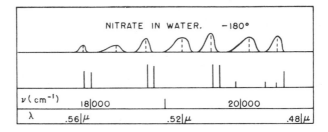

Fig. 1.21. Uranyl nitrate solution (1M). Fluorescence spectrum at −180°C after snap freezing and after slow cooling to same temperature. From Nichols and Howes (1919, Fig. 96).

immediate surroundings of each ion, phases containing cations, anions, and solvent molecules in true crystalline arrangement will arise if the rate of freezing is not fast compared to the rate of crystallization. The more dilute the solutions, the smaller the chance of the ions being assembled into a crystal before their diffusion is stopped by solidification of the medium and the greater the likelihood of the spectrum retaining the broad-banded structure characteristic of an undercooled solution.

As an example we reproduce Nichols and Howes' results obtained with uranyl nitrate. Figure 1.22 shows schematically the changes in the fluorescence spectrum of 1M $UO_2(NO_3)_2$ solution upon cooling: First, the number of diffuse fluorescence bands is increased from two at $+20°$ to four at $0°$ and $−18°C$; then, between $−18°$ and $−25°C$, a transformation occurs which leads to the appearance of three new diffuse double bands. At still lower temperatures, the longer-wave components of these double bands split into sharp doublets, while the shorter-wave components become weaker and remain diffuse. By very slow cooling, the diffuse components can be made to disappear altogether, while snap-freezing to $-180°C$ leads to a spectrum with both sets of bands still diffuse and about equal in intensity (Fig. 1.21).

Upon heating, the spectral transformations which have occurred in slow cooling between $-60°$ and $-180°C$ were reversed, but above $-60°C$ the change back to the broad double bands failed to

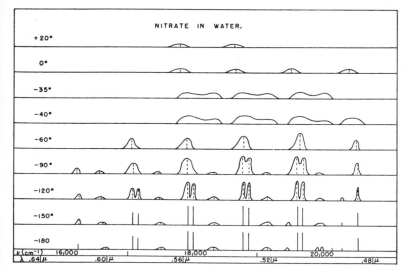

FIG. 1.22. Uranyl nitrate solution (1M). Changes in fluorescence spectrum upon cooling. From Nichols and Howes (1919, Fig. 97).

occur; at $-18°C$ (the cryohydrate point) the spectrum of the unfrozen solution reappeared.

As anticipated above, the changes were less sharp in 0.1M and 0.01M than in 1M solution.

The fluorescence bands which failed to become dissolved into sharp lines at $-180°C$ in neutral aqueous solution did so in the presence of a small excess of nitrate ions (Fig. 1.23). In the presence of a large excess of nitrate ions, on the other hand, all bands remained diffuse even at $-180°C$ (Fig. 1.24).

In 50 per cent aqueous alcohol the low-temperature fluorescence spectra were quite different from those of aqueous solutions (Fig. 1.25).

Some spectra obtained under these conditions (e.g. that of 0.1M uranyl nitrate in 50 per cent ethanol at $-185°C$) indicated co-existence of two sets of bands, one sharp and one diffuse. These may correspond to hydrated and ethanolated uranyl ions, respectively.

Germann (1922) inquired whether the five different fluorescence spectra of frozen uranyl nitrate solution, observed by Nichols and Howes, could all belong to the same crystal hydrate. Systematic density measurements and thermal analysis convinced him that, in addition to the hexahydrate, another hydrate, $UO_2(NO_3)_2.24H_2O$,

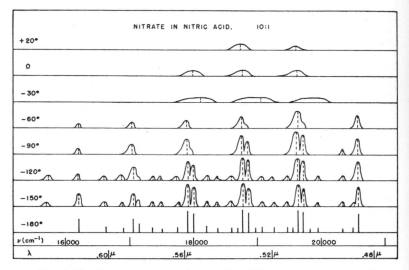

FIG. 1.23. Uranyl nitrate solution (1M). Fluorescence spectrum in presence of excess nitric acid. From Nichols and Howes (1919, Fig. 101).

stable between $-35°$ and $-20°C$, occurred in these systems. He interpreted Nichols and Howes' spectra as belonging to various mixtures of the hexahydrate with this "ikositetrahydrate."

Gordon (1950) measured the position of fluorescence bands in a frozen solution of UO_2SO_4 and found them to be identical with those of crystals of $UO_2SO_4.3H_2O$ (type II) obtained by fast crystallization.

Recently Hayakawa and Hirata (1959) have examined the spectrum and intensity of fluorescence of uranyl nitrate in (rapidly?)

frozen water solution as functions of increasing temperature. They studied solutions of composition $UO_2NO_3.6H_2O$; $UO_2NO_3.6H_2O$ (10 aq.); $UO_2NO_3.6H_2O$ (100 aq.). The appearances of their spectra are similar to those of Nichols and Howe. Their intensity findings, shown in Fig. 1.26, show a small temperature dependence for the hydrated samples with little water but a very strong temperature dependence between $-90°$ and $0°C$ for the dilute sample. The very rapid decline of intensity with temperature between $-50°$ and $-80°C$ was attributed by Hayakawa and Hirata to a loss of coherent

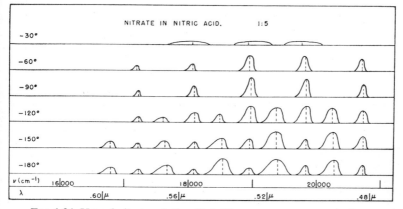

Fig. 1.24. Uranyl nitrate solution (1M). Fluorescence spectrum in large excess of nitric acid. From Nichols and Howes (1919, Fig. 104).

water–uranyl interaction owing to the allowance of molecular rotation in ice at temperatures above $\sim -60°C$.

5.9. Miscellaneous Observations

Ephraim and Mezener (1933) wanted to know whether a rule, discovered by Ephraim in the spectra of rare-earth salts, that the cation bands are shifted towards the shorter waves with increasing polarizing action of the anion, applies also to uranium. They noted that the data of Nichols and Howes in fact show a shift of uranyl bands in double salts towards shorter waves with increased polarizability—of the alkali ion. This shift is particularly clearly recognizable in fluorescence spectra.

Ephraim and Mezener's own measurements of *reflection spectra* of certain *uranyl halides*, such as $UO_2Br_2.7H_2O$, $UO_2F_2.3KF$,

$UO_2Br_2.2KBr.2H_2O$, and $UO_2Br_2.2NH_4Br$, at the temperature of liquid air, gave results in general agreement with the rule. *Double nitrates* were found to be unsuitable for comparison because of differences in the crystal system and consequent variations in the

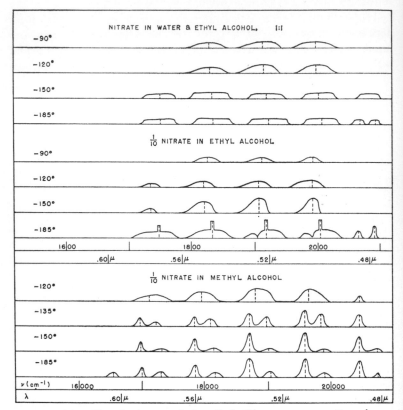

Fig. 1.25. Uranyl nitrate solution (1M). Fluorescence spectrum in water and alcohol. After Nichols and Howes (1919, Fig. 106).

spectrum. *Uranyl nitrate* crystals with 0, 2, 3, and 6 molecules of water also had very different spectra (cf. Section 5.6), but the intervals between bands in a given series showed a systematic decrease with increasing number of water molecules, n (from 885 cm^{-1} at $n = 0$ to 860 cm^{-1} at $n = 6$). Double sulfates exhibited shifts similar to those in double halides.

Ephraim and Mezener used these results (as well as similar observations with U(IV) and U(III) salts) to argue in favor of considering uranium as a "rare earth" rather than as a homologue of titanium and wolfram—a point of view which has later received support from the work on transuranium elements.

D. D. Pant (1950, 1952) discussed the origin of the weak, high-frequency *A* series of bands which appears in the fluorescence of some uranyl salts. Pant (1950) argued that the *A* series, which

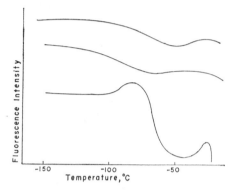

FIG. 1.26. Temperature dependence of fluorescence intensity of uranyl nitrate frozen into ice. Intensity units are arbitrary. From the data of Hayakawa and Hirata (1959).
Upper curve: $UO_2(NO_3)_2.6H_2O$.
Middle curve: $UO_2(NO_3)_2.6H_2O$ (10 aq.).
Lower curve: $UO_2(NO_3)_2.6H_2O$ (100 aq.).

appears at *ca.* 150 cm^{-1} above the corresponding lines of the *B* series in F$^-$, Cl$^-$, SO$_4^-$, CH$_3$COO$^-$, KSO$_4^-$, and Br$^-$ salts of uranyl, is caused by a low-lying electronic state rather than an impurity. He argued that the A_0 and B_0 bands undergo intensity reversal between absorption and fluorescence. He cited, as further evidence of a low-lying electronic state, the high temperature-independent paramagnetism of uranyl salts. The latter phenomenon, however, is readily understandable on the basis of high-lying antibonding states only (see Chapter 5, also Belford (1961)). Further, the electronic structure of uranyl ion in its ground state seems qualitatively well understood, and little room is left for postulating a low lying electronic state (see Chapter 5).

TABLE 1.27. FIRST MEMBERS OF *A* AND *B* SERIES OF BANDS OF DIFFERENT URANYL SALTS

Uranyl salt	Fluorescence spectrum		Absorption spectrum		$A_o - B_o$	Reference
	A_o	B_o	a_o	b_o		
Fluoride	20,234	20,082	20,234	20,082	152	Pant and Sakhwalkar (1944)
Bromide	20,390	20,249	20,392	20,254	159	Pant (1945)
Sulfate	20,566	20,323	20,571	20,327	243	Pant (1952a)
Sodium acetate	21,250	21,130	21,253	21,129	120	⎱ Dieke and Duncan (1949)
Potassium chloride	20,059	19,969	20,078*	19,978*	90	⎰
Potassium sulfate	20,454	20,389	20,470*	20,381*	65	
Acetate (anh.)	20,237	20,079	Data not available		158	Nichols and Howes (1919)
Acetate (cryst.)	20,732	20,588	20,746	20,893	144	Guilmart (1946)
Acetate (Swedish)	21,091	20,858	21,158	20,923	233	Cf. Pant and Pandey (1957)

* Observed at 20°K.

Later, Pant and Pandey (1957) reviewed some of the observed facts and proposed explanations of the A series of bands in many uranyl salts. Table 1.27, taken from their paper, shows frequencies

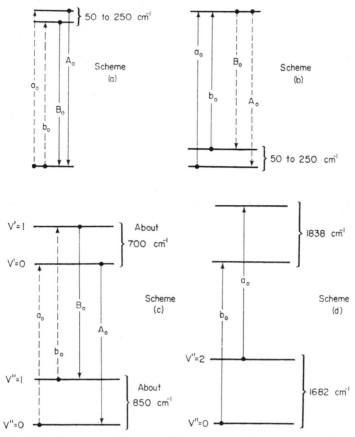

FIG. 1.27. Some suggestions regarding the origin of the A and B series of bands in spectra of uranyl salts. (Adapted from Pant and Pandey, 1957.) Scheme (*a*) was suggested by Pant (1945), scheme (*b*) by Pant (1950), scheme (*c*) by Guilmart *et al.* (1946), scheme (*d*) by Rao and Narsimham (1956).

of the leading bands. These bands have been explained by energy level diagrams of various kinds, shown in Fig. 1.27, in which the bands are labeled according to the nomenclature of Table 1.27.

Many workers have considered the A series to be caused by impurities, mixtures of hydrates, or solid state impurity levels (cf. Nichols and Howes, Dieke and Duncan, Pringsheim (1949)). However, Pant and Pandey think these bands are an integral part of uranyl salt spectra, because they appear in many different uranyl salts and because, in some instances, they have been reported to be stronger than the B bands in absorption. Scheme (d) of Fig. 1.27 seems unlikely because it would require an extremely high transition moment for the transition from the $v'' = 2$ level of the ground state to the vibrationless level of the second excited state, to compensate for the low value of the Boltzmann factor, which allows only a very small population at low temperature of a state 1682 cm^{-1} above the ground state. If the transition moment were so high, one would expect the a_0 band to be nearly as intense in fluorescence, compared to the b_0 band, as in absorption. This was not found. Scheme (c) seems to be open to the same objection. Pant and Pandey consider that either scheme (a) or scheme (b) may be correct.

CHAPTER 2

SPECTROSCOPY OF
URANYL COMPOUNDS IN SOLUTION

1. The Free (Hydrated) Uranyl Ion and the Products of Its Hydrolysis

1.1. *Absorption Spectra*

Free U^{+6} ions do not occur in solution; if a compound derived from this ion, such as UF_6, comes in contact with water, it is immediately hydrolyzed, i.e. associated with the anions of water, even at the lowest accessible pH values. The first step in this hydrolysis can be written as:

$$U^{+6} + 4OH^- \rightarrow UO_2^{++} + 2H_2O$$
$$\text{or} \quad U^{+6} + 2O^{--} \rightarrow UO_2^{++}$$

and leads to the divalent uranyl ion, which is stable over a considerable pH range. Further hydrolysis occurs in non-complexed solutions at about pH 2, and ends in precipitation; certain anions, such as the citrate ion, can prevent precipitation up to pH 10 by forming soluble complexes with uranyl ions (see Section 2).

Most of the solid U(VI) compounds are salts derived from the divalent uranyl ion. Their dissolution in water produces solutions whose spectrum is the result of superposition of the spectrum of free (hydrated) uranyl ion $\{UO_2^{++}\}_{aq}$ (perhaps $UO_2^{++}.6H_2O$) and of the spectra of complexes of this ion with the anions present in solution. In addition to simple complexes of the type $\{UO_2^{++}X^{-n}\}^{+(2-n)}$, complexes containing two or more uranyl ions bridged by divalent anions may occur. The stepwise hydrolysis of uranyl ions, in particular, probably involves the formation of two polyuranyl complexes, $\{(UO_2)_2O\}^{++} (= U_2O_5^{++})$ and $\{(UO_2)_3O_2\}^{++} (= U_3O_8^{++})$. A precise and systematic study of the extinction curves of solutions of varying compositions, concentration, acidity and ionic strength is needed for reliable interpretation of the absorption spectrum of a given uranyl salt.

To obtain the spectrum of the free (hydrated) uranyl ion, one has to use salt solutions that contain no complexes with the anions of water and of acids. For this purpose strongly acid perchlorate solutions are best, because ClO_4^- is the anion with the least tendency for complexing; Sutton (1947) found that adding sodium perchlorate to a 0.04M $UO_2(ClO_4)_2$ solution caused no change in spectrum up to a total concentration of 3M ClO_4^-. The presence of

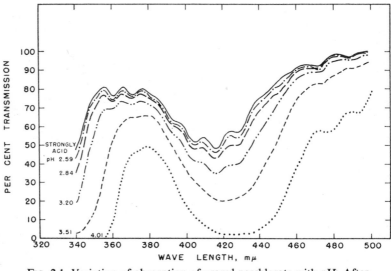

Fig. 2.1. Variation of absorption of uranyl perchlorate with pH. After Sutton (1947).

excess perchloric acid is the best means to prevent association of UO_2^{++} cations with the anions of water without introducing complexing with the anions of the acid.

Absorption curves of uranyl perchlorate solutions were first reproduced by von Kiss and co-workers (1942a, b); but they do not agree with the curves obtained in the more recent and careful measurements by Sutton and Ahrland.

The change in the absorption curve of a uranyl perchlorate solution in perchloric acid with decreasing concentration of the latter is shown in Fig. 2.1 (after Sutton). This figure indicates a strong increase in absorption throughout the spectrum at pH values above 2.5 (cf. Fig. 2.2, which shows T at 416 mμ as function of pH). Sutton attributed this change to a stepwise hydrolysis, beginning with the formation of the polyuranyl complexes, $(UO_2)_2O^{++}$ and $(UO_2)_3O_2^{++}$. This type of complexing can be represented in several ways: as a

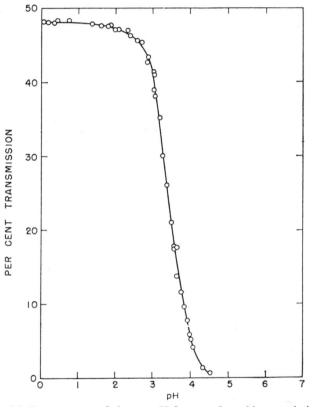

FIG. 2.2. Per cent transmission vs. pH for uranyl perchlorate solutions at $\lambda = 416$. Ionic strength $= 0.17226$.

substitution reaction of UO_2^{++} ions with H_2O molecules or OH^- ions, or as an association with O^{--} ions. (The concentration of the latter is extremely low so that hydrolysis is unlikely to proceed through their intermediary; but, formally, polyuranyl complexes of this type are most easily understood as products of association of

O^{--} anions with UO_2^{++} cations.) The three alternative interpretations are represented by the following pairs of equations:

Exchange reactions with water molecules:

$$2UO_2^{++} + H_2O \overset{K_1}{\rightleftharpoons} \{(UO_2)_2O\}^{++} (= U_2O_5^{++}) + 2H^+ \tag{1}$$

$$\{(UO_2)_2O\}^{++} + UO_2^{++} + H_2O \overset{K_2}{\rightleftharpoons} \{(UO_2)_3O_2\}^{++}$$
$$(= \{U_3O_8\}^{++}) + 2H^+ \tag{2}$$

Exchange reactions with hydroxyl ions:

$$2UO_2^{++} + 2OH^- \rightleftharpoons \{(UO_2)_2O\}^{++} + H_2O \tag{3}$$

$$\{(UO_2)_2O\}^{++} + UO_2^{++} + 2OH^- \rightleftharpoons \{(UO_2)_3O_2\}^{++} + H_2O \tag{4}$$

Associations with O^{--} ions:

$$2UO_2^{++} + O^{--} \rightleftharpoons \{(UO_2)_2O\}^{++} \tag{5}$$

$$\{(UO_2)_2O\}^{++} + UO_2^{++} + O^{--} \rightleftharpoons \{(UO_2)_3O_2\}^{++} \tag{6}$$

Sutton calculated the absorption curves (Fig. 2.3) of the three postulated ionic species using the following equilibrium constants derived from pH measurements:

$$K_1 = 1.24 \times 10^{-6} \tag{7}$$

$$K_2 = 2.5 \times 10^{-7} \tag{8}$$

(These constants are, of course, strongly dependent on ionic strength.)
The choice of equilibria (1) and (2), in preference to the simpler hydrolytic equilibria involving one uranyl ion only:

$$UO_2^{++} + H_2O \rightleftharpoons UO_2OH^+ + H^+$$
$$(\text{or } UO_2^{++} + OH^- \rightleftharpoons UO_2OH^+) \tag{9}$$

$$UO_2OH^+ + H_2O \rightleftharpoons UO_2(OH)_2 (= UO_3.H_2O) + H^+$$
$$(\text{or } UO_2OH^+ + OH^- \rightleftharpoons UO_2(OH)_2) \tag{10}$$

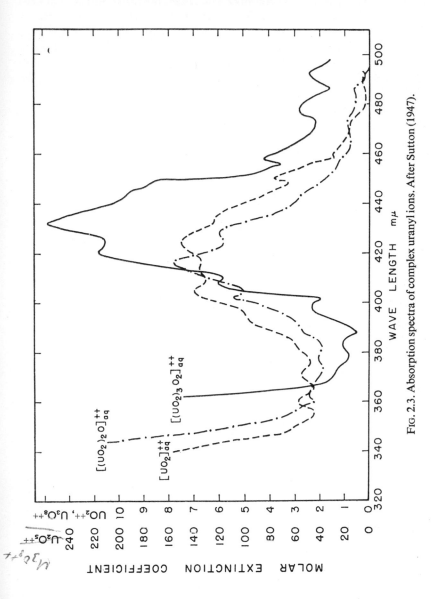

FIG. 2.3. Absorption spectra of complex uranyl ions. After Sutton (1947).

was first proposed by MacInnes and Longsworth (1942), who found that Equation (1) with $K_1 = 1.35 \times 10^{-6}$ accounted well for the results of pH measurements on stoichiometric UO_2Cl_2 [or $UO_2(NO_3)_2$] solutions, as well as for those of pH and conductance measurements on UO_3 solutions in hydrochloric acid, while Equation (9) could be used to represent the second but not the first type of data. The second hydrolysis step, too, they thought more likely to be of type (2) than of type (3), among other reasons, because the second alternative would have required UO_3 to be soluble in water, which is not the case. Sutton (1947) pointed out that further argument in favor of reaction sequence (1) (2) can be derived from the fact that U_3O_8, rather than UO_3, is deposited on the cathode in the electrolysis of uranyl solutions.

Robinson and Lim (1951) found that the vapor pressure lowering of uranyl perchlorate solutions increases when excess UO_3 is added. This agrees with the assumption that these solutions contain $U_2O_5^{++}$ rather than UO_2OH^+ ions.

The extinction curve of $\{UO_2^{++}\}_{aq}$ was derived by Sutton from the empirical absorption curve of uranyl perchlorate at pH < 2.5, a region where the concentrations of the complex ions are negligible; that of $\{(UO_2)_2O\}_{aq}^{++}$ was computed from the absorption spectrum at pH 2.5–3.0, where the third ionic species can be neglected. The extinction curve of this third species, $\{(UO_2)_3O_2\}_{aq}^{++}$, was estimated rather roughly from the empirical absorption curves at pH > 3.

According to Fig. 2.3, the complex ion $\{(UO_2)_2O\}_{aq}^{++}$ has a somewhat stronger absorption in the visible region than does the simple ion $\{UO_2\}_{aq}^{++}$; its absorption is relatively weaker in the region 360–410 mμ, and again becomes stronger below 360 mμ. The ion $\{(UO_2)_3O_2\}_{aq}^{++}$ is much more intensely colored than the other two; its absorption peak at 435 mμ reaches an estimated height of $\epsilon_{max} = 250$, whereas $\epsilon_{max} = 8$ for the two other species (at 418 mμ for $\{UO_2\}_{aq}^{++}$, and at 425 mμ for $\{(UO_2)_2O\}_{aq}^{++}$ respectively).

The wavelengths of the peaks of the absorption bands of the three ionic species postulated by Sutton, taken from the curves in Fig. 2.3, are listed in Table 2.1.

Comparison of the wavelength table given by Pringsheim (1937) for a 0.05M uranyl sulfate solution (without added acid) with Table 2.1 indicates that the spectrum obtained by Pringsheim must have been that of a partly hydrolyzed solution containing the ions UO_2^{++}

and $U_2O_5^{++}$. The same applies to McBrady and Livingston's (1946) absorption curve of a 0.01M solution of uranyl sulfate. Sutton gave Table 2.2 for the absorption coefficients of a stoichiometric uranyl perchlorate solution. The values in this table are averages of measurements in the concentration range 0.01–0.2M, the pH being kept below 2.0 to avoid hydrolysis. Beer's law was found to be valid, under these conditions, up to at least 3M.

TABLE 2.1. ABSORPTION BANDS OF URANYL IONS AND THEIR
COMPLEXES WITH WATER IONS AT ROOM TEMPERATURE
After Sutton

Band No.	$\{UO_2\}_{aq}^{++}$ (pH < 2.0)		$\{(UO_2)_2O\}_{aq}^{++}$		$\{(UO_2)_3O_2\}_{aq}^{++}$ pH > 3)	
	λ (mμ)	ν (cm^{-1})	λ (mμ)	ν (cm^{-1})	λ (mμ)	ν (cm^{-1})
1	(350)	(2857$_0$)	—	—	—	—
2	360	2778$_0$	363	2755$_0$	—	—
3	370	2703$_0$	—	—	372	2688$_0$
4	(381)	(2625$_0$)	377	2653$_0$	383	2611$_0$
5	392	2551$_0$	388	2577$_0$	396	2525$_0$
6	404	2475$_0$	405	2469$_0$	407	2457$_0$
7	416	2404$_0$	415	2410$_0$	420	2381$_0$
8	425	2353$_0$	430	2326$_0$	432	2315$_0$
9	(438)	(2283$_0$)	443	2357$_0$	441	2268$_0$
10	450	2222$_0$	—	—	448	2232$_0$
11	457	2188$_0$	456	2193$_0$	458	2183$_0$
12	472	2119$_0$	472	2119$_0$	478	2092$_0$
13	489	2045$_0$	487	2053$_0$	492	2033$_0$

In a second paper, Sutton (1949) gave extinction curves of uranyl perchlorate solutions for pH values up to pH 9.3. These curves are reproduced in Fig. 2.4. During the measurements the solutions showed no precipitation or formation of a Tyndall cone. However, after several hours' standing, a yellow precipitate formed.

It will be noted that in the main band region (400–450 mμ) absorption as a function of pH passes through a maximum somewhere in the region of pH 6–7 and then declines again. (On both sides of this region absorption increases steadily with pH.) Sutton interpreted this change in the absorption trend as evidence that the third and subsequent steps of hydrolysis are different from the first two; he

TABLE 2.2. THE MOLAR ABSORPTION COEFFICIENTS OF STOICHIOMETRIC
URANYL PERCHLORATE SOLUTION (0.01–0.2M)*

λ (mμ)	ϵUO_2^{++}	λ (mμ)	ϵUO_2^{++}	λ (mμ)	ϵUO_2^{++}	λ (mμ)	ϵUO_2^{++}
230	1175	300	59.5	370	2.82‡	440	3.02
2	1115	2	58.0	2	2.75†	2	2.89†
4	1055	4	56.2	4	2.54	4	2.65
6	1000	6	53.2	6	2.43	6	2.36
8	945	8	52.6	8	2.58	8	2.05
40	875	10	51.7	80	2.81	50	1.76
2	810	2	49.0	2	3.02	2	1.57
4	745	4	46.5†	4	3.16†	4	1.42
6	685	6	45.3	6	3.40	6	1.34†
8	620	8	42.9	8	3.86	8	1.19
50	565	20	40.6	90	4.38	60	1.02
2	505	2	37.5†	2	4.88	2	0.91
4	461	4	34.9	4	5.04	4	0.855
6	415	6	31.9	6	5.07†	6	0.835
8	378	8	27.3	8	5.36	8	0.855
60	338	30	22.5†	400	5.97	70	0.890
2	299	2	19.9	2	6.69	2	0.90†
4	270	4	17.6	4	6.99‡	4	0.745‡
6	248	6	14.2	6	6.91†	6	0.500
8	229	8	10.53†	8	6.58	8	0.300
70	208	40	8.42	10	6.60	80	0.215
2	190	2	7.23	2	6.96	2	0.175
4	171	4	5.88	4	7.51	4	0.185
6	159	6	4.42†	6	7.82‡	6	0.230
8	144	8	3.44	8	7.51†	8	0.310
80	130	50	3.07	20	6.72	90	0.315‡
2	120	2	2.80	2	6.07	2	0.220†
4	108	4	2.44	4	5.88	4	0.110
6	99	6	2.36	6	5.96	6	0.053
8	89	8	2.76	8	6.09‡	8	0.039
90	80	60	3.05†‡	30	5.86†	500	0.018
2	73.5	2	2.86	2	5.20		
4	68.2	4	2.47	4	4.48		
6	64.5	6	2.40	6	3.80		
8	61.8	8	2.63	8	3.31		

* Error limits
±0.5% at 230 mμ
±1.0% at 270 mμ
±0.3% from 320 to 450 mμ
±0.5% at 460 mμ
±1.0% at 470 mμ
±3.0% at 480 mμ
±5.0% at 500 mμ

† Bands are indicated in these positions in 0.05M UO_2SO_4 solution according to Pringsheim (1937).

‡ Peaks.

suggested that they occurred by the addition of hydroxyl ions to the triuranyl complex:

$$U_3O_8^{++}+OH^- \rightleftharpoons U_3O_8OH^+ \tag{11}$$

$$U_3O_8OH^++OH^- \rightleftharpoons U_3O_8(OH)_2, \text{ etc.} \tag{12}$$

The assumption that $U_2O_5^{++}$ and $U_3O_8^{++}$ are the first products of hydrolysis of $UO_2(ClO_4)_2$ is confirmed, according to Sutton, by cryoscopic measurements. These show that dissolution of solid UO_3 in a $UO_2(ClO_4)_2$ solution occurs without increase in the number of osmotically active particles:

$$UO_2^{++}+UO_3 \rightleftharpoons U_2O_5^{++} \tag{13}$$

Sutton's second assumption—that the formation of polyuranate complexes linked by O bridges stops at $U_3O_8^{++}$, and that further complexing occurs by association with OH^- ions—was based primarily on non-spectroscopic evidence, such as the shape of the pH titration curves. Transference experiments confirm the appearance of uranium-bearing *anions* at alkaline pH values. Sutton's analysis of the several inflection points on the pH titration curve of uranyl perchlorate indicated the successive formation of $U_2O_5^{++}$, $U_3O_8^{++}$, $U_3O_8OH^+$, $U_3O_8(OH)_2$, $U_3O_8(OH)_3^-$, and $U_3O_8(OH)_4^{--}$.

The relative amounts of these species in the uranyl solutions used in Sutton's spectroscopic studies are illustrated by Fig. 2.5. According to this figure, spectrum II in Fig. 2.4 corresponds to a mixture of $U_3O_8OH^+$ with some $U_3O_8(OH)_2$ and a small amount of $U_3O_8(OH)_3^-$; spectrum III, to a mixture of about equal amounts of $U_3O_8(OH)_3^-$ and $U_3O_8(OH)_4^{--}$; and spectrum IV, to a solution containing twice as many divalent as monovalent anions.

Independently of Sutton's measurements, data on the hydrolysis of uranyl salts and its spectroscopic effects have been collected by other investigators. The review article by Dounce, Flagg, Fanta, Tishkoff, and Lan (1949) gives some such data (obtained in connection with toxicological studies) on uranyl acetate solutions. In 0.2M acetate buffer (HAc + NaAc) the absorption spectrum of uranyl acetate shows a change with increasing pH. A curve is given, showing a rapid increase of the ratio $\epsilon_{446m\mu} : \epsilon_{440m\mu}$ between pH 3.0 and 4.5. Two absorption curves for the visible region, one obtained at

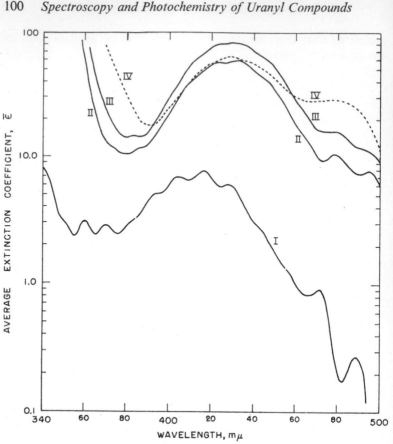

Fig. 2.4. Absorption spectra of uranyl perchlorate sodium hydroxide solutions.

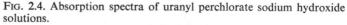

$$\bar{\epsilon} = \frac{\text{Optical density}}{\text{Cell length} \times \text{Total uranium concentration (independent of species)}}$$

Curve I: Acid solution, pH < 1.5.
Curve II: 10 cc 0.01M $UO_2(ClO_4)_2$ + 16 cc 0.0085 NaOH pH 4.89.
Curve III: 10 cc 0.01M $UO_2(ClO_4)_2$ + 25 cc 0.0085 NaOH pH 6.31.
Curve IV: 10 cc 0.01M $UO_2(ClO_4)_2$ + 30 cc 0.0085 NaOH pH 9.30.
No precipitate was observed in these solutions. There was no colloidal particle formation (Tyndall effect) until the solutions had been standing for an hour or longer.

pH 3.5 and one at pH 4.7, indicate that at the higher pH a new, or strongly enhanced, band appears with a peak at 446 mμ. It can be tentatively identified with the 443 mμ band of $U_2O_5^{2+}$ in Table 2.1.

(The authors discussed these results in reference to formation of uranyl acetate complexes, but they are more likely to be due to hydrolysis.)

Neuman, Havill, and Feldman (1949) mentioned that the hydrolysis of UO_2^{++} (which they interpreted as formation of UO_2OH^+) can be detected polarographically only at pH $\geqslant 4.2$. The difference between this result and Sutton's data (pH $\geqslant 2.5$, cf. Fig. 2.2) may be due in part to the use of more dilute uranyl salt solutions (5×10^{-4}M in polarography vs. > 0.1M in spectrophotometry); according to Equation (1), the percent hydrolysis should increase in the region of low hydrolysis proportionally to $[UO_2^{++}]/[H^+]^2$.

The absorption spectrum of uranyl perchlorate solutions was measured also by Ahrland (1949). The curves he gave are very similar to those of Sutton (Fig. 2.1); they show the practical independence of ϵ upon pH between pH 0.1 and 2.7 over the range 240–440 mμ. In the region 240–320 mμ (not studied by Sutton) the absorption rises with decreasing wavelength (cf. Table 2.2). Shoulders are indicated at 310, 275, and perhaps also at 240 mμ.

The pH 4.1 absorption curve was measured by Ahrland only above 300 mμ; it is similar to Sutton's curve for pH 4.0 in Fig. 2.1.

Ahrland then proceeded to make pH measurements in uranyl perchlorate solutions (2×10^{-3} to 6×10^{-2}M) and calculated from them the average number, n, of complexly bound OH^- ions per uranyl ion at different uranyl salt concentrations and acidities. He concluded, from the shape of $\bar{n} = f(\text{pH})$ curves, that polyuranyl complexes are involved in hydrolysis even when the total salt concentration is as low as 5×10^{-3}M. By extrapolating $\bar{n}$ to $1/[H^+] = 0$ at different total uranyl concentrations, and plotting the result (n_0) against this concentration, a curve $\bar{n}_0 = f[UO_2^{++}]_0$ was constructed. Its extrapolated value at $[UO_2^{++}]_0 = 0$ was used to calculate the complex dissociation constant, K_1', for the first monouranyl complex ($UO_2^{++}OH^-$); from its initial slope, it was possible to calculate the complex dissociating constant, K_1'', of the first diuranyl complex, presumably $UO_2^{++}O^{--}UO_2^{++}$. The so-calculated values were as follows:

$$K_1' = 2 \, (\pm 0.4) \times 10^{-5};$$

$$K_1'' = 4 \, (\pm 1) \times 10^{-3}$$

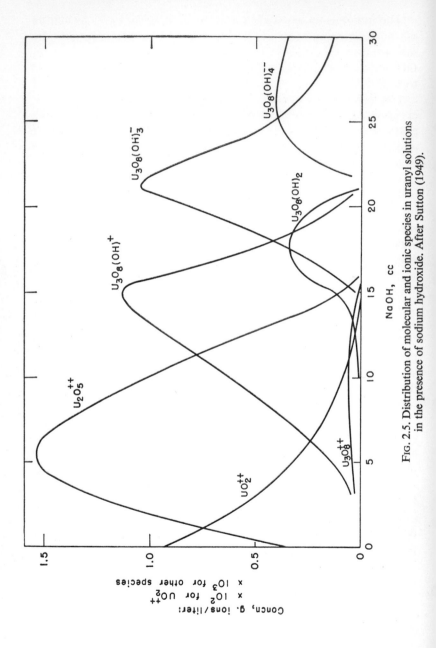

Fig. 2.5. Distribution of molecular and ionic species in uranyl solutions in the presence of sodium hydroxide. After Sutton (1949).

Ahrland thus agrees with Sutton in postulating early formation of diuranyl complexes, but assumes an effective competition by monouranyl complexes, whereas according to Sutton, addition of OH^- ions begins to play a role only after UO_2^{2+} has been complexed to $U_3O_8^{2+}$.

The low value of the extinction coefficients of UO_2^{2+} ($\epsilon_{max} \simeq 8$, cf. above) indicates a "prohibited" electronic transition (cf. Kasha (1949)); the prohibition apparently becomes less strict in the $U_3O_8^{2+}$ complex, where the extinction coefficient (referred to one g atom uranium!) reaches 240 (even this is low compared to average extinction coefficients in bands corresponding to "permitted" transitions, which are of the order of 10^4, or even 10^5). The natural mean lifetime of an excited state corresponding to an absorption band covering the range 400–500 mμ, with an average decadic molar extinction coefficient $\bar{\epsilon}$, is:

$$\tau_0 \simeq \frac{1.05 \times 10^{19}}{\int \epsilon_\nu d\nu} \lambda_0^2 = \frac{2.1 \times 10^{10}}{\bar{\epsilon} \times 1.5 \times 10^{14}} = \frac{1.4 \times 10^{-4}}{\bar{\epsilon}}$$

or $\qquad \tau_0 = 1.4 \times 10^{-4}$ for $\bar{\epsilon} = 1$ $\qquad\qquad\qquad$ (14)

The "actual" lifetime, τ, as derived from fluorescence measurements, is somewhat *longer*—about 5×10^{-4} sec—in uranyl solutions as well as in solid uranyl salts (cf. Table 3.1). Since τ is related to the "natural" lifetime τ_0 (to which Equation 14 refers) by the equation

$$\tau = \phi \tau_0 \qquad\qquad\qquad (15)$$

where ϕ, the quantum yield of fluorescence, is < 1, τ should be *shorter* than τ_0. This paradox may be due to the fact that ϵ, estimated from the absorption spectrum, includes transitions to several electronic states, while an ϵ value corresponding to the transition to the F state only should be properly used in Equation (14).

In any case, it seems that the yield of fluorescence in uranyl salt solutions must be high. No experimental determination of this yield has been made, but a rough estimate of ϕ for *solid* potassium uranyl sulfate has in fact indicated a value of the order of 1. This means, incidentally, that in uranyl salt crystals, too, the natural lifetime of excitation could not be much longer than 5×10^{-4} sec, which is two orders of magnitude less than the lifetime calculated by Dieke from intensity measurements of single absorption lines at low temperatures. This discrepancy was pointed out in Chapter 1.

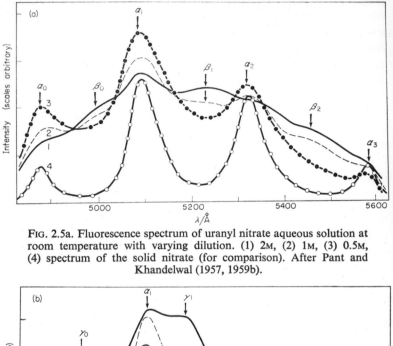

FIG. 2.5a. Fluorescence spectrum of uranyl nitrate aqueous solution at room temperature with varying dilution. (1) 2M, (2) 1M, (3) 0.5M, (4) spectrum of the solid nitrate (for comparison). After Pant and Khandelwal (1957, 1959b).

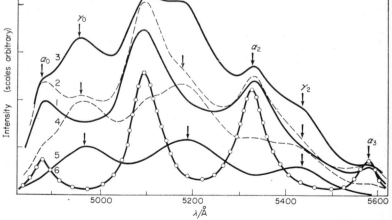

FIG. 2.5b. Fluorescence spectrum of uranyl nitrate aqueous solution at room temperature with varying dilution (continued). (1) 0.5M, (2) 0.2M, (3) 0.025M, (4) 0.006M, (5) 0.0015M, (6) spectrum of the solid nitrate (for comparison). After Pant and Khandelwal (1957, 1959b).

1.2. *Fluorescence Spectra*

The effects of varying uranyl concentration and pII upon the distribution of uranium-bearing molecular species can be seen in fluorescence as well as in absorption spectra of aqueous uranyl solutions. Pant and Khandelwal (1957, 1958, 1959a, 1959b) studied fluorescence of aqueous solutions of uranyl acetate, nitrate, and perchlorate as functions of concentration, pH, and added anion. The results of these studies are shown in Figs. 2.5a–i.

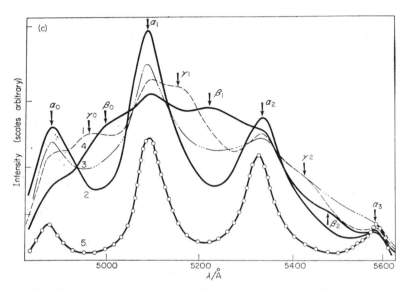

FIG. 2.5c. Fluorescence spectrum of uranyl nitrate solution with varying quantity of nitric acid (continued). Proportion of HNO_3 by volume: (1) 0.1%, (2) 30%, (3) 40%, (4) 50%, (5) 75%, (6) spectrum of the solid nitrate (for comparison). After Pant and Khandelwal (1959b).

The fluorescence spectra of uranyl nitrate solutions, Pant and Khandelwal noted, contain several band systems—four of them clearly evident—which appear and disappear together. These four obvious series were named α, β, γ, α'. Generally, the α and β systems were present at high uranyl concentrations; the α system, at intermediate concentrations ($\sim 0.5M$); both α and γ systems, at low uranyl concentrations; the γ system, at high pH; and the α' system, at extremely high HNO_3 concentrations.

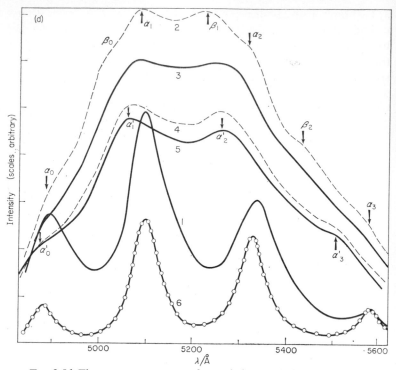

FIG. 2.5d. Fluorescence spectrum of uranyl nitrate solution with varying quantity of nitric acid. U-concentration constant at 0.08M. Concentration of HNO_3 used: 68%. Proportion of HNO_3 by volume: (1) 0%, (2) 0.1%, (3) 10%, (4) 30%, (5) spectrum of the solid nitrate (for comparison). After Pant and Khandelwal (1959b).

Further, the β system appears when HNO_3 is added to a solution having only the α system. In the light of these observations, and of the results obtained from absorption studies—discussed elsewhere in this chapter and repeated by Pant and Khandelwal—Pant and Khandelwal made the following species assignments:

$$\alpha \ \text{——} \ UO_2^{++}$$

$$\beta \ \text{——} \ UO_2NO_3^+$$

$$\gamma \ \text{——} \ U_2O_5^{++}$$

$$\alpha' \ \text{——} \ UO_2(NO_3)_2$$

Two further observations regarding the spectra of the basic uranyl nitrate solutions were made: (1) a large excess of base yields further hydrolyzed species and more complex fluorescence spectra, and (2) the γ band system is similar in its characteristics to the reported spectrum of hydrated UO_3 (cf. Dieke and Duncan).

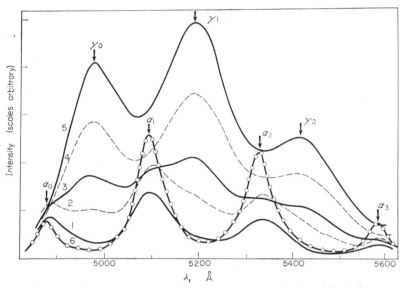

FIG. 2.5e. Fluorescence spectrum of uranyl nitrate solution with varying quantity of NaOH. U-concentration constant at 0.3M. NaOH used: ~ 0.002M. (1) 0%, (2) 0.1%, (3) 0.3%, (4) 0.5%, (5) 1.0% NaOH by volume, (6) spectrum of the solid nitrate (for comparison). After Pant and Khandelwal (1957, 1959b).

To test their assignments of the α and γ bands, Pant and Khandelwal (1959a) studied the fluorescence spectra of solutions of uranyl perchlorate as functions of pH. The results in accord with the above interpretation, are the following: (1) No α' or β band systems appeared under any conditions, (2) the two systems α and γ appeared when the predominant species should have been UO_2^{++} and $U_2O_5^{++}$ respectively, (3) a further drastic change in the spectrum occurred with the addition of large amounts of alkali. The α and γ systems, as observed in the perchlorate and nitrate solutions respectively are compared in Table 2.2a, which shows that the nature of the anion has little effect on the spectrum.

TABLE 2.2a. WAVELENGTHS OF α AND γ BANDS
After Pant and Khandelwal (1959a)

Designation	Wavelength (Å)	
	Perchlorate solution	Nitrate solution
α_0	4880	4888
γ_0	4980	4990
α_1	5100	5108
γ_1	5185	5185
α_2	5335	5350
γ_2	5405	5420
α_3	5580	5610
γ_3	5660	

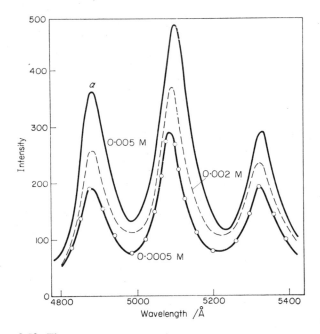

FIG. 2.5f. Fluorescence spectra of uranyl perchlorate solution at different concentrations at room temperature. (The solutions are acidic and the intensity scale is arbitrary.) After Pant and Khandelwal (1959a).

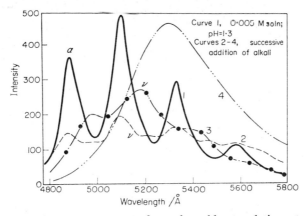

Fɪɢ. **2.5g.** Fluorescence spectra of uranyl perchlorate solutions at room temperature, showing the effect of increasing pH. (Curve 1, 0.005M solution of perchlorate, pH 1.3; curves 2–4 represent the spectra obtained with successive additions of alkali. Intensity scale is arbitrary.) After Pant and Khandelwal (1959a).

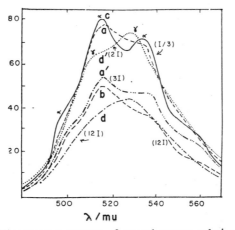

Fɪɢ. **2.5h.** Fluorescence spectra of uranyl acetate solutions at room temperature. (Curves *a*, aqueous only 0.0026ᴍ; curve *a'*, same, 0.00052ᴍ; curve *b*, in 0.4% acetic acid. Curve *c*, in 0.1% NaOH; curve *d*, in 0.3% NaOH, immediately after addition; curve *d'*, same, after standing overnight.) Greek letters refer to types of spectra. After Pant and Khandelwal (1958).

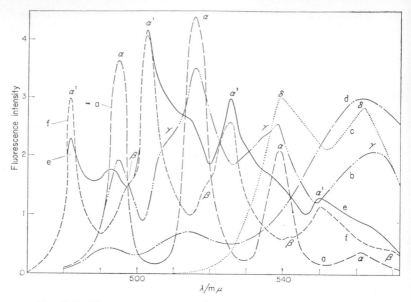

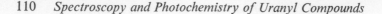

FIG. 2.5i. Fluorescence spectra of uranyl acetate solutions at 77°K, 0.0026M. (Curve *a*, aqueous; curves *b*, *c*, *d*, with successive additions of NaOH; curves *e*, *f*, with successive additions of acetic acid.) The Greek letters refer to band systems recognized by Pant and Khandelwal (1958), to whom this figure is due.

2. Absorption Spectra of Uranyl Ions Complexed with Acid Anions

2.1. *Effect of Inorganic Anions on Uranyl Spectrum in Solution*

For a long time observations had indicated that the spectrum of aqueous solutions of uranyl salts of strong inorganic acids—nitric, hydrochloric, sulfuric, etc.—is affected by the anions present in solution. However, the data had been neither precise nor systematic enough to tell whether these differences indicated the formation of definite complexes. (Thus, marked spectral changes could occur, without the formation of complexes, in consequence of the influence of ions on the bulk properties of the medium, such as its dielectric constant; or as a result of long-range order effects; or, in concentrated solutions, as a result of transient interaction between ions during their encounters.) More recently, the spectra of chloride, sulfate and nitrate solutions have been studied with better precision and interpreted in terms of complex formation.

Many of the older observations dealt only with the *position* of band peaks; others, in a qualitative way, with changes in the *intensity* of different bands. The following is a brief review of the results of these studies.

The earliest measurements were assembled and converted to international wavelength scale by Kayser, in Volume 3 of his *Handbook of Spectroscopy* (1905, p. 418). Absorption band peaks are given there for aqueous solutions of uranyl acetate, chloride, fluoride, nitrate, (mono)phosphate, and sulfate. As an example, Table 2.3 gives the (corrected) values of the band peaks observed by Morton and Bolton (1873). It shows that, with few exceptions, the bands of the nitrate are located at the shortest waves, followed by those of chloride, sulfate, acetate, fluoride and phosphate.

TABLE 2.3. ABSORPTION PEAKS OF URANYL SALTS IN AQUEOUS
SOLUTION AT ROOM TEMPERATURE
After Morton and Bolton (1873), corrected by Kayser (1905)

	Band No.						
	1	2	3	4	5	6	7
Nitrate	488	472	455	440	428	416	404
Chloride	—	475	457	440	429	—	—
Sulfate	495.5	475	457	443.4	431.5	420	408
Acetate	489	476	461	444	432	420	405
Fluoride	—	478	462	446	433	419.5	405.5
Mono-phosphate	506	477.5	461.5	448	434.5	424	—

For the interpretation of these shifts, the effects of the *concentration* of anions and of *temperature* are significant.

Concentration of the anions can be changed in two ways: either by increasing the concentration of the uranyl salt, or by adding another compound of the same anion, such as an alkali salt, or free acid. These studies are best carried out by *substitution*, keeping constant the total ionic strength and the acidity. Also, care should be taken to use the pH range where uranyl ions do not undergo any of the hydrolytic changes described in Section 1. No such precautions have been taken in the early measurements with which we are dealing now.

Concentration Effects. Knoblauch (1891) found that the *positions* of the two extreme long wave bands of uranyl nitrate did not change in the concentration range of $UO_2(NO_3)_2$ from 1M to 3×10^{-3}M; the same was found for a 1 : 450 change of concentration of uranyl acetate and a 2500 : 1 change of concentration of uranyl chloride. However, Knoblauch found these bands to be relatively *stronger* in dilute solution (indicating a deviation from Beer's law).

Jones and Strong (1910a) reproduced photographs of the absorption spectra of aqueous solutions of the following systems:

UO_2Cl_2 (1; 0.75; 0.5; 0.33; 0.25; 0.16 and 0.125N)

UO_2Cl_2 (0.2N) + $AlCl_3$ (2.43N)

UO_2Cl_2 (0.2N) + $ZnCl_2$ (saturated)

UO_2Cl_2 (0.2N) + HCl (concentrated)

The last three systems were investigated to observe the effect of a high concentration of Cl^- ions at constant concentration of UO_2^{++}. The absorption bands broadened with increasing UO_2Cl_2 concentration (the product concentration times cell depth being constant). The ultraviolet band merges with the nearest violet band.

TABLE 2.4. ABSORPTION BANDS OF UO_2Cl_2 (0.2N SOLUTION)
After Jones and Strong (1910)

UO_2Cl_2	—	402.5	417	431.5	446	456	474	492
+ $ZnCl_2$ (sat.)	—	411.5	424.5	—	440 diff.	460	477	493
+ $AlCl_3$ (2N)	401	413.5	427	442	448	462	479	495
+ HCl (conc.)	401.5	415	428	442	448	463.5	480	495

The positions of the observed band centers (which do not shift significantly with concentration) are shown in Table 2.4. In addition, very narrow, weak bands were noted at 518.5, 520, 600, 602, 604 and 607 mμ. Addition of calcium chloride caused all bands to broaden. The effect of aluminium chloride was even stronger; the bands shifted to the red by up to 3 mμ; some increased considerably in intensity. Zinc chloride and concentrated hydrochloric acid produced similar changes, but the red shift was less pronounced with zinc chloride than with aluminium chloride or hydrochloric acid.

Similarly, concentrated nitric acid was found to increase the intensity of $UO_2(NO_3)_2$ bands, but the band shift caused by this acid was toward the violet.

Von Kurelec (1927) measured the shift of the peaks of the first two absorption bands of uranyl nitrate (3.454 g $UO_2(NO_3)_2$ in 14 ml H_2O), caused by addition of an increasing quantity of sulfuric acid, and found that at $[H_2SO_4]/[HNO_3] = 1.2$, the bands assumed the positions characteristic of uranyl sulfate. This may indicate replacement of nitrate ions in association with uranyl cations by sulfate ions.

TABLE 2.5. SHIFT OF $UO_2(NO_3)_2$ ABSORPTION BANDS BY SULFURIC ACID
After von Kurelec (1927)

[H_2SO_4] (g/14 ml solution)	Band	
	I	II
0	487.0	470.0
0.473	489.7	473.5
0.788	489.6	473.6
0.867	489.7	473.7
0.946	489.9	473.9
1.576	490.3	474.4
UO_2SO_4 in H_2O	490.4	474.2

No shift was observed when 0.47 g HNO_3 was added to a solution of 4.57 g UO_2SO_4 in 14 ml H_2O. Addition of nitric acid to UO_2Cl_2 solution also was ineffective. This agrees with the assumption that the tendency of uranyl ions for complexing is smaller with NO_3^- than with Cl^- and SO_4^{--} ions.

Only when nitric acid was added to UO_2Cl_2 solution in large excess and the mixture heated until gas evolution and brown coloration occurred, did the UO_2^{++} bands shift to positions characteristic of a nitrate solution.

When hydrochloric acid was added to uranyl nitrate, a shift similar to that caused by sulfate was observed. At about $[HCl]/[HNO_3] = 1$, the band reached a position close to that in pure UO_2Cl_2 solution.

Pierce (1929) found that chloride in low concentrations has no marked effect on the absorption spectrum of uranyl salt solution, but that *saturated* potassium chloride changes the spectrum almost as strongly as 0.01M oxalic acid, indicating the formation of complexes. (It will be noted that quenching of uranyl fluorescence by chloride ions sets in at much lower concentrations and therefore cannot be attributed to complex formation.)

Pringsheim (1937) found similar evidence of interaction of uranyl ions with *iodide* ions at potassium iodide concentrations of the order of 0.01–0.1M. The absorption coefficient of 0.05M UO_2SO_4 at 365 mμ was increased by a factor of 4 by the addition of 0.1M KI.

The *temperature effect* on the absorption bands of simple uranyl salts in aqueous solution was first noted by Bremer (1890) [cf. Bremer (1892) and Kayser (1905, p. 419)]. He found that with UO_2SO_4 as well as with $UO_2(NO_3)_2$ solution, heating shifts the band peaks towards the red (by 1.2–1.6 mμ between 20° and 80°C). Morton and Bolton (1873) found the same rule to be followed by several double salts.

Jones and Strong (1910a, b, 1911a) photographed the spectrum of uranyl *chloride* (1N) at 6°, 18°, 34°, 52°, 68° and 82°C. With increasing temperature, the ultraviolet absorption limit moved toward the visible, from 355 to 370 mμ; the strong blue-violet band shifted at the same time from 400–445 mμ to 395–460 mμ. In more dilute (0.0156N) solution, the temperature effect was much less pronounced. In uranyl *nitrate* solutions in water (1N and 0.0156N), the results were similar, with the ultraviolet absorption edge shift (343 $\rightarrow$ 355 mμ) being the most prominent effect. The blue-violet band extended, at 79°C, from 390 to 445 mμ.

In uranyl *sulfate* solutions in water (1N and 0.0156N), the ultraviolet edge advanced between 5° and 84°C from 350 to 360 mμ. The blue-violet band extended at low temperature from 390 to 440 mμ (in concentrated solution) or 395 to 445 mμ (in dilute solution) and at high temperature from 385 to 445 mμ or 390 to 450 mμ, respectively. Other bands also were shifted by heating: from 457, 473 and 491 mμ, to 459, 474.5 and 492.5 mμ, respectively, in 1N solution; and from 472 and 489.5 mμ to 473.5 and 491.5 mμ respectively, in N/64 solution.

Jones and Strong (1911b, 1912) reproduced the spectra of uranyl nitrate in nitric acid, of uranyl chloride in hydrochloric acid, and of uranyl sulfate in water and in sulfuric acid, at temperatures from 10° to 70–80°C. The shifts in acid solutions were in the same direction (i.e. towards longer wavelengths) as in pure water, but were much less extensive, by about 1 mμ in the case of nitrate in nitric acid, and 1.5 mμ in that of chloride in hydrochloric acid. Sulfate in sulfuric acid showed a marked shift only in the blue-violet band.

Jones and Guy (1913b) reproduced absorption spectra of 0.2N and 0.02N uranyl nitrate solutions in water, at temperatures from 20 to 120°C and from 20 to 165°C, respectively. The spectrogram shows general band widening and shift of the centers of some bands towards longer waves with increasing temperature. Broad and diffuse bands appear at the higher temperatures—in 0.02N solution at 510, 560 and 620 mμ.

Similar spectrograms were given for 0.166 and 0.2N uranyl sulfate in water at 20–185°C and 20–165°C respectively. The centers of the bands at 477.5 and 432.5 mμ moved by as much as 2.5 mμ upon heating, while that of the 475.0 mμ remained in its original position. The weak and diffuse bands at 510, 560 and 620 mμ seemed in this case to be unaffected by temperature. These experiments indicated that only very weak complexing occurs between uranyl and nitrate ions and that association is somewhat stronger with sulfate, and still stronger with chloride ions.

Betts and Michels (1949) made the first more precise spectrophotometric study of solutions of uranyl sulfate and uranyl nitrate. They pointed out that definite complex formation with sulfate ions is indicated, in addition to earlier polarographic studies, by the observation that isotopic exchange of uranium between uranyl ions, U^{+4} ions and U^{+6} ions is much more rapid in sulfate than in perchlorate solutions. The absence of complexing in the latter solution, shown by Sutton's spectrophotometric study (p. 92) was confirmed by Betts and Michels, who extended the range in which the spectrum shows no changes attributable to complexing, to $[UO_2^{++}] = 0.02–0.5M$ and $[HClO_4] = 2–6M$ (at $[H^+] = 2M$).

In sulfate solutions (also at $[H^+] = 2M$), with a total ionic strength of $\eta = 2.65$ (sulfuric acid being treated as a monobasic acid), comparison of absorption curves of solutions with a constant value of $([UO_2^{++}] + [HSO_4^-])$ ($= 0.240M$), but variable ratio $[UO_2^{++}]/[HSO_4^-]$, revealed an increase of average molar extinction coefficients (in the range 420–450 mμ) with increasing proportion of uranyl ions, $x = [UO_2^{2+}]/([UO_2^{2+}] + [HSO_4^-])$, reaching a peak at the ratio $x = 0.5$ and decreasing at $x > 0.5$. According to Job, this indicates the formation of a one-to-one uranyl bisulfate complex. The effect of H^+ concentration on the results indicated that the complexing reaction is:

$$UO_2^{2+} + HSO_4^- \rightleftharpoons UO_2SO_4 + H^+$$

rather than $\qquad UO_2^{2+} + HSO_4^- \rightleftharpoons UO_2HSO_4^+$

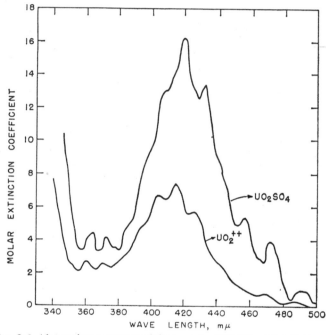

FIG. 2.6. Absorption spectrum of the complex UO_2SO_4. After Betts and Michels (1949).

The spectrum of the species UO_2SO_4, derived from these experiments, is shown in Fig. 2.6. The equilibrium constant is:

$$K(UO_2SO_4) = ([UO_2SO_4]/[UO_2^{2+}] [HSO_4^-]) = 2.50 \pm 0.17 \text{ (mole/l)}^{-1}$$

for $\eta = 3.48$. This value was derived from the spectra of two solutions, both 0.02M in HSO_4^-; it was confirmed by calculating extinction values for other mixtures of same ionic strength and acidity, and comparing them with experimental values.

A similar study of the uranyl nitrate system led to Fig. 2.7a for the spectrum of the species $UO_2NO_3^+$, and to an equilibrium constant

$$K(UO_2NO_3^+) = \frac{[UO_2NO_3^+]}{[UO_2^{++}][NO_3^-]} = 0.21 \pm 0.01 \ (\text{mole/l})^{-1} \quad (16)$$

at $[H^+] = 2.00$, and $\eta = 5.38$ (equilibrium constant calculated from the spectra of two solutions with $[UO_2^{++}] = 0.0605$M, and $[NO_3^-]$

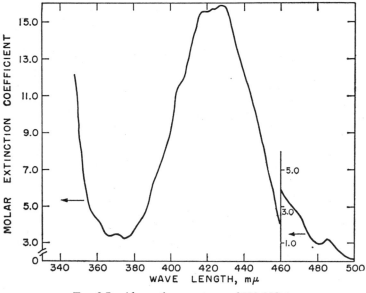

FIG. 2.7a. Absorption spectrum of $UO_2NO_3^+$.

$= 1.28$ and 2.56M respectively; checked by comparing calculated and observed spectra of other solutions of same acidity and ionic strength).

In looking for higher nitrate complexes at the higher concentrations, Betts and Michels found only slight deviations of observed from the calculated spectra at $\eta = 7.05$ $[K(UO_2NO_3^+) = 0.270 \pm 0.007]$. These deviations were in the direction of stronger absorption, as expected for a higher complex, but they were so small that Betts and Michels considered them to be due to slight variations of

K with [UO_2^{2+}] (at constant η), rather than to the formation of deeper-colored higher complexes. Pant and Khandelwal (1959b), however, believed that their absorption and fluorescence spectra showed evidence for a species $UO_2(NO_3)_2$ at HNO_3 concentrations over 50 per cent; this species has a band system nearer to the blue than the other species.

According to a note by Arden (1949), potentiometric and conductometric measurements indicate the formation of the following complexes in uranyl sulfate solutions:

$$UO_2SO_4;\ U_3O_8^{2+};\ (UO_2OH)_2SO_4;\ U_3O_8OH^+;\ UO_2(OH)_2;$$
$$U_3O_8(OH)_2$$

The formation of a *trinitro* complex from uranyl nitrate and concentrated nitric acid in certain organic solvents will be described in Section 3 of this chapter.

Ahrland (1951c) measured extinction curves of 0.033M (or 0.015M) $UO_2(ClO_4)_2$ solutions in 0.25M (or 0.10M) $HClO_4$, to which NaCl (0.25–0.75M), NaBr (0.75M) or $NaNO_3$ (0.75M) was added, the ionic strength being adjusted to $\eta = 1.0$ by $NaClO_4$. The curves showed slight, but real differences, indicative of weak complexing. Assuming a 1–1 complex only, its equilibrium constant could be calculated, for uranyl *chloride*, as

$$K_1 = \frac{[UO_2Cl^+]}{[UO_2^{2+}]\,[Cl^-]} = 0.5 \pm 0.3\ (\text{mole/l})^{-1}\quad (20°C)$$

For all three salts the first complexing constant at 20°C was determined potentiometrically; the resulting values were 0.8, 0.5 and 0.5 (± 0.2) (mole/l)$^{-1}$ for the *chloride*, *bromide*, and *nitrate*, in this order. The last value can be compared with Betts and Michels' result (0.21 ± 0.01 at $\eta = 5.38$ and 25°C).

A similar study of *sulfate* (Ahrland, 1951b) gave Fig. 2.8a for the absorption spectra at different sulfate concentrations, and Fig. 2.8b for the molar absorption coefficient at 310 mμ as function of [sulfate] and three different [uranyl] values. Again, only monouranyl complexes of UO_2^{2+} with SO_4^{2-} are indicated, with the association constants

$$K_1 = 56 \pm 6\ (\text{mole/l})^{-1}\qquad K_2 = 450 \pm 50\ (\text{mole/l})^{-2}$$

The first constant, valid at 20°C and $\eta = 1.0$, can be compared with Betts and Michels' value of 59.5 ± 4 (mole/l)$^{-1}$. (Ahrland makes objections against the method used by Betts and Michels.)

The association constants derived from potentiometric methods were:

$$K_1 = 50 \pm 10 \ (mole/l)^{-1}$$

$$K_2 = 350 \pm 150 \ (mole/l)^{-2}$$

$$K_3 = 2500 \pm 1000 \ (mole/l)^{-3}$$

Association constants of mixed acetate–sulfate complexes, $UO_2^{++}Ac^-SO_4^{--}$ and $UO_2^{++}Ac_2^-SO_4^{--}$, also were estimated potentiometrically.

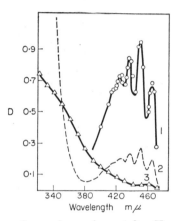

Fig. 2.7b. Spectra of uranyl complexes (after Komarov, 1959). (1) UO_2^{++}, 0.035M; $KHCO_3$, 0.10M; KNO_3, 5M; 1 cm cell. (2) $UO_2(NO_3)_2$, 9.6×10^{-4}M in 0.01M $KHCO_3$; 10.16 cm cell. (3) $K_3[UO_2(CO_3)_2.OOH]$, 5×10^{-4}M, in 100 per cent excess of $KHCO_3$ and 400 per cent excess of H_2O_2; 1 cm cell.

Komarov (1959) studied the formation of the tricarbonato uranyl ion $[UO_2(CO_3)_3]^{-4}$, of the hydroperoxydicarbonato uranyl ion $[UO_2(CO_3)_2O_2H]^{-3}$, and of other species in the system $UO_2(NO_3)_2$–$KHCO_3$–H_2O_2–H_2O. He determined equilibrium constants by a spectrophotometric method, which he discussed in detail. Figure 2.7b shows spectra obtained by him and by Blake *et al.* (1956) for these complexes.

2.2. *Complexing with Organic Ions*

The spectroscopic evidence of uranyl ion complexing with anions of organic acids is much stronger than in the case of mineral acids but here, too, older data are insufficient for satisfactory quantitative analysis, and new systematic measurements, under controlled conditions of acidity and ionic strength, are yet needed. Much progress is being made in this area, however.

Early data on the absorption spectrum of uranyl *acetate* in the visible range were mentioned on p. 111 (cf. Table 2.3). Jones and Strong (1910a, 1911b) noted that the long-wave edge of the blue-violet absorption band of a 0.04M solution of this salt moved from 450 mμ at 6°C to 460 mμ at 75°C.

Henri and Landau (1914) measured the absorption coefficients of several uranyl salt solutions in the medium ultraviolet (236–330 mμ). The results are shown in Table 2.6. A substantial increase in absorption is caused by the addition of oxalate or acetate. Henri and Landau saw in this an example of "photochemical exaltation"; according to this concept, the absorption of light by a mixture of molecular species that can react with each other photochemically is stronger than the sum of the absorption of the components.

A parallelism between enhanced absorption and photochemical reactivity is in fact possible, but the latter cannot be considered as *cause* of the former. What is essential is that the two components form a more or less stable complex. Light absorption can then cause the transfer of an electron from one part of the complex (e.g. the anion), to another part (e.g. the cation); the absorption band is an "electron transfer band." Such a transfer is equivalent to an internal oxidation–reduction; the complex may then—but does not need to—dissociate into an oxidized and a reduced product (e.g. into a reduced uranyl ion and an oxidized oxalate ion). If the anion–cation electron transfer band lies in the same region as the absorption bands of one (or both) of the separate ions, the effect of complexing will be to enhance absorption in this region. Whether or not the lifting of the electron into the transfer band will lead to a photochemical change depends on the amount of vibrational energy of a certain type required for this change and the probability of conversion of electronic excitation energy into vibrational energy of this kind. This probability may be large or small, both in photochemically unstable and in photochemically stable complexes.

TABLE 2.6. EFFECT OF DIFFERENT ANIONS ON THE ABSORPTION COEFFICIENTS OF URANYL IONS IN ULTRAVIOLET After Henri and Landau (1914)

Solution contains	Wavelength (mμ)									
	236	243.5	251.0	259.2	272.4	289.5	300.1	307.6	318.6	330.6
$UO_2(NO_3)_2$	2020	1350	675	540	295	160	125	108	65	27
UO_2SO_4	1350	1000	720	545	375	200	108	81	54	—
UO_2Cl_2	1050	890	540	490	320	275	170	—	—	—
$UO_2(CH_3COO)_2$	2200	1825	1575	1300	970	810	630	500	320	210
$UO_2(NO_3)_2 + H_2C_2O_4$	—	—	2480	1950	1390	780	540	440	300	—
$UO_2SO_4 + H_2C_2O_4$	3225	2850	2445	2030	1440	640	410	280	190	—
$UO_2Cl_2 + H_2C_2O_4$	—	—	1610	1380	1010	585	370	260	180	—
$UO_2(CH_3COO)_2 + H_2C_2O_4$	3160	2670	2280	1840	1230	—	—	—	—	—
$UO_2C_2O_4$	2770	2380	1990	1690	1230	580	435	290	165	120
Oxalic Acid*	88	64	57	—	49	22	5	2	—	—

* Figures in this row show how much light oxalate alone would have absorbed at the different wavelengths. Henri and Landau noted that ϵ(oxalate), added to $\epsilon(UO_2(NO_3)_2)$ (top row in Table 2.6) is smaller than ϵ of the mixture ($UO_2(NO_3)_2$ + oxalate), and considered this difference as "photochemical exaltation"; we interpret it as evidence of complex formation.

$$\log_{10}(I_0/I) = \epsilon c d$$

c in mole U/liter. Acid concentration not specified.

The change of absorption spectrum observed by Henri and Landau upon mixing of uranyl salts with acetic or oxalic acid seems to consist in a strong general enhancement of absorption, rather than a shift of the absorption band; this is a reason for attributing it to a new excited state, not possessed by the separate ions. Often, however, the absorption bands of complexes are not much more intense than those of the non-complexed ions, but only appear so because they shifted towards longer waves, thus enhancing the

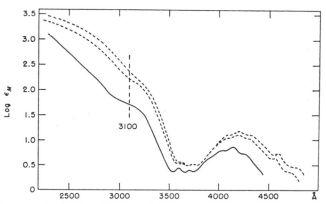

FIG. 2.8a. Molar decadic extinction curves of uranyl sulfate complexes (after Ahrland, 1951b). Solid line: uranyl ions (free). Dashed lines: $[UO_2^{++}]_0 = 0.01M$; $[sulfate]_0 = 0.05M$ (lower curve), $0.2M$ (upper curve). $[UO_2^{++}]_0 =$ total concentration of free and bound uranyl. $[Sulfate]_0 =$ total concentration of sulfate used (uranyl sulfate + sodium sulfate). A small correction is made for association of SO_4^{--} ions with H^+ ions. (Enough perchloric acid is added to suppress hydrolysis of uranyl ions.) Ionic strength $\eta = 1.0$ adjusted by $NaClO_4$.

absorption in the visible and near ultraviolet. In this case, one does not need to postulate a new electronic level in the complex, but can assume that complexing merely lowers the energy of an excited state belonging to one of the free ions. In further developing the picture, we note that "free ions," in the case of aqueous solutions, means hydrated ions; some of their strong ultraviolet absorption bands may be (and probably are) due to the transfer of an electron from the hydration sphere to the central cation, or vice versa. (The much weaker bands in the visible and near ultraviolet, on the other hand, are likely to be caused by prohibited transitions within the ion itself.) The effect of complexing with an anion is to introduce it into the hydration sphere of the cation. This may merely make the electron transfer to or from the water envelope easier (thus shifting the absorption band towards longer waves); or it may permit a new kind of transfer, in which the electron originates (or ends), not in the hydration sphere, but in the anion. This new electronic transition produces a general enhancement of absorption in the region of the new electron transfer band.

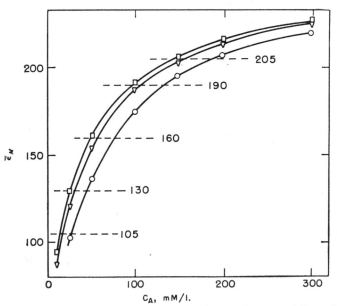

FIG. 2.8b. Average molar decadic extinction coefficient at 310 mμ in uranyl+sulfate solution as function of total sulfate concentration C_A (free sulfate ions + sulfate ions complexed with uranyl). ◯ $[UO_2^{++}]_0$ = 0.030M. ▽ $[UO_2^{++}]_0$ = 0.010M. ☐ $[UO_2^{++}]_0$ = 0.003M. Horizontal lines cut the several curves at points corresponding to constant concentration of free anions.

With these general remarks concerning enhanced absorption of complex ions (compared to that of non-complexed, hydrated ions) prompted by Henri and Landau's "photochemical exaltation" concept, we return to the experimental data obtained with uranyl ions and organic acids.

Somewhat more systematic measurements than those of Henri and Landau were carried out by Ghosh and Mitter (1928). They observed the enhancement of ultraviolet absorption of 5×10^{-4}M and 10×10^{-4}M uranyl solutions by the addition of various organic acids (0.005M to 1M), and found effects which they attributed to the formation of 1–1 complexes between uranyl ions and the acid, with an equilibrium constant K_c:

$$K_c = \frac{[UO_2^{++}A]}{[UO_2^{++}][A]} = \frac{[C]}{([U]_0 - [C])([A]_0 - [C])} \tag{17}$$

where $[C]$ is the concentration of the complex, and $[U]_0$ and $[A]_0$ are the total concentrations of uranyl salt and acid respectively.

Spectroscopic evidence of the formation of a uranyl tartrate complex was obtained by Hakomori (1927); he noted that increased addition of Rochelle salt to 0.02N uranyl sulfate solution causes the ultraviolet absorption to move from 335 to 360 mμ, when a 1 : 1 ratio is reached, and then to recede again.

By analogy with the hydrolysis equilibria discussed in Section 1, the possibility of formation of polyuranyl ions should not be forgotten. However, Ahrland (1949, 1951) found, with several inorganic (HCl, HBr, HNO$_3$, H$_2$SO$_4$) and organic (acetic, monochloracetic, thiocyanic) acids, no evidence of complexes containing more than one uranyl ion. Even considering 1–1 complexes only, Equation (17) is unsatisfactory, because $[A]$ denotes *total acid*, no distinction being made between acid anions and neutral acid molecules. Even if relatively few free ions are present in weak acids at $A_0 \geqslant 0.1$M, the most important complex species may still be that containing anions, e.g.

$$UO_2^{++} + HCOO^- \rightleftharpoons UO_2HCOO^+ \tag{18}$$

Equation (17) must therefore be replaced by one involving the dissociation constant of the acid, D, in addition to the complexing constant K:

$$K = \frac{[UO_2^{++}A^-]}{[UO_2^{++}][A^-]} = K_c \left(\frac{[H^+]}{D} + 1 \right) \tag{19}$$

When acid dissociation is practically complete (i.e. when $D \gg [H^+]$) we have

$$K \simeq K_c$$

and Ghosh and Mitter's procedure becomes admissible (leaving out "second order" effects, such as the—generally quite considerable—dependence of the complexing constant on ionic strength). In the case of weak dissociation ($[H^+] \gg D$), on the other hand, we have

$$K \simeq K_c \frac{[H^+]}{D}, \quad \text{or} \quad K_c \simeq \frac{KD}{[H^+]} \simeq K \sqrt{\frac{D}{A_0}} \qquad (20)$$

and thus see that Ghosh and Mitter's "constant," K_c, cannot remain constant except in buffered solutions ($[H^+] = $ const.), while in the absence of a buffer the observed values of the "constant" K_c will decrease with increasing concentration of the acid. In the region of very weak dissociation K_c will be inversely proportional to $\sqrt{A_0}$.

Ghosh and Mitter's K_c calculations could have given a correct picture of the relative strength of complexing with different acids only if their measurements had been made in the region of approximately complete dissociation; in fact, however, they were made mostly in the region of weak dissociation, where the apparent "complexing constants," K_c, are smaller the weaker the acid. With very weak dissociation, when Equation (20) is valid, K_c/K will be proportional to $\sqrt{D}$ at any given concentration of the added acid; in other words, of two acids with equal *true* complexing constants, K' and K'', the one with the higher dissociation constant, D, will appear to form more stable complexes:

$$K_c' \simeq \sqrt{\frac{D'}{D''}} K_c'' \qquad (21)$$

One can imagine the acid anions as having a choice of complexing, either with H^+ ions or with UO_2^{++} ions. The tendency for complexing with hydrogen ions is generally greater than that for complexing with uranyl ions (K is smaller than $1/D$!). The number of H^+ ions available (i.e. in practice, in unbuffered solution, the total acid concentration, $[A]_0$) was in Ghosh's experiments much higher than the total number of available uranyl ions. Therefore, the concentration of free acid anions was determined mainly or exclusively by $[A]_0$ and D, and the concentration of uranyl complexes was in its turn determined by the concentration of free acid anions.

Similarly, the uranyl ions have a choice of association either with the acid anions or with the anions of water (OH^- and O^{--}).

Improved calculation should take into consideration also the hydrolysis equilibria of the uranyl ion, described in Section 1, which become important at pH > 2. Finally, the equilibrium constants depend on ionic strength, so that measurements should be made at known and constant ionic strength.

When Equation (17) is valid, the complexing constant, K_c, can be calculated, together with the absorption coefficient, ϵ_c, of the complex $[UO_2^{++}A]$, by measuring the absorption coefficient $\bar{\epsilon}$ (the average molar absorption coefficient referred to the total uranyl content) at a given wavelength, λ, with two different concentrations of total added acid, A_0.

Each measured value of $\bar{\epsilon}$ can be expressed by an equation

$$\bar{\epsilon} = \frac{[C](\epsilon_c - \epsilon_u + [U]_0 \epsilon_u)}{[U]_0} \tag{22}$$

with two unknowns: $[C]$ = concentration of complex, and ϵ_c = absorption coefficient of complex, while ϵ_u, the absorption coefficient of non-complexed uranyl ions, can be presumed to be known from measurements made without added acid. Two such equations, together with two equations of type (17) for the two concentrations A_0, provide four equations with four unknowns, which can be solved.

Ghosh and Mitter tabulated K_c values (Table 2.7) and the absorption coefficients, ϵ_c (Table 2.8) calculated in this way for the several acids they have studied. However, closer scrutiny reveals, in the first place, that the values designated by them as "absorption coefficients of the complex" (i.e. ϵ_c) are not these coefficients, but *differences* between them and the absorption coefficients of free uranyl ions (i.e. $\bar{\epsilon}_c - \epsilon_u$, cf. Equation (22)). This error has been corrected in Table 2.8. Furthermore, no indication can be found in the paper of Ghosh and Mitter as to whether their absorption coefficients were based on decadic or natural logarithms. Since in some later papers from Ghosh's laboratory natural logarithms were specified, we presume that the same was true of the values of Ghosh and Mitter as well.

The absorption coefficients given by Henri and Landau (Table 2.6) are generally lower than those given by Ghosh and Mitter; this may be due to the fact that the (unspecified) concentrations of the

TABLE 2.7. COMPLEXING CONSTANTS OF URANYL IONS WITH ORGANIC ACIDS
After Ghosh and Mitter (1928)

Acid	Formula	K_c (mole/l)$^{-1}$	$D \times 10^4$	$\sqrt{D} \times 10^2$	$\dfrac{K_c}{\sqrt{D}}$ (mole/l)$^{-1}$
Formic	HCOOH	10	176	13	77
Acetic	CH$_3$COOH	6	17.5	4.2	143*
Propionic	CH$_3$CH$_2$COOH	4	14	3.7	108
Oxalic	HOOC COOH	115	65,000	254	45
Malonic	HOOC CH$_2$ COOH	80	1600	40	200
Succinic	HOOC CH$_2$ CH$_2$ COOH	50	66	8.2	610
Glycolic	CH$_2$OH COOH	15	—	—	—
Lactic	CH$_3$ CHOH COOH	20	—	—	—
Tartaric†	HOOC CHOHCHOH COOH	20	1100	33	60
Mandelic	C$_6$H$_5$ CHOH COOH	50	—	—	—

* Ahrland (1951a) calculated $K = 240$ (mole/l)$^{-1}$ for the first association constant of uranyl with acetate ions at 20°C, $\eta = 1.0$.
† Rana Char (1942) calculated $K_c \simeq 10$ from optical rotation measurements; cf. Chap. 4.

$$K_c(\text{mole/l})^{-1} = \frac{[\text{complex}]}{[\text{free uranyl}] \times [\text{free acid}]} \; ; \; D = \frac{[H^+][A^-]}{[AH]} \; (\text{mole/l})^{-1}$$

TABLE 2.8. EFFECT OF COMPLEXING ON ABSORPTION SPECTRUM OF URANYL IONS IN AQUEOUS SOLUTION
After Ghosh and Mitter (1928)

Complex with	Wavelength (mμ)									
	250.7	254.5	260.0	272.2	277.0	296.1	327.4	336.4	343.5	366.0
None*	304.3	260.9	239.1	130.4	108.7	65.2	(< 43.5)	—	—	—
Formate	565.2	391.3	396.6	—	152.2	91.3	—	—	—	—
Acetate	—	608.7	513.0	360.9	287.0	152.2	—	—	—	—
Propionate	908.7	808.7	780.4	—	395.7	213.0	—	117.4	63.0	—
Oxalate	—	—	—	—	—	534.8	239.1	—	—	—
Malonate	—	—	934.8	521.7	408.7	165.2	(52.2)	—	—	7.39†
Succinate	630.4	491.3	469.6	421.7	221.7	156.5	(78.3)	—	—	—
Glycolate	—	760.9	595.7	—	287.0	139.1	(56.5)	—	—	—
Lactate	—	782.6	673.9	—	369.6	195.7	(91.3)	—	—	—
Tartrate	—	956.5	752.2	—	360.9	256.5	(195.7)	(130.4)	—	—
Mandelate	—	—	—	630.4	421.7	273.9	(130.4)	(104.3)	(65.2)	—‡

* Uranyl nitrate solution 5 × 10⁻⁴M (cf. p. 112 about complexing with nitrate).
† Ghosh, Banerjee, and Bhatta (1936).
‡ See data of Ghosh, Naraganmuoti, and Ray in Table 4.23; an ϵ value of 15 is given there for λ436 mμ.

$\epsilon = \log_{10}(I_0/I)/cd$
c = total concentration of uranium in mole/l
d = light path in cm

acids used by Henri and Landau probably were not high enough to achieve complete complexing. (The values of Ghosh and Mitter were extrapolated to complete complexing, but extrapolation must have been unreliable because of disregard of changes in acid dissociation with the concentration of the acid in unbuffered solution.) The same criticism applies to the value in the last column given by Ghosh, Banerjee and Bhatta (1936) for the absorption coefficient of uranyl ions at 366 mμ in 0.1M succinic acid.

The approximate proportionality between the values of K_c and $\sqrt{D}$ in Table 2.7 supports the hypothesis that association occurs mainly between cations and anions (and *not* between cations and neutral acid molecules), and that the "constants" K_c of the weaker acids measure their acid strength rather than the stability of their uranyl complexes.

Some figures for the effect of oxalic acid on the absorption spectrum of uranyl sulfate in the *visible* and the *near-ultraviolet* (above 346 mμ) were given also by Pringsheim (1937). They are shown in Tables 2.9 and 2.10.

TABLE 2.9. EFFECT OF OXALATE ON AVERAGE ABSORPTION
COEFFICIENTS OF URANYL SULFATE
After Pringsheim (1937)

λ (mμ)	346.6	361.2	365.0	404.7	435.8
UO$_2$SO$_4$ (0.05M)*	67	5.3	2.2	8.5	6
Same + H$_2$C$_2$O$_4$ (0.005M)	200	20	11	10.5	7.5

* According to p. 96, these values correspond to a product of hydrolysis rather than to free UO$_2$++ ions.

$$\epsilon = \log_{10}(I_0/I)/cd; \; c \text{ in mole U/liter}$$

TABLE 2.10. AVERAGE ABSORPTION COEFFICIENT OF URANYL IONS (0.02M)
AT 365.0 mμ, AS FUNCTION OF CONCENTRATION OF ADDED OXALIC ACID
After Pringsheim (1937)

$\dfrac{[H_2C_2O_4]}{[UO_2SO_4]}$	0	1/16	1/8	1/4	1/2	1	2
ϵ (365.0 mμ)	2.2	2.9	3.7	4.9	7.2	11.1	12.4

$$\epsilon = \log_{10}(I_0/I)/cd; \; c \text{ in mole U/liter}$$

Table 2.10 shows that complexing is not complete even when more than one molecule of $H_2C_2O_4$ (0.02M) are present per molecule of uranyl sulfate; this indicates that the figures in Table 2.9 must be much lower than the true absorption coefficients of the uranyl oxalate complex.

A systematic spectroscopic study of uranyl complexes in solution has been undertaken by Ahrland. His first paper (1949a) dealt with hydrolysis (cf. Section 1). He then (1949b) proceeded to study the complexing of UO_2^{++} ions by *monochloracetic acid*, using the range below pH 3, where hydrolysis is insignificant. Potentiometric measurements indicated that no polyuranyl complexes were formed; the spectroscopic data were interpreted correspondingly. The spectrum of a 10^{-2}M solution of uranyl perchlorate showed, in the presence of 0.1M chloroacetate buffer, a general enhancement of absorption between 300 and 450 mμ. No exact spectral curves were determined, but absorption at 313 mμ was studied as function of concentration. The result could be explained by assuming a sequence of three complexing steps (in the range from $[A] = 0.02$M to $[A] = 0.4$M; the three complex dissociation constants (for 20°C and $\eta = 1$) were calculated with the following results:

$$UO_2^{++}A^- \qquad K_1 = 24 \pm 3 \text{ (mole/l)}^{-1}$$

$$UO_2^{++}A^{--} \qquad K_2 = 150 \pm 40 \text{ (mole/l)}^{-2}$$

$$UO_2^{++}A_3^{---} \qquad K_3 = 350 \pm 150 \text{ (mole/l)}^{-3}$$

Potentiometric measurements gave, for the same constants, the values 27.5, 195 and 625, respectively.

Ahrland (1949c) studied in the same way UO_2^{++} complexes with *thiocyanate* ions. Figure 2.8c shows the effect of thiocyanate (0.03–0.16M) on the absorption spectrum of 0.03M uranyl perchlorate. Again, no polynuclear complexes were found; dissociation constants of three monouranyl complexes were derived from extinction measurements at 366 mμ. The following values (for 20°C and $\eta = 1$) were obtained:

$$UO_2^{++}A^- \qquad K_1 = 5.7 \text{ (mole/l)}^{-1}$$

$$UO_2^{++}A_2^- \qquad K_2 = 5.5 \text{ (mole/l)}^{-2}$$

$$UO_2^{++}A_3^{---} \qquad K_3 = 15 \text{ (mole/l)}^{-3}$$

Ahrland (1951a) then made a similar potentiometric and spectroscopic measurement on uranyl *acetate*. Figure 2.8d shows the spectra
between 250 mμ and 500 mμ of uranyl solution in different acetate
buffers. The wavelength 260 mμ was chosen for the calculation of
acetate complexing constants, since at $\lambda > 260$ mμ, the hydrolysis
effect on the spectrum became significant (as shown by the divergence
of curves 2–6). By plotting the molar extinction coefficient as a

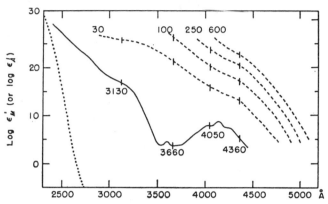

FIG. 2.8c. Molar decadic extinction curves of uranyl thiocyanate
complexes (after Ahrland, 1949c). Solid line: uranyl ions (free).
Dashed lines: $[UO_2^{++}]_0 = 0.0331$M; $[thiocyanate]_0 = 0.030$, 0.100,
0.250, and 0.600M respectively. Dotted line: thiocyanate alone,
$\epsilon_A = (\log I_0/I)/[thiocyanate]_0 D$. $[UO_2^{++}]_0 =$ total concentration of
uranyl (complexed and free). $[Thiocyanate]_0 =$ total concentration of
thiocyanate (in 0.1M HClO$_4$ to avoid hydrolysis of uranyl; no correction
for incomplete dissociation of thiocyanic acid needed; constant ionic
strength $\eta = 1.0$ adjusted by NaClO$_4$).

function of acetate concentration, for three different uranyl concentrations, Fig. 2.8e was obtained. For each value of ϵ (horizontal
lines in the figure), the values of [acetate] are found to be linear
functions of the corresponding values of [uranyl], indicating that
only mononuclear complexes are formed. The following association
constants were calculated:

$$K_1 = 240 \ (mole/l)^{-1}; \quad K_2 = 2.3 \times 10^4 \ (mole/l)^{-2}; \quad K_3 = 2.2 \times 10^6$$
$(mole/l)^{-3}$ for 20°C and ionic strength 1.0.

Table 2.10a summarizes the complexing constants derived by
Ahrland for mononuclear uranyl ions with several inorganic and
organic ions.

TABLE 2.10a. EQUILIBRIUM CONSTANTS OF REACTIONS
$$UO_2^{++} + nA^- = UO_2^{++}A_n^{-n}$$
20°C; ionic strength 1.0
After Ahrland (1949, 1951, 1953, 1956)

A^-	$n = 1$ $(\text{mole/l})^{-1}$	$n = 2$ $(\text{mole/l})^{-2}$	$n = 3$ $(\text{mole/l})^{-3}$	$n = 4$ $(\text{mole/l})^{-4}$
OH^-	2×10^9*			
F^-†	3.5×10^4 (± 0.4)	7.8×10^7 (± 0.8)	2.9×10^{10}; (± 0.4)	6.5×10^{11} (± 1.5)
Cl^-	0.5 (± 0.3)			
SO_4^{--}	56 (± 6)	450 (± 50)		
CH_3COO^-	240 (± 10)	2.3×10^4 (± 0.2)	2.2×10^6 (± 0.3)	
CH_2ClCOO^-	24 (± 3)	150 (± 40)	350 (± 150)	
$HOCH_2COO^-$	265 (± 15)	9.1×10^3 (± 0.6)	1.6×10^5 (± 0.2)	
CNS^-	5.7 (± 0.3)	5.5 (± 1)	15 (± 5)	

* Ahrland gives 2×10^{-5} mole/l for $[UO_2^{++}OH^-][H^+]/[UO_2^{++}]$ (cf. p. 101); assuming $[H^+][OH^-] = 10^{14}$, we calculate $[UO_2^{++}OH^-]/[UO_2^{++}][OH^-] = 2 \times 10^9$ (mole/l)$^{-1}$.

† Johnson, Kraus, and Young (1954) presented ultracentrifuge studies as evidence for species such as $(UO_2)_2F_6^{--}$ in aqueous fluoride solutions of UO_2F_2, with the dimerization constant equal to 3.

✳ Foley and Anderson (1949) observed the effect of *sulfosalicylic acid* on the spectrum of an aqueous solution of uranyl acetate. Figure 2.9 shows the absorption curves of a 5×10^{-3}M solution of UO_2Ac_2 (pH 4.5) (curve I) and of a 7.5×10^{-4}M solution of UO_2Ac_2 to which 4.25×10^{-3}M sulfosalicylic acid has been added (pH 4.65) (curve II). Although the added acid does not absorb in the visible, and the concentration of UO_2^{2+} is lower by a factor of 6.7, absorption curve II lies much higher than curve I. The acetate curve probably corresponds to a solution containing hydrolyzed uranyl ions ($[(UO_2)_3O_2]^{++}$ according to Sutton's Fig. 2.3) and uranyl acetate complexes. According to Tables 2.6 and 2.8, the uranyl acetate complexes absorb strongly in the far ultraviolet; but their formation does not affect significantly the visible and near-ultraviolet spectrum, which remains similar to that of nitrate. The sulfosalicylate complex, on the other hand, absorbs strongly in the visible and near ultraviolet. Foley and Anderson noted that addition of increasing amounts of acetate buffer caused absorption in the visible region to become weaker, indicating competition of acetate with sulfosalicylate for uranyl ions.

By plotting the difference between the optical density, at selected wavelengths, of the mixture and of an equal amount of uranyl salt without sulfosalicylic acid, as a function of the ratio $x = [UO_2^{++}]/$

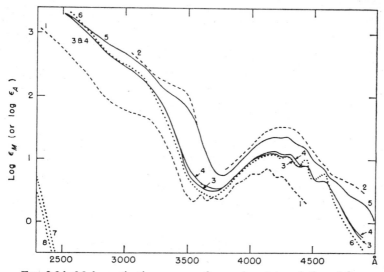

FIG. 2.8d. Molar extinction curves of uranyl acetate solutions (after Ahrland, 1951a). Curve 1: uranyl ion. Curve 2: same, partially hydrolysed $[UO_2^{++}]_0 = 0.033M$, pH 4.1). Curves 3, 4, 5: uranyl acetate complexes with $[UO_2^{++}]_0 = 0.010M$, $[acetate]_0 = 0.030M$, in acetic acid–acetate buffers 5 : 1, 2 : 1, and 0.5 : 1 respectively. Curve 6: same, with $[UO_2^{++}]_0 = 0.010M$, $[acetate]_0 = 0.060M$, in acetic acid–acetate buffer 2 : 1. Curves 7, 8: acetic acid–acetate buffers 5 : 1 and 0.5 : 1 respectively. $[UO_2^{++}]_0 =$ total concentration of free and complexed uranyl; $[acetate]_0 =$ total concentration of acetate used. (A small correction must be made for the effect of acetic acid on the concentration of free acetate ions.) Complexing of uranyl with acetate strong enough to prevent hydrolysis in above buffers. Ionic strength $\eta = 1.0$ adjusted by NaClO$_4$.

$([UO_2^{++}] + [SSA])$, Foley and Anderson obtained, for $\lambda = 400, 420,$ 440 and 460 mμ, symmetrical curves with peaks at $x = 0.5$. As first pointed out by Job, this is a proof of formation of a 1 : 1 complex. The same result was obtained at pH 4.6, 5.1, and 6.1. The optical density was highest at pH 4.5–4.7, and declined at both lower and higher pH values. The decline at low pH values was considered as indicating that the complex formation occurred with the divalent anion of the sulfosalicylic acid ($pK = 2.86$); the decline at high pH values was ascribed to hydrolysis.

The extinction coefficients of the complex were determined by using a solution containing a 9 : 1 excess of the complexing anions;

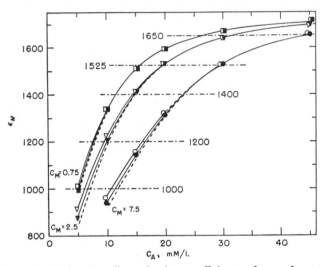

FIG. 2.8e. Molar decadic extinction coefficients of uranyl acetate complex solutions as function of total concentration of acetate C_A (free + complexed with uranyl). ■, □: $[UO_2^{++}]_0 = 0.00075\text{M}$; ▼, ▽: $[UO_2^{++}]_0 = 0.0025\text{M}$; ●, ○: $[UO_2^{++}]_0 = 0.0075\text{M}$. Open signs: [acetic acid] : [acetate] = 5; full signs: [acetic acid] : [acetate] = 2. Dashed lines extrapolated to $[H^+] = \infty$ (no hydrolysis). The points in which a horizontal $\epsilon_M = $ const. crosses the several curves correspond to the same concentration of free anions.

they were $\epsilon = 403$ at 440 mμ and $\epsilon = 432$ at 460 mμ. Using these values, the concentration of the complex was calculated in different mixtures, and thence the dissociation constant was derived:

$$K = \frac{[UO_2^{++}][R]}{[UO_2^{++}R]} = (1.3 \pm 0.8) \times 10^{-4}\ (\text{mole/l})^{-1} \qquad (23)$$

corresponding to a *complexing* constant of between 5000 and 20,000. An improved method of calculation, using solution pairs of constant ionic strength, with the same complex concentration, but different ratios of the components, led to a more precise value:

$$K = (1.93 \pm 0.08) \times 10^{-4} \quad (25°C)$$

or $1/K \simeq 5200$. This corresponds to a free energy of association

$$\Delta G = -5.06 \text{ kcal} \quad (25°C)$$

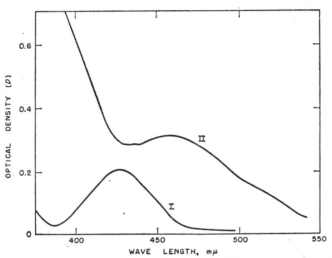

FIG. 2.9. Effect of sulfosalicylic acid on absorption spectrum of uranyl ions (after Foley and Anderson, 1949). Curve I: 5×10^{-3}M UO_2Ac_2. Curve II: 7.5×10^{-4}M $UO_2Ac_2 + 4.25 \times 10^{-3}$M sulfosalicylic acid.

Raising the temperature increases the complexing, but the increase is slight, indicating a small negative heat of formation.

Concentration $[R]$ in Equation (23) refers to total acid, which at the pH of maximum color depth is completely dissociated into R^{--} and $2H^+$. A complex of a divalent anion and a divalent cation (UO_2^{++}) is neutral as a whole, but Foley and Anderson suggested that the uranyl sulfosalicylate complex is a "zwitterion," $^+UO_2R^-$.

Foley and Anderson found that addition of 0.18M acetate to 0.002M sulfosalicylate reduces the optical density at 460 mμ from 0.643 to 0.242; this indicates a ratio of association constants of the order of 10^2, i.e., an acetate complexing constant of the order of 50.

This can be compared with the value of 240 $(\text{mole}/\text{l})^{-1}$ derived by Ahrland (for 20°C and $\eta = 1.0$), and also with the value of $K_c/\sqrt{D}$ given in the last column of Table 2.7. If it is assumed that the latter corresponds to an average acetic acid concentration of $\bar{A}_0 \simeq 0.1\text{M}$ (it was calculated from measurements between 0.005 and 1M), the corresponding value of K is

$$K = \frac{K_c\sqrt{A_0}}{\sqrt{D}} \simeq 40 \ (\text{mole}/\text{l})^{-1}$$

Since complexing of uranyl ions with organic acids is of great importance for the behavior of uranium in the living organism, it has been also studied by toxicologists. Electrochemical methods (polarography, transference, etc.) have been used by them, and only a few spectroscopic observations have been made. The results obtained up to 1947 were summarized by Dounce *et al.* (1949). One important general result of electrochemical studies is that they indicated, in all systems studied, the formation of higher complexes in addition to the 1 : 1 complexes whose existence appeared sufficient to explain the above-described spectroscopic results of other investigators. For example, in acetate buffers (NaAc + HAc) a neutral complex, probably $UO_2^{2+}Ac_2^{--}$, was indicated at $[Ac^-] > 0.025\text{M}$ by transference measurements at 20°C, and at $[Ac^-] > 0.05\text{M}$ by polarographic measurements at 25°C. An anionic uranyl acetate complex, probably $UO_2^{2+}Ac_3^{---}$, also was observed in transference experiments. Its relative concentration was independent of the concentration of neutral acetic acid molecules and only dependent on that of the Ac^- ions, as expected for a complex in whose formation only acetate *ions* take part.

Absorption changes observed in 0.2M acetate buffers with varying pH, described in the same review, probably refer to hydrolysis rather than formation of uranyl acetate complexes (as assumed by the review). They have been therefore described in Section 1 of this chapter.

Polargraphic studies have been continued by the Rochester toxicological group with other organic acids, such as pyruvic, malic, and particularly citric, by Neuman *et al.* [Neuman and Havill (1948), Rodgers and Neuman (1948), and Neuman, Havill and Feldman (1949)]. They led to the conclusion that dicarboxylic acids generally have a stronger tendency for association with uranyl ions than acetic acid, even when—as in the case of succinic acid—their dissociation constant is not higher than that of acetic acid. It was surmised that complexing with dibasic acids involves formation of 5-, 6- or 7-membered rings with both carboxyls. In fact mixing uranyl nitrate (pH 2.8) with oxalic acid (pH 1.6) lowered the pH to 1.3, indicating that uranyl ions displaced a second proton from the monobasic oxalic acid anion.

A further complication of the complexing mechanism was found in these studies: it was deduced that the 1 : 1 uranyl citrate complex forms a rather stable *dimer*. The formation of the dimer was described by Neuman *et al.* (1949) in the following way:

$$UO_2^{++} + H_2Cit^- \rightarrow UO^{++}HCit^{--} + H^+$$

$$2\{UO_2^{++} HCit^{--}\} \rightarrow \{(UO_2^{++})_2 H^+ (Cit^{---})_2\} + H^+ \quad (= dimer^- + H^+)$$

giving for the dissociation constant the expression

$$K_d = \frac{[UO_2^{++}] [H_2Cit^-]}{[H^+]^{3/2} [dimer^-]^{1/2}} \tag{24}$$

A value of 0.18 ± 0.08 was calculated for K_d at pH 2.9–3.6 and a total uranyl concentration of 5×10^{-4}M.

The uranyl citrate system was further studied spectroscopically by Feldman, Neuman, and Havill (1949). Figure 2.10a represents the optical density of uranyl salt solutions with and without added citric acid in the alkaline region (pH 7.5) and in the acid region (pH 3.75). The steep change of absorption (at 320 mμ) as a function of pH in the regions < 3 and 5–7 (Fig. 2.10b) indicates successive formation of two complexes; the second one is stable up to pH 11 (while non-complexed uranyl nitrate solution of the same concentration precipitates above pH 4.5).

The complex that is stable at pH 3.85 has the composition 1 UO_2^{++} : 1 citrate, as shown by the plot of absorption coefficients (at 320, 330, or 350 mμ) as function of $[UO_2^{++}]/\{[UO_2^{++}] + [citrate]\}$ (Fig. 2.10c). The authors assume, on the basis of previously described electrochemical results, that this complex is present mainly as a dimer, and calculated its dissociation constant according to Equation

(24). The K_d values obtained were 0.04 for 1×10^{-4}M uranyl solution (pH 3.16–3.69) and 0.065 for 5×10^{-4}M solution (pH 3.03). The agreement with the previously given potentiometric value ($K = 0.18$) is only in the order of magnitude; it is suggested that the spectroscopic values are more reliable.

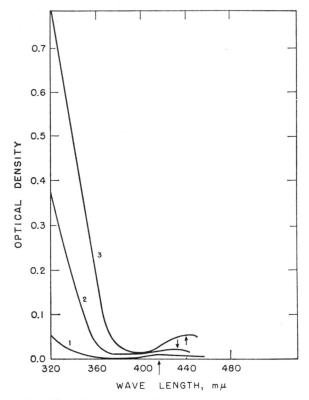

FIG. 2.10a. Absorption spectra of uranyl chloride and uranyl citrate.

The nature of the more strongly colored complex present at pH 7.5 has not been clarified, but it seems to involve a uranyl : citrate ratio > 1, perhaps 1.5.

The absorption curves of aqueous solutions of a number of complex uranyl salts (mainly of the aldimine series) have been measured by von Kiss and co-workers in their extensive study of the spectra

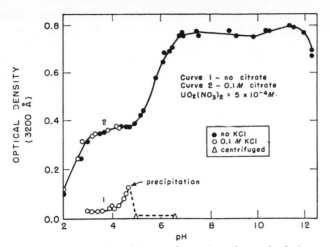

FIG. 2.10b. The effect of pH on absorption of uranyl solutions.

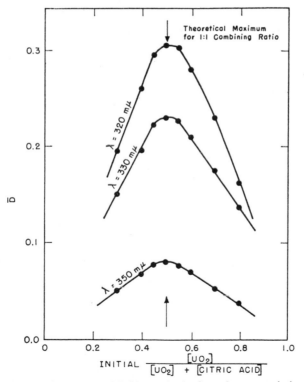

FIG. 2.10c. Application of Job's method of continuous variations to the study of the uranyl citrate complex at pH 3.85 ± 0.03.

of such complexes [see von Kiss and Nyiri (1942b), and von Kiss, Csokan and Nyiri (1942a)].

Spectra of uranyl salts complexed with organic bases (or their salts) in organic solvents will be discussed in the next section. Some part-aqueous systems, such as the system uranyl nitrate and tetrabutyl ammonium nitrate and concentrated nitric acid, will be included in this discussion.

3. Spectra of Uranyl Compounds in Organic Solvents

3.1. *Absorption Spectra*

Most comparisons of uranyl salt spectra in different solvents suffer from the lack of information concerning the nature of molecular species—neutral or ionized—present in solution, or concerning the extent and geometry of inner-shell specific solvation.

The first extensive comparisons of this type were made by Deussen (1898). He measured the positions of ten uranyl bands (486–369 mμ) in water, methanol, ethanol, acetone, glycerol, amylol, acetic ester, and ether. Addition of 50 per cent C_2H_5OH to water was found to shift all bands towards the red, but the direction of the shift was reversed in 80 per cent and 100 per cent ethanol. Addition of glycerol to water caused a shift of all bands towards the red; this shift increased with the amount of glycerol.

Jones and Strong (1910a) photographed the absorption spectra and estimated the positions of the band peaks of uranyl chloride and uranyl nitrate, in water, methanol, ethanol, glycerol, acetone, and in binary mixtures of these solvents, and also of uranyl acetate in water and in methanol.

They noted that the absorption bands were considerably stronger in methanol than in water; the band peaks were sharper and were generally shifted towards the red. Beer's law was found to hold between 0.06N and 0.25N solutions of uranyl chloride in ethanol. Addition of calcium chloride had almost no effect on the absorption spectrum of uranyl chloride in methanol (in contradistinction to the behaviour of the same compound in aqueous solution).

A summary of the band positions of uranyl chloride in different solvents, including those above mentioned, and also some investigated in a subsequent study by Jones and Strong (1912), is given in Table 2.11.

TABLE 2.11. ABSORPTION BANDS OF URANYL CHLORIDE
IN DIFFERENT SOLVENTS
After Jones and Strong, (1910a, 1912)

Solvent	Band centers (mμ)						
	1	2	3	4	5	6	7
H_2O	492	474	456	446	431.5	417	402.5
CH_3OH	493	476	459	446.5	434.5	422	409
C_2H_5OH	490	475	458	440	—	425	410
C_3H_7OH	491	475	458	458	446.0	423	410
i-C_3H_7OH	—	475	456	436	—	425	410
C_4H_9OH	497	—	475	456	439	424	410
i-C_4H_9OH	490	—	472	456	440	—	—
$(C_2H_5)_2O$	—	—	463	444	430	416	404
CH_3OOCH_3	492	479	462	444	428	416	403
Glycerol	505	472	454	440	426	414	402.5
Formamide	484	—	465	445	—	—	—

The same authors observed the effect of temperature on the absorption spectra of uranyl chloride in acetone (22–195°C), of uranyl nitrate in propanol (20–145°C), and of both these salts in isobutanol (20–115°C) and methyl sulfate.

Von Kurelec (1927) made a comparison of the positions of the four lowest frequency bands of uranyl nitrate in 44 organic solvents: 13 aliphatic alcohols and glycols, 7 aliphatic aldehydes, 8 aliphatic acids, 9 esters of such acids, 4 nitriles, ether, acetone, and citronellal.

In all solvents, ionizing and non-ionizing, the position of the absorption bands of uranyl nitrate was approximately the same. For example, the center of the first band lay in aqueous solutions between 483 mμ (conc. HNO_3) and 493 mμ (conc. HCl) and in organic solvents between 483.4 mμ (glacial acetic acid) and 490.4 mμ (glycol). Similarly, the center of the second band lay between 468 and 478 mμ in aqueous solutions, and between 466.6 and 472.9 mμ in organic solutions.

Within a homologous series (e.g. the series of saturated straight chain alcohols, from CH_3OH to $C_8H_{17}OH$), a "red shift" could be observed with increased index of refraction of the solvent (cf. Table 2.12). (No similar regularity is noticeable in Table 2.11.)

In *mixed organic solvents*, early observations indicated preferential association of uranyl salts (or their ions) with one of the components.

Thus, Hartley (1903) concluded from spectroscopic evidence that when hydrated uranyl nitrate is dissolved in ether the spectrum remains that characteristic of uranyl ions in water.

Jones and Strong (1910a) noted that addition of as little as 8 per cent water to a uranyl chloride solution in methanol caused the uranyl bands to shift appreciably towards their position in aqueous solution. Similarly, addition of 10 per cent glycerol to methanol caused the spectrum of uranyl chloride to assume the character of that in pure glycerol.

Jones and Strong (1912) and Jones (1913a) asserted that the broadened and shifted bands observed in uranyl salt solutions in methanol upon addition of water can be interpreted as the result of

TABLE 2.12. SHIFT OF AN ABSORPTION BAND OF $UO_2(NO_3)_2$
IN A SERIES OF SOLVENTS
von Kurelec (1927)

Solvent	mμ	η
CH_3OH	465.0	1.3326
C_2H_5OH	465.8	1.3614
C_3H_7OH	466.3	1.3859
C_4H_9OH	467.9	1.3991
$C_5H_{11}OH$	467.2	1.4078
$C_8H_{17}OH$	467.4	1.4314

mutual superposition of "methanolate bands" and "hydrate bands," a conclusion which they used as an argument supporting the solvate theory of solutions. To test this theory was the main motivation of the long series of studies devoted to absorption spectra of inorganic salts by Jones and co-workers, and summarized in Jones and Strong's monographs in 1910 and 1911. (The most convincing examples of the coexistence of bands characteristic of individual solvents in a mixed solvent were found by Jones in solutions of U(IV) salts, such as UBr_4.)

Müller (1940) observed that the ultraviolet absorption edge of uranyl nitrate is shifted towards the longer waves, and the absorption appears stronger when ether is substituted for water as solvent. The effect is stronger the more dilute the uranyl solutions.

Mathieson (1949) studied the absorption spectra of uranyl nitrate in two ketones: acetone and methyl ethyl ketone, and, for comparison, in diethyl ether and water. He found, in ketonic solutions, a sharp enhancement of the long-wave absorption peaks, and a general increase in absorption intensity above 330 mμ. He attributed these spectral changes to complex formation. Stable crystalline complexes with the composition $UO_2(NO_3)_2Me_2CO.3H_2O$ and $UO_2(NO_3)_2MeEtCO.3H_2O$ could in fact be crystallized from these solutions. A similar complex, $UO_2(NO_3)_2Et_2O.3H_2O$, was obtained from ethyl ether.

A similar study was carried out by Kaplan, Hildebrandt and Ader (1950a), who measured the spectra of uranyl nitrate solutions in methyl isobutyl ketone ("hexone"), cyclohexanone, and acetone. Since nitrates of organic bases are known to enhance the extractability of uranyl nitrate into methyl isobutyl ketone, the effect of these compounds on the uranyl spectrum also was investigated.

Figure 2.11 shows that the absorption spectra of uranyl nitrate (hexahydrate?) are very similar in the three ketones. Beer's law is followed (in hexone) at least up to 0.1M. Addition of tetrabutyl ammonium nitrate, NBu_4NO_3 (as well as that of tributylammonium nitrate, pyridinium nitrate or methyl isobutyl ketazinium nitrate), produces a striking spectral change. Four bands in the long-wave part of the spectrum become strongly enhanced, without apparent change in their positions. The increase of the absorption coefficient in this part of the spectrum is a linear function of concentration of the added tetrabutyl ammonium nitrate; the increase ceases abruptly when a molecular ratio $[UO_2(NO_3)_2] : NBu_4NO_3 = 1$ is reached. This points to the formation of a 1 : 1 complex, for which the following composition is suggested:

$$UO_2(NO_3)_2 + NO_3^- \rightleftharpoons UO_2(NO_3)_3^-$$

The method of continuous variations (comparison of spectra of mixtures with constant total amount of the two nitrates, but varying proportion, x, of uranyl nitrate) showed the average absorption coefficient (at 455 and 470 mμ) to rise with x up to $x = 0.5$, and then to decrease—as expected for a 1 : 1 complex whose absorption is stronger than that of the two components (Fig. 2.12). The linearity of the change, and the consequent extreme sharpness of the peaks at $x = 0.5$, indicate that the complex is very stable.

Kaplan *et al.* point out that the argument does not depend on the extent of the ionic dissociation of uranyl nitrate in the organic

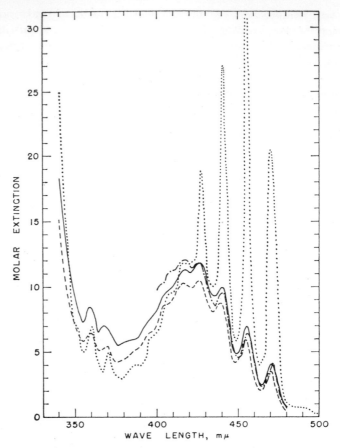

FIG. 2.11. Absorption spectra of uranyl nitrate in some ketonic solvents.
——————— 0.02M uranyl nitrate in acetone.
– – – – – – 0.02M uranyl nitrate in methyl isobutyl ketone.
— · — · — 0.02M uranyl nitrate in cyclohexanone.
· · · · · · · · · 0.02M uranyl nitrate, 0.02M tetrabutylammonium nitrate in acetone.

solvent in the absence of NBu_4NO_3; the maximum in Fig. 2.12 corresponds to three nitrate radicals present per one uranyl group.

Volod'ko, Sevchenko and Umreiko show a similar spectrum for tetraethylammonium uranyl trinitrate hexahydrate in acetone (1960).

A similar spectral change can be produced by the addition of nitric acid (instead of NBu_4NO_3) to a solution of uranyl nitrate in hexone. However, even at a nitric acid concentration of 0.78M, the absorption between 420 and 480 mμ is increased only about half as much as it is in 0.02M NBu$_4$NO$_3$. The authors suggest that nitric acid addition leads to an equilibrium

$$UO_2(NO_3)_2 + HNO_3 \overset{K}{\rightleftharpoons} HUO_2(NO_3)_3$$

and that the neutral complex HUO$_2$(NO$_3$)$_3$ has practically the same spectrum as the complex ion UO$_2$(NO$_3$)$_3^-$. With these two assumptions they calculate:

$$K = 1.1 \pm 0.2 = \frac{[HUO_2(NO_3)_3]}{[UO_2(NO_3)_2][HNO_3]} \text{mole l}^{-1} \tag{25}$$

The close agreement they find between K values calculated from two absorption vs. nitric acid concentration curves (at 454 and 469 mμ respectively) by using for the complex ion the (previously determined) extinction coefficients of the complex molecule, is quoted by them as confirmation of the postulated identity of the two spectra.

Adding NBu$_4$NO$_3$ to a UO$_2$NO$_3$ solution containing large excess of nitric acid causes a further sharp rise of the absorption bands, even if the amount of organic nitrate added ($\sim$ 0.1M) is small compared to that of the nitric acid already present ($\sim$ 1M). The effect of NBu$_4$NO$_3$ is not quite as strong in the presence as in the absence of nitric acid, and the final spectrum, obtained upon "saturation" with NBu$_4$NO$_3$, is the same with and without acid. Kaplan *et al.* pointed out that the addition of a certain amount of strong nitric acid also implies the addition of 1.6 molecules of water per molecule of added nitric acid; apparently the presence of this amount of water does not affect significantly the spectrum of the uranyl trinitrate complex.

Comparison of the action of several nitrates shows NBu$_4$NO$_3$ and NPr$_4$NO$_3$ (Pr = n-propyl) to be equally effective (in acetone as solvent); with a tertiary amine (2-n-hexylpyridine), complexing is less complete (88 per cent in 0.02M UO$_2$(NO$_3$)$_2$ + 0.02M hexylpyridinium nitrate). This cannot be ascribed to an acid–base dissociation of HNC$_{11}$H$_{17}$NO$_3$ ($\rightleftharpoons$ HNO$_3$ + NC$_{11}$H$_{17}$), since addition of nitric acid does not affect the absorption. Rather, one has to assume a relatively low complexing constant of the tertiary amine ($\sim$ 3 × 10^3, as against $> 10^5$ with the quaternary ammonium salts). In hexone solution, too, pyridinium nitrate proves to be a less effective complexing agent than the quaternary ammonium nitrates. This (as well as the still lesser effect of nitric acid) may be related to the stronger complexing action of NO_3^- ions compared to RNO_3 molecules. (The larger size of the anion $UO_2(NO_3)_3^-$, compared to

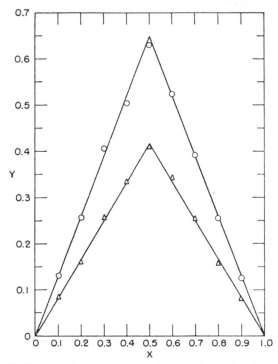

FIG. 2.12. Reaction between uranyl nitrate and tetrabutylammonium nitrate in methyl isobutyl ketone.
$\bigcirc = 455\ m\mu$　　$\triangle = 470\ m\mu$

NO_3^-, ought to make the ionization tendency of the complex $RUO_2(NO_3)_3$ stronger than that of the molecule RNO_3.)

The molecule $UO_2(NO_3)_2$ is, according to the estimate of Kaplan *et al.*, practically non-ionized in ketonic solvents, such as acetone or hexone, in the concentrations used, while molecules such as NBu_4NO_3 may be 40 or 70 per cent dissociated in these solvents. Consequently the significant complexing processes are those coupling the neutral molecules $UO_2(NO_3)_2$ with the molecules RNO_3 and the ions NO_3^-. The complexing is more stable the stronger the dissociation $RNO_3 \rightarrow R^+ + NO_3^-$.

The neutral complex $RUO_2(NO_3)_3$ itself undergoes ionic dissociation into R^+ and $UO_2(NO_3)_3^-$, while the neutral molecules $UO_2(NO_3)_2$ disproportionate into $UO_2NO_3^+$ and $UO_2(NO_3)_3^-$. Trinitratouranyl anions can thus arise in three different ways: by association of uranyl nitrate with NO_3^- ions, by association of the same salt with organic nitrates followed by ionic dissociation, and by disproportionation.

As mentioned before, the authors assume the spectroscopic difference between ionized and non-ionized complexes, $UO_2(NO_3)_3^-$ and $RUO_2(NO_3)_3$, to be insignificant; if this is so, the concentration ratio of these two forms cannot be derived from spectroscopic observations.

Further evidence for the formation of the trinitrato-uranyl complex is adduced by Kaplan *et al.* from solubility and solvent distribution measurements, and ionic transference observations.

The same investigators (Kaplan, Hildebrandt, and Ader, 1950b) also measured the spectra of uranyl nitrate in dioxane, pyridine, propanol, chloroform and other solvents, with and without addition of tetrabutyl ammonium nitrate, or of tertiary ammonium nitrates.

In some of the solutions studied, a darkening of color and turbidity appeared after several hours standing, indicating slow reaction of uranyl nitrate with the solvent. In cellosolve and dibutyl carbitol, the reaction occurred within a few minutes, making accurate spectroscopic measurements impossible.

All spectra had in common a broad band extending (in 0.02M solution) from about 380–500 mμ, with a peak around 425 mμ. The most important difference between the various spectra is in the four maxima between 420 and 480 mμ, whose enhancement by organic nitrates was first noted in ketones (Fig. 2.11). The same strong effect of organic nitrates—attributed above to the formation of a trinitro complex—was noted in some other solvents, while in others only a minor effect was observed.

Figure 2.13 shows the spectra of uranyl nitrate in water, in dilute (0.5M) and strong (16M) nitric acid. The somewhat stronger absorption in water compared to dilute nitric acid must be due to partial hydrolysis (cf. Section 1). The effect of concentrated nitric acid in enhancing the long-wave peaks, presumably by trinitrate complex formation, was mentioned above.

The similar effect of *acetone*, also mentioned above (see Fig. 2.11), is represented in Fig. 2.14 in relation to the water content of the acetone, and the addition of tetrabutylammonium nitrate.

The absorption spectrum of $UO_2(NO_3)_2$ in *dioxane* (Fig. 2.15) is rather similar to that in water, but the maxima in the 400–430 mμ region are somewhat flattened, while the structure at longer waves is somewhat better resolved. It is, however, much less pronounced

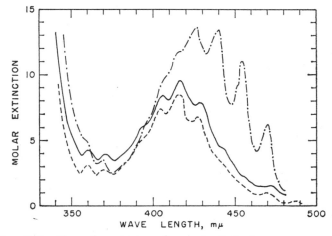

FIG. 2.13. Absorption spectra of uranyl nitrate in some aqueous solutions.

——————— 0.02M $UO_2(NO_3)_2$ in H_2O.
– – – – – – 0.00974M $UO_2(NO_3)_2$ in 0.514M HNO_3.
— · — · — 0.02M $UO_2(NO_3)_2$ in 16M HNO_3.

than in acetone, even in the presence of NBu_4NO_3. Presence of up to 20 per cent water causes a general enhancement of the absorption curve, without significant change in shape, but at 40 per cent water the spectrum acquires the shape typical of aqueous solutions. NBu_4NO_3 cannot be added to pure dioxane solution without causing precipitation; addition of 2-hexylpyridinium nitrate causes a marked enhancement of the long-wave bands, but the effect is much weaker than in ketonic solvents.

The absorption curves in *ethanol* and *propanol* (Fig. 2.16) are similar to those in dioxane above 430 mμ, but the absorption is

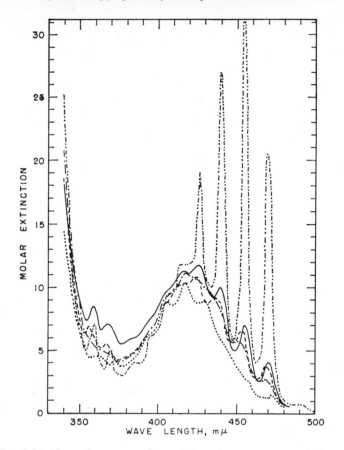

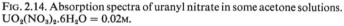

FIG. 2.14. Absorption spectra of uranyl nitrate in some acetone solutions. $UO_2(NO_3)_2.6H_2O = 0.02M$.

———————— Dry acetone.
– – – – – 10% water, 90% acetone.
— · — · — 20% water, 80% acetone.
· · · · · · · · · 40% water, 60% acetone.
– · · — · · – Dry acetone, 0.02M in NBu_4NO_3.

stronger. Addition of 0.04M NBu_4NO_3 to propanol solution, or of 0.04M $HNEt_3NO_3$ to ethanol solution, raises the absorption somewhat, but causes no selective enhancement of the long-wave bands.

In *chloroform* (containing about 0.7 per cent alcohol), $UO_2(NO_3)_2$. $2H_2O$ is appreciably soluble, so that solutions 0.015M in uranyl

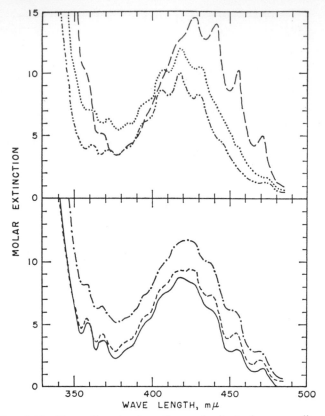

Fig. 2.15. Absorption spectra of uranyl nitrate in some dioxane solutions. $UO_2(NO_3)_2.6H_2O = 0.02M$.

———————— Dry dioxane.
– – – – – – 10% water, 90% dioxane.
— · — · — 20% water, 80% dioxane.
· · · · · · · · 40% water, 60% dioxane.
– · · – · · – · 60% water, 40% dioxane.
—— —— —— 5% water, 95% dioxane, 0.04M NBu_4NO_3.

nitrate could be prepared. Its spectrum (Fig. 2.17) is similar to the solution of uranyl nitrate hexahydrate in dioxane. NBu_4NO_3 increases the solubility markedly, and the resulting solution has the same type of spectrum as is found in strongly complexed ketonic solutions.

In *pyridine*, the absorption spectrum of uranyl nitrate is quite different from that in other solvents (Fig. 2.18). Addition of

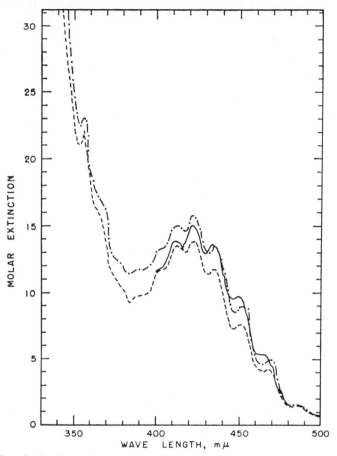

Fig. 2.16. Absorption spectra of uranyl nitrate in some alcoholic solutions.

——————— 0.02M $UO_2(NO_3)_2$ in ethanol.

– – – – – – 0.02M $UO_2(NO_3)_2$ in n-propanol.

— · — · — 0.02M $UO_2(NO_3)_2$ + 0.04M NBu_4NO_3 in n-propanol.

NBu_4NO_3 causes a general increase in absorption above 380 mμ, and a shift of the peak to longer waves, but produces no selective enhancement of the bands above 410 mμ.

Figure 2.19 shows the spectra of $UO_2(NO_3)_2.6H_2O$ dissolved in *nitroethane, ethyl acetate*, glacial *acetic acid*, and *tetraethylene glycol dibutyl ether*. They are rather similar to that in acetone, and in all

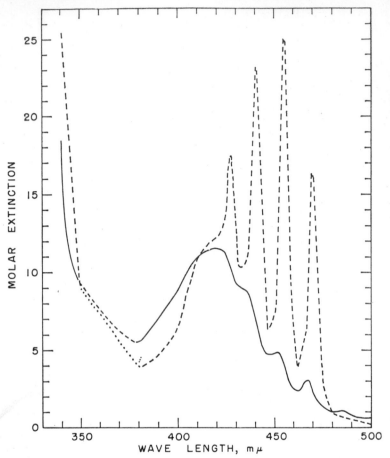

Fig. 2.17. Absorption spectra of uranyl nitrate in chloroform–0.7 per cent ethanol.

———— 0.0154M $UO_2(NO_3)_2.2H_2O$.

– – – – – 0.02M $UO_2(NO_3)_2.2H_2O + 0.02M$ NBu_4NO_3.

of them, with the exception of that in acetic acid, addition of an organic nitrate produces the same selective enhancement, although not always in equally extreme form. In acetic acid, the changes are more complex, probably indicating complexing with acetate ions.

For comparison, the spectrum of uranyl *perchlorate* solutions in methyl isobutyl ketone (with and without NBu_4NO_3) was also

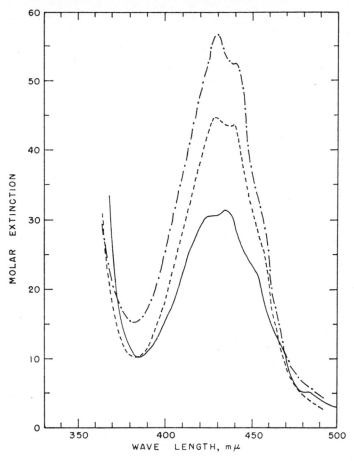

FIG. 2.18. Absorption spectra of uranyl nitrate in pyridine.
$UO_2(NO_3)_2 \cdot 6H_2O = 0.02M$.

——————— No added reagent.

– – – – – 0.1M NBu_4NO_3.

— · — · — 0.8M NBu_4NO_3.

measured (Fig. 2.20). The changes are similar to those described
above for nitrate solutions.

Tables 2.12a and 2.12b summarize the above-described results.
In discussing the absorption curves in Figs. 2.13–2.19, Kaplan *et al.*
note that the spacing of the bands is approximately the same

TABLE 2.12a. The Effect of Added Nitrates, RNO_3, on the Absorption of Uranyl Nitrate in Organic Solvents

Solvent	H_2O (%)	R	(RNO_3) (M)	$\epsilon_{470} - \epsilon_{464}$*	$\epsilon_{455} - \epsilon_{448}$*	$\epsilon_{441} - \epsilon_{434}$*
Acetone	0		0	1.6	2.1	0.5
	0	NBu₄†	0.02‡	15.8	24.9	16.6
	10	NBu₄†	0.02	2.9	4.3	
	20	NBu₄†	0.02	0.7	1.0	
Nitroethane	0		0	2.4	3.3	1.9
	0	HNEt₃§	0.02‡	13.8	22.2	14.9
Chloroform‖		NBu₄†	0.02‡	12.3	18.7	12.9
Ethyl acetate	0		0	0.7	1.3	0.4
	0	HNEt₃§	0.02	10.3	15.9	11.4
$C_{16}H_{34}O_5$¶	0		0	0.7	0.8	0.5
	0	HNEt₃§	0.02	9.2	13.5	9.5
	0	HNEt₃§	0.04	10.6	17.3	13.0
Dioxane	0	HNC₁₁H₁₇**	0.02	3.2	5.1	2.7
	0	HNC₁₁H₁₇**	0.04	5.2	8.3	5.4
	0	HNC₁₁H₁₇**	0.08	6.5	10.8	7.5
	5	NBu₄†	0.02	0.5	1.3	0.4
	5	NBu₄†	0.04	0.8	1.7	1.3

* $\epsilon\lambda$ = Molar extinction coefficient at λ mμ. Wavelengths of the maxima vary by ± 1 mμ among the different solvents; minima vary by ± 2 mμ. Extinctions given are those at the actual maxima and minima in the particular solvent.

† Tetra-n-butylammonium.

‡ Further increase in the nitrate concentration caused no appreciable increase in the peak heights.

§ Triethylammonium.

‖ Containing 0.7 per cent ethanol.

¶ Tetraethylene glycol dibutyl ether.

** 2-n-Hexylpyridinium.

(710–746 cm^{-1}; average 727 cm^{-1}) in all six solvents where it could be measured (the bands in pyridine are too diffuse).

The most remarkable result is the sharpness of the bands ascribed to the trinitrouranyl complex. The authors compare this spectrum (above 380 mμ) with that of solid uranyl cesium nitrate. (For the sake of this comparison, the sharp lines of the crystal, as measured by Dieke *et al.* (cf. Chapter 1) at 20°K, are "smeared out" over a 2 mμ range to simulate the effect of temperature. The lines of the

TABLE 2.12b. SPACING OF THE ABSORPTION BANDS IN
URANYL NITRATE SOLUTIONS

Solution	No. of bands measured	Average spacing (cm^{-1})	Average deviation (cm^{-1})
Water	11	725	110
Acetone	10	735	80
UO$_2$(NO$_3$)$_3^-$ in			
acetone	10	722	80
Nitroethane	4	710	27
Dioxane	10	722	110
Propanol	10	746	91
		Mean 727 ± 9	83

"magnetic" series are omitted because they are known to disappear
with rising temperature.) Kaplan *et al.* find a remarkable similarity
between the two spectra (Fig. 2.21), and conclude that the position
of the three NO$_3^-$ ions in respect to the UO$_2^{++}$ ion must be similar
in both cases. [In UO$_2$Rb(NO$_3$)$_3$, where this position is known

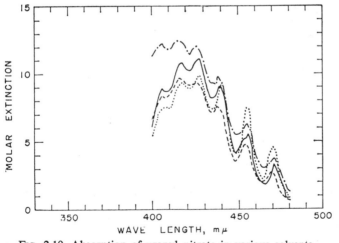

FIG. 2.19. Absorption of uranyl nitrate in various solvents.
UO$_2$(NO$_3$)$_2$.6H$_2$O = 0.02M.
———— Glacial acetic acid.
– – – – – Ethyl acetate.
— · — · — Tetraethylene glycol dibutyl ether.
· · · · · · · · Nitroethane.

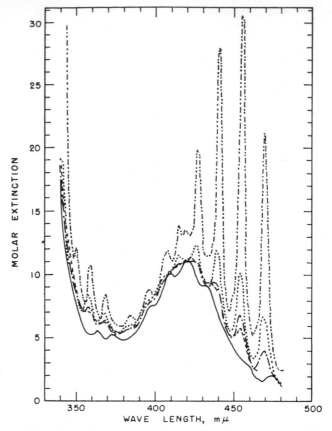

FIG. 2.20. Absorption spectra of methyl isobutyl ketone solutions containing uranyl perchlorate. $UO_2(ClO_4)_2 = 0.02M$.
———————— No added reagent.
– – – – – – 0.02M NBu_4NO_3.
— · — · — 0.03M NBu_4NO_3.
. . . . 0.04M NBu_4NO_3.
– · · – · · – · 0.06M NBu_4NO_3.

from X-ray analysis, the three nitrate groups are arranged symmetrically around the O—U—O axis.]

In discussing the molecular species which may be present in the various solutions studied, Kaplan *et al.* noted that apart from the striking change caused by formation of the trinitrouranyl complex, other spectroscopic changes observed were small, and thus difficult to analyze quantitatively. However, they thought to recognize six spectral types:

Type A. Sharp peaks at 426, 441, 456, 470 mμ (typical example: uranyl solution in acetone + NBu$_4$NO$_3$).

Type B. Distinct, but weaker peaks in same positions [e.g. UO$_2$(NO$_3$)$_2$ in acetone *without* NBu$_4$NO$_3$].

Type C. No marked peaks > 380 mμ, except for one broad maximum at $\sim$ 420 mμ [e.g. UO$_2$(NO$_3$)$_2$ in dioxane].

Type D. Very little structure > 430 mμ; three peaks between 400 and 430 mμ [e.g. UO$_2$(NO$_3$)$_2$ in water].

Type E. Similar to type C above 440 mμ, but absorption stronger. Three peaks in the region 410–440 mμ; stronger absorption < 400 mμ than in types A–D [e.g. UO$_2$(NO$_3$)$_2$ in propanol].

Type F. Diffuse absorption [UO$_2$(NO$_3$)$_2$ in pyridine].

The authors interpreted spectra of the types A, B, C, and D as indicative of a diminishing number of NO$_3^-$ ions in association with the UO$_2^{++}$ ion. Type A was ascribed above to the UO$_2$(NO$_3$)$_3^-$ ion [or the HUO$_2$(NO$_3$)$_3$ molecule]. Type B may then indicate a *di*nitrate complex, UO$_2$(NO$_3$)$_2$, type C, a *mono*nitrocomplex, UO$_2$NO$_3^+$, and type D (exhibited, e.g., by uranyl nitrate in water) the non-complexed ion UO$_2^{++}$. The existence of a dinitrocomplex is made plausible by quantitative analysis of the five curves in Fig. 2.20. If trinitrate were the only complex formed, its concentration in the five solutions would have had to be 0, 0.0067, 0.01, 0.013, and 0.02M respectively; if, in addition to the trinitrate, only a (stable) mononitrate were formed, the trinitrate concentrations would have had to be 0, 0, 0.005, 0.01, and 0.02M. With a (stable) dinitrate complex, the trinitrate concentrations would be zero in the first four solutions and 0.02M in the last one. The actual trinitrate concentrations, calculated from the curves on the assumption that the enhancement of absorption in the four peaks is caused by trinitrate alone, are as follows: 0, 0.0016, 0.0024, 0.0052, and 0.02M. A plausible interpretation of these numbers is that a dinitrate complex *does* exist, and has absorption bands in the same positions as those of the trinitrate, but considerably weaker than the latter. If this hypothesis is correct, then the dinitrate complex predominates in 0.02M solutions of uranyl nitrate in the following solvents: 16M

HNO$_3$, acetone, methyl isobutyl ketone, ethyl acetate, nitroethane and glacial acetic acid. Because of the low dielectric constant of solvents, such as dioxane, which show type C spectra (Fig. 2.15), the mononitrate complex—which we assumed produces these spectra—cannot be present in them as a free cation. The authors

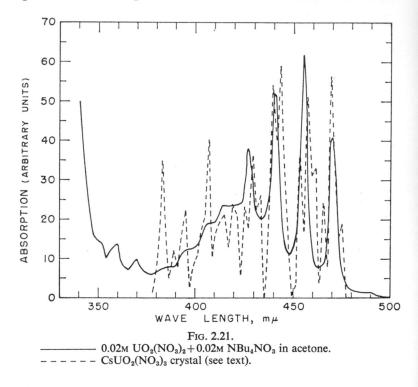

FIG. 2.21.
————— 0.02M UO$_2$(NO$_3$)$_2$ + 0.02M NBu$_4$NO$_3$ in acetone.
– – – – – – CsUO$_2$(NO$_3$)$_3$ crystal (see text).

suggest that it is solvated and then associated with a solvated nitrate anion, thus:

$$[(UO_2NO_3^+)_{solv.}(NO_3^-)_{solv.}]$$

Within a given spectral type, minor differences occur that can be attributed to solvation by different solvents. In the case of solvent mixtures containing water, partial hydrolysis also must be taken into consideration.

The peculiar effect of pyridine (type F spectrum) can be tentatively attributed to coordination of UO$_2^{2+}$ with the nitrogen atoms in

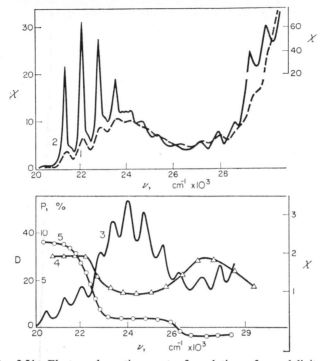

Fig. 2.21a. Electron absorption spectra for solutions of uranyl dinitrate (1) and trinitrate (2) in acetone, and for a monocrystal of uranyl nitrate (3). The figure also shows the polarization spectrum (4) and the absorption dichroism (5) for a uranyl nitrate monocrystal. (X is the molar absorption coefficient; P is the degree of polarization for the radiation; D is the absorption dichroism.) After Volod'ko, Sevchenko, and Umreiko (1960a).

pyridine molecules (in all the other cases, the only coordination taken into account was that with oxygen atoms).

The solvation of uranyl ions by alcohols must be particularly strong to account for the type E spectra exhibited by solutions in these solvents. Addition of NR_4NO_3 leads to the formation of the trinitrate complex in acetone, methyl isobutyl ketone, ethyl acetate, nitroethane and chloroform, but *not* in acetic acid, dioxane, pyridine, or alcohols.

Some of these interpretations appear speculative, but they are quite similar to those suggested independently by other observers for the explanation of the spectra of other nitrates in mixed solvents.

Vdovenko, Pilovskij, and Kuzina (1957) added pyridinium nitrate and anilinium nitrate to acetone solutions of uranyl nitrate. They observed the very sharp band system characteristic of the uranyl trinitrato species. In another series of experiments they studied the two-phase distribution between water and diethyl ether of uranyl nitrate and nitric acid. Again, the sharp spectrum of $UO_2(NO_3)_3^-$ appeared in the organic phase when sufficient HNO_3 was added.

Volod'ko, Sevchenko and Umreiko (1960) argued that the principal spectral change, following transition from dinitrato to trinitrato complexes of the uranyl ion, occur in the second and fourth spectral region; they suggested that the altered symmetry of the trinitrato complexes causes the selection rules valid for these transitions to change. It is difficult to say whether this can be reconciled with the assumption of McGlynn and Smith (1960) that admixture of spectral region 4 is responsible for the intensity in regions 1 and 3, and that admixture of region 5 is responsible for the intensity in region 2. (See Fig. 2.2a).

Another study of the visible and ultraviolet absorption spectrum of $UO_2(NO_3)_2.6H_2O$ in organic solvents was reported by Jezowska–Trzebiatowska and Bartecki (1958). Their data are summarized in Table 2.12c and displayed in Figs. 2.21b, c.

Evidence seems to exist for complex formation between uranyl nitrate and most solvents. Those solvents of highest dielectric constant and also of highest complexing ability seem to produce higher-energy transitions. The effect upon intensity and line breadth, however, is more pronounced than the frequency shifts.

Figure 2.21d illustrates the failure of attempts to correlate parameters of the visible and ultraviolet absorption spectrum with the dielectric constants of the solvents. The reason for this is, most likely, that it is very difficult to separate the effects of direct co-ordination by solvent molecules from general solvent effects. Certainly, the dielectric constant of the solvent would affect the transition frequencies, the U—O bond length, etc. A knowledge of the effect would be a valuable aid in establishing band assignments and details of the uranyl ion electronic structure. We hope that some clever experimenters will find a way clearly to establish the directions and magnitudes of the dielectric shifts.

Rao and Rao (1959) studied complex formation and visible spectra

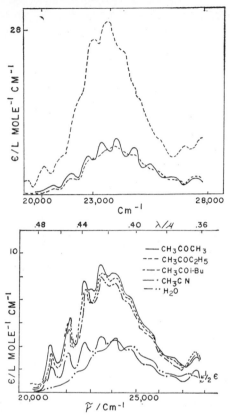

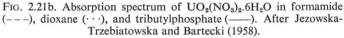

FIG. 2.21b. Absorption spectrum of $UO_2(NO_3)_2.6H_2O$ in formamide (– – –), dioxane (· ·), and tributylphosphate (——). After Jezowska-Trzebiatowska and Bartecki (1958).

FIG. 2.21c. Spectra of $UO_2(NO_3)_2.6H_2O$ in various solvents. After Jezowska-Trzebiatowska and Bartecki (1958).

in aqueous solutions of uranyl with substituted phenols. Each phenol was shown to form a 1 : 1 complex with the uranyl ion. One purpose of the study was to determine the direction of the spectral shift of uranyl with the basicity of the ligand; however, the spectra are not sufficiently similar to give an unambiguous answer (see Fig. 2.21e). It looks as though the main maximum ($\lambda \sim 420$ mμ, $\epsilon \sim 200$) shifts to higher frequency and the shoulder ($\lambda \sim 480$ mμ) to lower frequency with increasing donor power of the ligand (p-Cl > p-H > p-HSO$_3$ > p-NO$_2$).

Ishidate (1957) and Yamane (1957) studied the formation and the absorption spectra, in the ultraviolet and visible regions, of several uranyl β-diketone chelates. They found, in each case, that two moles of β-diketone added to each mole of uranyl. The crystals isolated from the solutions had compositions and showed absorption maxima in aqueous ethanol (50 to 99 per cent) as indicated in the following table:

$$(R_1COCHCOR_2)_2UO_2.nH_2O$$

R_1	R_2	n	$\lambda_{max}^{(1)}/m\mu$	$\epsilon^{(1)}$	$\lambda_{max}^{(2)}/m\mu$	$\epsilon^{(2)}$
ϕ	CH_3	2.5	375	6300	320	22,300
ϕ		1.5	404	23,300	345	30,900
ϕ	ϕ	2.5	395	16,500	335	27,600
ϕ	N	0	400	17,700	335	20,300
ϕ	m-$NO_2\phi$	1.5	~ 399	15,000	330	18,300
ϕ	o-$NO_2\phi$	0	390	12,300	325	17,700
ϕ	p-$NO_2\phi$	1.5	406	16,000	340	12,300
ϕ	m-$NH_2\phi$	0	400	16,400	335	25,000
ϕ	p-$NH_2\phi$	0	410	30,000	365	30,000
ϕ	o-$MeO\phi$	0	400	14,500	335–340	22,800
ϕ	m-$MeO\phi$	0	400	16,800	335	26,000
ϕ	p-$MeO\phi$	0	404	20,900	345	35,500

Though the ultraviolet absorption spectrum of the chelate is in each case richer than that of the chelating agent, all of it is probably attributable to ligand, or possibly to charge transfer from the perturbed ligand to uranium. Generally, a chelating metal atom splits the near-ultraviolet absorption band of β-diketonic ligands

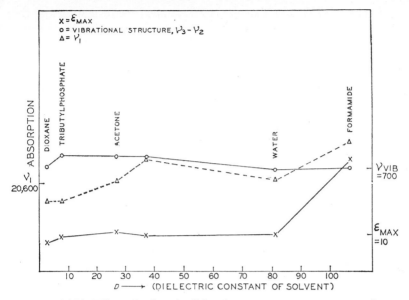

Fig. 2.21d. Effect of solvent's dielectric constant upon spectrum of $UO_2(NO_3)_2.6H_2O$.

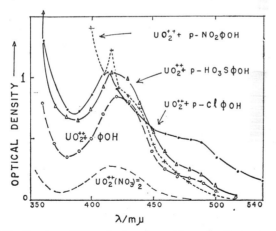

Fig. 2.21e. Spectra of Uranyl–phenol complexes in aqueous solution, pH ~ 4.5. Taken from Rao and Rao (1959). In each case the solution contained 0.0055M $UO_2{}^{++}$, 0.0110M $NO_3{}^-$, 0.00826M RØOH.

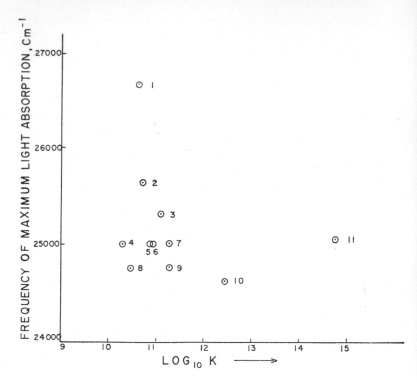

FIG. 2.21f. Uranyl complexing constants (determined by Ishidate and Yamane, 1957) and absorption frequencies.

$$K = \frac{[UO_2A_2.nH_2O.mEtOH]}{[UO_2^{++}][A^-]^2}$$

m, n unknown, and may vary from compound to compound.

$$A^- = \text{anion} \quad \begin{matrix} R-CCHC-\varnothing \\ \parallel \quad \parallel \\ O \ominus O \end{matrix}$$

Measurement was for 99 per cent EtOH medium.

1. CH_3.
2. $o\text{-}NO_2\varnothing$.
3. $\varnothing$.
4. $o\text{-}CH_3O\varnothing$.
5. $m\text{-}NH_2\varnothing$.

6. $m\text{-}CH_3O\varnothing$.
7.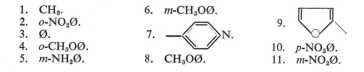
8. $CH_3O\varnothing$.

9.
10. $p\text{-}NO_2\varnothing$.
11. $m\text{-}NO_2\varnothing$.

into two or more clearly separated bands. Ishidate and Yamane noted that the position of both bands ($\sim$ 340 and $\sim$ 400 mμ) in the chelate spectrum was related to the position and intensity of the band ($\sim$ 400 mμ) in the chelating agent.

Ishidate and Yamane calculated apparent chelate equilibrium constants from their spectroscopic data. They used Job's method to study the complex formation. As we see in Fig. 2.21f, no correlation appears between transition frequency and chelate stability. None would be expected if the transition were within the ligand.

The visible absorption spectrum of the uranyl ion in several β-diketone chelates has been observed. Sacconi and Giannoni (1954) presented spectra of several benzoylacetone uranyl salts. Some of their results are shown in Fig. 2.21g. They found the spectra in the visible to be sensitive to solvent and particularly to the presence of water in it.

Belford, Martell, and Calvin (1960) studied the effect of fluorine substitution on the absorption bands of uranyl acetylacetonate. They found that the structure of the uranyl spectrum in the visible region is completely smeared out in the acetylacetonate, somewhat smeared out—but still distinguishable—in the trifluoroacetyl-acetonate, and very clear in the hexafluoroacetylacetonate (Fig. 2.21h). Unfortunately, the chelates with weaker bases (that is, with fluorine-containing ligands) could be isolated only as hydrates and it is unknown what the effect of the water of hydration (or coordination) is. The vibrational structure appeared to have on the average, wider spacing in the trifluoro than in the hexafluoro acetylacetonate. The average spacing measured over several prominent peaks was $\sim$ 812 cm^{-1} for the trifluoro and $\sim$ 776 cm^{-1} for the hexafluoro compound. However, these values do not give reliable values of the vibration frequencies in the excited states, because individual variations in spacing were quite large— $\sim$ 100 cm^{-1}. Also, it appeared that the most basic chelating groups (Acac > F$_3$Acac > F$_6$Acac) shifted the uranyl absorption very slightly to the red. Again, the uncertainty introduced by the different degrees of hydration of these chelates and by the fact that the shifts are only by a few millimicrons makes it difficult to use such data as sensitive tests of the nature of these transitions.

A finding that is very important in interpreting uranyl chelate spectra in organic solvents was made by Comyns, Gatehouse, and

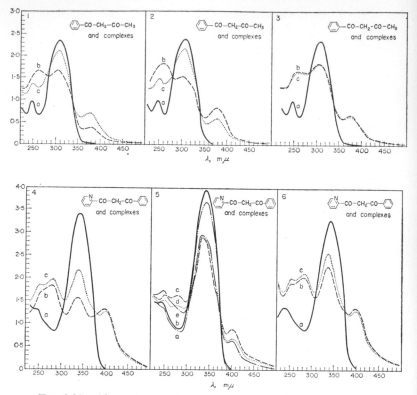

FIG. 2.21g. Absorption spectra of some uranyl β-diketones according to Sacconi and Giannoni (1954).

1. *a*, Benzoylacetone in anhydrous and 98% EtOH; *b*, UO$_2$(benzac)$_2$ in anhydrous EtOH; *c*, UO$_2$(benzac)$_2$ in 98% EtOH.

2. *a*, Benzoylacetone in anhydrous and aqueous Et$_2$O; *b*, UO$_2$(benzac)$_2$ in anhydrous Et$_2$O; *c*, UO$_2$(benzac)$_2$ in aqueous Et$_2$O.

3. *a*, Benzoylacetone in anhydrous and 98% MeOH; *b*, UO$_2$(benzac)$_2$ in anhydrous MeOH; *c*, UO$_2$(benzac)$_2$ in 98% MeOH.

4. *a*, Benzoylpicolinoylmethane in anhydrous and 98% EtOH; *b*, UO$_2$(picmet)$_2$ in anhydrous EtOH; *c*, UO$_2$(picmet)$_2$ in 98% EtOH.

5. *a*, Benzoylpicolinoylmethane in anhydrous Et$_2$O; *b*, Benzoylpicolinoylmethane in aqueous Et$_2$O; *c*, UO$_2$(picmetH)$_2$(NO$_3$)$_2$ in anhydrous EtOH; *d*, UO$_2$(picmetH)$_2$(NO$_3$)$_2$ in 98% EtOH; *e*, UO$_2$(picmetH)$_2$(NO$_3$)$_2$ in aqueous Et$_2$O.

6. *a*, Benzoylpicolinoylmethane in anhydrous and 98% MeOH; *b*, UO$_2$(picmetH)$_2$(NO$_3$)$_2$ in anhydrous MeOH; *c*, UO$_2$(picmetH)$_2$-(NO$_3$)$_2$ in 98% MeOH.

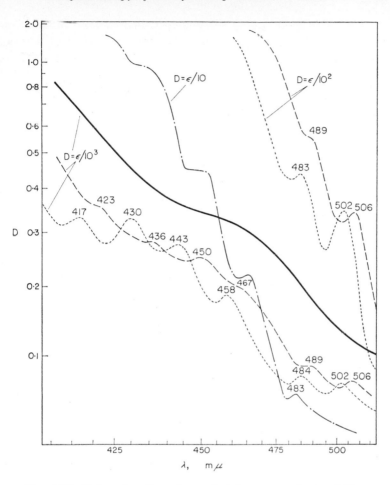

Fig. 2.21h. Enlarged section of uranyl chelate spectra in the visible: bisacetylacetono ——, bistrifluoroacetylacetono — — —, and bishexafluoro – – – uranyl chelates in 1.0×10^{-3} and 1.0×10^{-2}M chloroform solution. Also uranyl dinitrate hexahydrate — · —, 1.0×10^{-1}M in dioxane; fresh preparation. After Belford, Martell, and Calvin (1960).

Wait (1958). They discovered that anhydrous acetylacetonate raises the boiling point of benzene to the extent expected for a *dimer*. Since that observation was made at 80°C, it is quite possible that higher polymers are favored at room temperature or below it.

Comyns, Gatehouse, and Wait suggested that the low volatility of anhydrous uranyl acetylacetonate indicates that it is polymeric also in its crystalline form. Several structures can be imagined for the dimer in solution; in some of them the OUO group would be no longer symmetrical and the "symmetric stretch frequency," ν_s, would be allowed in the infrared absorption spectrum.

Examples of possible structures are shown below:

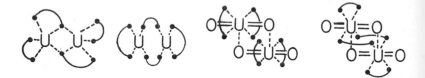

Whatever the form of the dimer molecule, its existence casts suspicion on the form of all uranyl chelates in organic solution. It means that if structural or other information is to be obtained from their solution spectra, careful studies ought to be made of their degree of association.

Comyns, Gatehouse, and Wait (1958) measured solution spectra of uranyl acetylacetonate (anhydrous) in ethanol and in benzene. These spectra, shown in Fig. 2.21i, reveal a very large solvent effect. Probably the uranyl chelate is monomeric but highly solvated in ethanol; the authors were able to isolate a solid ethanolate. At any rate, the ethanol solutions showed much weaker absorption than the benzene solutions, which were comparable with the chloroform solutions examined by Belford, Martell, and Calvin (1960).

3.2. *Fluorescence Spectra*

Sevchenko and Volod'ko (1956) investigated the fluorescence of uranyl salts in organic solvents at room temperature and at liquid air temperature. They state that all solutions of uranyl nitrate, chloride, sulfate, or acetate in alcohols, glycerine, formalin, acetone, butylacetate, ethylacetate, and other organic solvents luminesce at sufficiently low temperatures but with lower quantum efficiency than shown by the corresponding crystals.

One question to be settled was whether the frozen solutions actually contained uranyl salt microcrystals as fluorescent bodies.

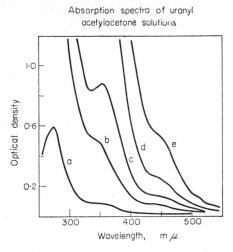

Absorption spectra of uranyl
acetylacetone solutions

FIG. 2.21i. After Comyns, Gatehouse, and Wait (1958).
a, c, e, in ethanol, in 10 cm cell, 3.60×10^{-6}, 3.60×10^{-5}, and 1.80×10^{-4}M respectively; *b, d,* in benzene, in 1 cm cell, 1.85×10^{-4} and 9.23×10^{-4}M respectively.

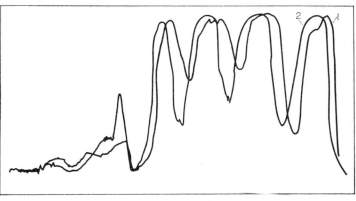

Wavelength ➡

FIG. 2.21j. Microphotograms of fluorescence spectra of solutions of uranyl nitrate in (1) formalin and (2) isobutanol ($-185°$C). The positions of peaks are given in the text. After Sevchenko and Volod'ko (1956).

TABLE 2.12c. WAVELENGTHS (mμ), FREQUENCIES (cm⁻¹), AND MAXIMUM EXTINCTION COEFFICIENTS OF ABSORPTION BANDS IN $UO_2(NO_3)_2 \cdot 6H_2O$ SOLUTIONS

After Jezowska-Trzebiatowska and Bartecki (1958)

Solvent		1	2	3	4	5	6	7	8	9	10
H₂O	λ	485	468.2	455	438.2	426.5	414.2	403.2	389	382	366
	σ_n	20,618	21,358	22,050	22,760	23,450	24,143	24,800	25,700	26,300	27,300
	ϵ_n	0.4	0.95	1.6	3.8	7.2	8.96	7.9	5.8	3.4	3.0
Acetone	λ	485	468.2	452	439	425.6	414.2	406	393.2	382	361.5
	σ_n	20,618	21,358	22,150	22,779	23,496	24,143	24,650	25,432	26,300	27,662
	ϵ_n	0.48	4.11	6.4	9.54	11.13	10.3	8.4	5.5	3.1	3.5
Methylethyl ketone	λ	485	468.2	453	439	425.6	414.2	406	393.5	382	362
	σ_n	20,618	21,358	22,077	22,779	23,496	24,143	24,650	25,400	26,300	27,600
	ϵ_n	0.66	3.55	5.88	8.79	10.35	9.65	8.0	5.3	2.9	3.4
Methylisobutyl ketone	λ	485	468.2	452	437.8	425.6	416	406	393.2	381.5	363.6
	σ_n	20,618	21,358	22,150	22,841	23,496	24,037*	24,650	25,432	26,200	27,500
	ϵ_n	0.69	3.38	5.47	8.85	10.0	9.5	7.8	5.2	3.0	3.0
Dioxane	λ	488	468.2	453	438	425.6	417	406.5	392.5	377	363.6
	σ_n	20,480	21,358	22,077	22,800	23,496	23,500	24,600	25,500	26,578	27,500
	ϵ_n	0.22	1.1	2.6	5.8	7.74	8.2	7.2	4.6	2.92	3.0
Formamide	λ	478	461	446.5	435	423.2	412.5	400	387.5	371.1	360.9
	σ_n	20,876	21,700	22,400	22,990	23,629	24,250	25,000	25,800	26,946	27,710
	ϵ_n	4.8	6.21	16.0	26.8	29.85	24.8	16.2	9.67	8.27	9.6
TBP	λ	488	470	453	439	427	416	402.6	390	378.9	363.6
	σ_n	20,480	21,280	22,077	22,779	23,419	24,037	24,838	25,640	26,391	27,500
	ϵ_n	0.63	1.71	3.54	6.61	8.82	9.74	8.14	5.25	3.2	3.0
Acetonitrile	λ	481	468.2	452	437.8	425.6	412.2	402	390	376	363.4
	σ_n	20,768	21,358	22,150	22,841	23,496	24,260	24,881	25,640	26,588	27,517
	ϵ_n	0.49	4.14	7.09	8.3	9.69	9.21	7.3	4.74	2.78	3.36
Acetylacetone	λ			453				400			
	σ_n			22,000				25,000			
	ϵ_n			260				580			

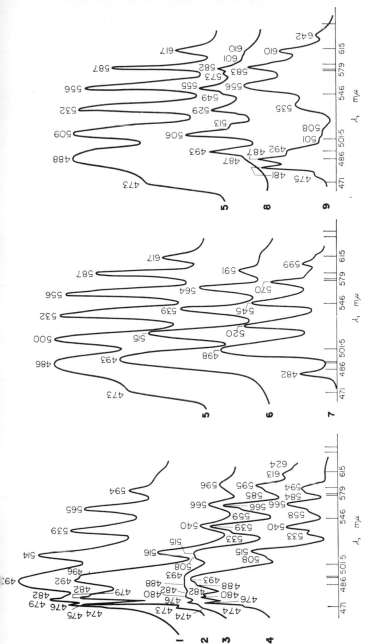

Fig. 2.21k. Microphotograms of fluorescence spectra of solutions of uranyl acetate, 0.1M at −185°C, in (1) methanol, (2) ethanol, (3) isoamyl alcohol, (4) butanol, (6) acetone, (7) ethyl acetate, (8) water, and (9) glycerine. The crystal spectrum at 20°C—curve (5)—is shown for comparison. After Sevchenko and Volod'ko (1956).

To this end Sevchenko and Volod'ko recorded fluorescence spectra of uranyl nitrate in acetone, glycerine, isobutanol, and formalin at −185°C. Figure 2.21j shows the comparison between the formalin and isobutanol solutions. The spectra are quite different and are not resolved into the pattern of sharp lines generally seen in crystal or microcrystal specimens of uranyl salts. The band maxima were located as follows:

Formalin	483	504	527	581	614	646 mμ	
i-Butanol	480	508	533	559	585	605	650 mμ

Whether these observations really prove that microcrystals are not responsible for the luminescence of frozen solutions is debatable; at least they prove that the solvent is present in the luminescing molecules.

Sevchenko and Volod'ko made a considerably more detailed study of the fluorescence of uranyl acetate in organic solvents at −185°C. Some of their results are shown in Figs. 2.21k. Because of the strong dependence of the intensity distribution (among the various bands) upon the nature of the solvent, they argued that fluorescence is a cooperative process in which both uranyl and solvent molecule participate, and cannot be ascribed to uranyl ion alone.

4. Raman Spectrum of Uranyl Salt Solutions

Pringsheim and Yost (1929) first observed the Raman spectrum of a concentrated uranyl sulfate solution (in sulfuric acid) and found a single frequency of 870 cm^{-1}, obviously corresponding to the main vibrational frequency of the ground state of UO_2^{++}, revealed by the fluorescence spectrum.

Conn and Wu (1938) investigated the Raman spectrum of saturated solutions of uranyl nitrate, chloride and sulfate, and found *two* vibrational frequencies (cf. Table 2.14). According to Chapter 1, these are the symmetric and the bending frequency respectively of the UO_2^{++} group. However, since the bending frequency should be

"Raman-inactive" in linear molecules, Conn and Wu preferred an angular model of the uranyl ion, in which the "symmetric" vibration

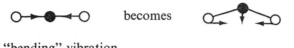 becomes

and the "bending" vibration

 becomes

with the result that both are now permitted in the Raman spectrum.

Satyanarayana (1942) used a saturated solution of uranyl chloride in water, adding potassium bromide to quench fluorescence. After 24 hr exposure, with the mercury line 546.1 mμ as exciting line, he was able to measure *five* Raman frequencies (Table 2.13).

TABLE 2.13. RAMAN FREQUENCIES OF UO_2Cl_2 IN WATER
Satyanarayana (1942)

Raman frequency (cm^{-1})	197	226	853	865	909
Intensity	2	2	0	10	1
Interpretation	ν_b''	ν_b'	ν_s''	ν_s'	ν_a

Table 2.13 shows, in addition to the double bending and symmetric vibration frequencies, a single antisymmetric frequency, ν_a, at 909 mμ. Similarly to Conn and Wu, Satyanarayana considered the occurrence of Raman frequencies other than ν_s evidence of non-linear structure; he calculated (by means of the Penn–Sutherland theory) a value of 140° for the ⟨angle⟩ angle. As a tentative explanation of the doubling of the frequencies ν_b and ν_s he suggested partial ionization, with some photons scattered by uranyl ions and some by undissociated uranyl chloride molecules. Satyanarayana also found that the 865 cm^{-1} Raman line was strongly polarized.

Crandall (1947, 1949) measured the Raman lines of uranyl chloride solutions of different concentrations and compiled Table 2.14, which includes the earlier results of Conn and Wu, and of Satyanarayana.

TABLE 2.14. RAMAN FREQUENCIES IN URANYL SALT SOLUTION
After Crandall

Frequency	Perchlorate (sat.) (Crandall)	Chloride			Nitrate (sat.) (Conn, Wu)	Sulfate (sat.) (Conn, Wu)
		Saturated		1.2M UO_2Cl_2 1.0M HCl 1.2M NH_4Cl (Crandall)		
		Conn, Wu	Satyanarayana			
ν_s (symmetric)	880	860	865, 853*	864	863	860
ν_a (asymmetric)	—	—	909*	—	—	—
ν_b (bending)	199*	210	226, 197	204	210	210

* Weak lines.

Crandall considered the difference between the frequencies in uranyl perchlorate solution and in the solutions containing other anions as an indication of complexing (of which incomplete dissociation, suggested by Satyanarayana, is a special case). The doublet structure found in Satyanarayana's experiments can then be interpreted as indicating the presence of two types of complexes. Crandall suggested that complexing may be responsible for an angular structure (if the occurrence of prohibited Raman lines is to be considered as proof that the UO_2^{++} ions, which is linear in crystals, becomes angular in solution) or, alternatively, for the violation of exclusion rules theoretically valid for linear structures (if the UO_2^{++} ion is assumed to remain linear in solution).

Crandall's experiments were made in connection with O^{18} exchange studies between uranyl ions and water. These studies indicated that the non-complexed ion has the simple structure

$$[O = {}^+U^+ = O]^{+2}$$

with four covalent bonds, and made unlikely the structure

$$\begin{bmatrix} {}^-HO & & OH^- \\ & (U^{+6}) & \\ {}^-HO & & OH^- \end{bmatrix}^{+2}$$

with four ionic bonds between a central U^{+6} ion and four OH^- anions. (If the second model were correct, a fast isotopic exchange of uranyl oxygen with water could be expected.)

The question of the shape of the UO_2^{++} ion in solution was again taken up by Sutton (1952). He compared the Raman spectra of the following solutions: (*a*) UO_2Cl_2, saturated, in water, (*b*) same, saturated with hydrochloric acid, (*c*) same, saturated with calcium chloride, (*d*) same, saturated with UO_3; and (*e*) $UO_2(NO_3)_2$, saturated. Figures 2.22a–e were obtained with the mercury line 546.1 mμ in 2–8 hr exposure.

The "prohibited" ν_a frequency (about 980 cm^{-1}) is not recognizable in (*a*), but appears clearly in (*b*) and (*c*), where Cl^- ions were present in large excess. Sutton considers this evidence of formation of complexes of UO_2^{++} with Cl^-, in which the entrance of Cl^- ions into the hydration spheres of the cations: $UO_2^{++}.6H_2O + Cl^- \rightarrow UO_2^{++}Cl^-.5H_2O$, creates an asymmetric electric field that makes the prohibited transition possible. (Using the UO_2F_2 crystal structure as a model, Sutton postulated that water molecules form a puckered

ring around the O—U—O axis, with an $O-U\diagup\!\!\!\!\diagdown\!\!\!\!\!{}^{OH_2}_{O}$ angle of about 73°.)

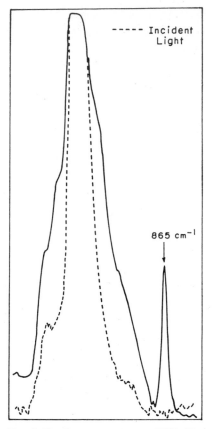

FIG. 2.22a. Raman spectrum of UO_2Cl_2.

The even more pronounced appearance of the ν_a frequency in uranyl chloride solution saturated with UO_3 (Fig. 2.22d) can be attributed to the formation of complex polyuranyl ions

$$UO_2^{++} + UO_3 \rightarrow \{UO_2^{++}\!-\!O^{--}\!-\!UO_2^{++}\}^{++} (= U_2O_5^{++})$$

(cf. Section 1), in which the O^{--} ion in the "bridge" exercises a similar (but stronger) asymmetric electric influence on the linear UO_2^{++} ions as does the Cl^- ion in the chloride complexes.

The occurrence in nitrate solution (Fig. 2.22e) of the ν_a frequency, with an intensity intermediate between those in Figs. 2.22b, c on the

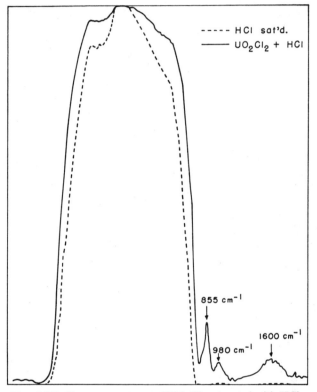

Fig. 2.22b. Raman spectrum of UO_2Cl_2 saturated with HCl.

one hand and Fig. 2.22d on the other, is taken by Sutton as confirmation of the conclusion of Betts and Michels (1949) that the uranyl ion has a stronger tendency to complex with NO_3^- ions than with Cl^- ion (for contradictory evidence, see Section 2.1). In this case (Sutton suggests) two adjacent water molecules in the hydration sphere can be replaced by two nitrate oxygens ($UO_2^{++}.6H_2O + NO_3^- \rightarrow UO_2^{++}NO_3^-.4H_2O$).

The ν_b frequency is not separated from the mercury line in Figs. 2.22a–e because of insufficient dispersion; however, its presence is revealed by the distortion of the shape of this line, which is least pronounced in curve (a) and stronger in curves (b–e).

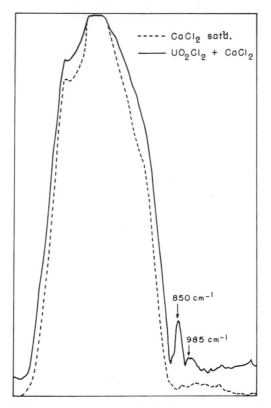

FIG. 2.22c. Raman spectrum of UO_2Cl_2 saturated with $CaCl_2$.

Sutton suggested that if the above argument is correct, the prohibited lines can be expected to be weaker in complex ions of higher symmetry, such as the trinitratouranyl ion, which is formed, according to Kaplan *et al.* (1950a, b), in uranyl nitrate solutions in organic solvents in the presence of quaternary ammonium nitrates.

5. Infrared Spectra of Uranyl Compounds in Solution

Until 1952, most of the spectroscopic work on uranyl solutions had been done in the region above $10,000 \text{ cm}^{-1}$. A significant advance was the report by Jones and Penneman (1953) on infrared

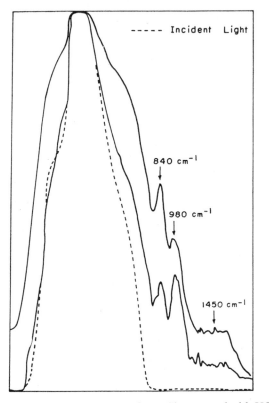

FIG. 2.22d. Raman spectrum of UO_2Cl_2 saturated with UO_3.

absorption spectra of uranyl (and of analogous transuranyl) salts in aqueous $HClO_4$ solution. They used very short optical paths (0.005 mm) and very concentrated solutions ($\geqslant 0.25\text{M } UO_2^{++}$) to overcome the water interference.

When the concentration of $HClO_4$ was greater than 1 molar, no change of UO_2^{++} frequencies was observed over a tenfold range of UO_2^{++} concentration (from 0.25M to 2.5M). This was taken as evidence that UO_2^{++} is not involved in polymerizations or hydrolyses in this composition range. The assumption agrees well with the general results of uranyl hydrolysis studies mentioned previously.

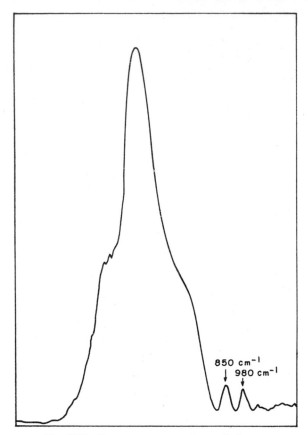

FIG. 2.22e. Raman spectrum of uranyl nitrate.

Jones and Penneman's curves are shown in Fig. 2.23. The strong band (ν_a) of XO_2^{++} is located at 965 ± 1, 969 ± 1, 962 ± 1, and 939 ± 1 cm^{-1} for X = U, Np, Pu, and Am respectively. We may presume that the species being observed are hydrated O—X—O^{++} ions, and from the similarity of the spectra we may infer that the geometry and bond strengths of the transuranyl ions are nearly the same as in uranyl itself. There is little doubt that the strong band is the asymmetric stretching band seen at 900–960 cm^{-1} in various solid uranyl salts, both in fluorescence and in infrared absorption measurements by many workers.

The absorption frequency for this series of ions does not seem to be a monotonic function of atomic number. Measurements of the

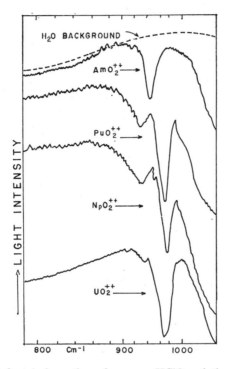

Fig. 2.23. Infrared absorption of aqueous HClO$_4$ solutions. Path = 5 micron. Absorption over 1000 cm^{-1} is caused by ClO$_4^-$. $\epsilon \simeq 500$ l mole^{-1} cm^{-1} for strong band of each XO$_2^{++}$ ion. After Jones and Penneman (1952).

lattice constant for the series NaXO$_2$(CH$_3$CO$_2$)$_3$ (Zachariasen, 1948a; Jones, 1955; Ellinger, 1954) imply that the O—X—O length does decrease monotonically with atomic number. However, as Jones (1955) has pointed out, only the asymmetric stretching frequencies were observed. Jones attempted to make a correction for the linear O—X—O groups, using the potential energy function

$$2V = k_{X-O}[\Delta R_1^2 + \Delta R_2^2] + k_{12}(\Delta R_1)(\Delta R_2) + k_\alpha(\Delta\alpha)^2$$

where R_1, R_2, and α are the two distances and the angle k_{12} is the bond interaction force constant of the ion. Taking values for k_{X-O} and k_{12} which fit the observed frequencies ν_a and ν_s in solid $NaXO_2(CH_3CO_2)_3$, and using the k_{12} thus obtained, together with ν_a for the aqueous solutions, he estimates k_{X-O} for X = U, Np,

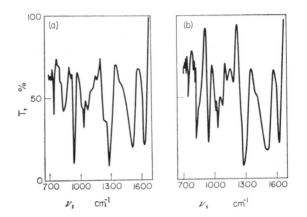

FIG. 2.24. After Volod'ko, Sevchenko, and Umreiko (1960). Infrared spectra (per cent transmission) of solutions of uranyl nitrates in acetone: (*a*) $UO_2(NO_3)_2.6H_2O$, (*b*) $UO_2(NO_3)_3(C_2H_5)_4N.6H_2O$. Concentration, 0.2M. Cell thickness, 0.05 mm.

Pu, Am in aqueous solution to be a monotonically decreasing function of atomic number. With serious reservations, we infer with Jones that increasing nuclear charge on the central ion tends to shorten the X—O bonds, but that the simultaneous addition of electrons about the central ion weakens the bond resistance to small stretches.

The infrared absorption spectra of acetone solutions of dinitrato and trinitrato complexes of uranyl ion were reported and discussed by Volod'ko, Sevchenko, and Umreiko (Fig. 2.24) in 1960. They found bands in the trinitrato complex at 1624, 1510, 1275, 1175, 1122, 1076, 1025, 1010, 954, 845, 828, 811, 797, 744, 734, 717, 705 cm^{-1}, and nearly the same spectrum for the dinitrato, with some alterations of relative band intensities and also some small shifts in frequency. Gatehouse, Livingstone, and Nyholm (1958) had found evidence that "free" nitrate ion has an infrared absorption band at 1390 cm^{-1}, while "bound" nitrate ion does not have this band, but does have one around 1500 cm^{-1}. Accordingly, Volod'ko *et al.* assumed that the three nitrate groups in the trinitratouranyl molecule, and the two nitrates of the dinitratouranyl molecule are "covalently bound" to the uranyl ion.

CHAPTER 3

URANYL FLUORESCENCE INTENSITY AND DECAY

1. Preliminary Remarks on Slow-decaying Fluorescence

It seems advisable to preface the description of the experimental results in the field of the fluorescence of uranyl salts with brief remarks about intensity measurements of slowly decaying fluorescence (of which that of uranyl salts is the best-known example). When working with dyestuffs or other organic compounds whose fluorescence stops almost instantaneously (more exactly, within 10^{-7} sec) after the cessation of illumination, the intensity of fluorescence usually is measured in the *steady state of illumination*. In the determination of the yield, the amount of light energy (or the number of quanta) emitted per second in the steady state is compared with the amount of light energy (or the number of quanta) absorbed during the same period. In experiments on slow-decaying fluorescence or phosphorescence (for differentiation between these two see below, p. 191) on the other hand, emission often is excited by a flash, and *momentary* intensity of emission is measured at various times after the flash and integrated graphically; alternatively, the total energy emitted after a single flash can be determined by an integrating instrument. In this case, the term "yield of fluorescence" often is taken to mean the ratio of the total light energy emitted after a flash to the amount of light energy absorbed in the flash. Whether the yield determined in this way is identical (or almost identical) with the yield in steady light depends on the duration of the flash, t_f, compared to the (actual, not natural) lifetime of the excited state, τ. If the flash is long compared to this lifetime, as in typical fluorescent dyestuffs ($\tau_n < 10^{-7}$ sec, while the flash may last several microseconds or even milliseconds), a stationary state is reached at the end of the flash (assuming the intensity of the flash is uniform through its duration); the total integrated emission of light after the flash, which we call L, is then *independent* of the duration of the flash, and the yield calculated from this emission is *inversely proportional* to this duration. If, however, the flash is *short* compared to the natural lifetime of the excited state (as can easily occur in the case of uranyl fluorescence, where t is of the order of 10^{-4} sec), the number of excited molecules present at the end of the flash, and with it, the initial intensity of emission, F_0 (as well as the integral of the emitted energy, L), must increase with the duration of the flash. In the limiting case, when $t_f \ll \tau$, both F_0 and L must become *proportional* to t_f, and the yield, derived from the measurement of L, is *independent* of the duration of the flash.

Let us assume that the number of non-excited uranyl ions in a unit volume of fluorescent material is $[UO_2^{++}]$. This number is not markedly depleted even in very strong light, because, for all practically attainable light intensities, the interval between two successive excitations of a given uranyl ion is long compared to the lifetime of excitation, so that every ion spends much more time in the non-excited than in the excited state. The rate of formation of excited molecules, in a layer which is situated at depth l and which is optically so thin as to be practically uniformly illuminated, is, in a parallel beam of monochromatic light:

$$+\frac{d[UO_2^{++*}]}{dt} = \epsilon I_l [UO_2^{++}] = \epsilon I_0 e^{-\epsilon[UO_2^{++}]l} [UO_2^{++}] \qquad (1)$$

where I_0 is the number of einsteins of quanta impinging on unit area (1000 cm^2) per unit time (1 sec), ϵ the molar absorption coefficient (with base e), which is inversely proportional to the *natural* lifetime of the excited state, τ_0, and $[UO_2^{++}]$ the concentration of uranyl ions in moles/liter. Since we have assumed illumination with a parallel beam of monochromatic light, the light intensity will decline with depth, l, as a simple exponential function (as assumed in Equation 1). Integration of this equation over a layer of total thickness l_0 gives, as could be expected:

$$\frac{d\left[\int_0^{l_0}[UO_2^{++}*]dl\right]}{dt} = \epsilon[UO_2^{++}]\int_0^{l_0} I_l\,d_l$$

$$= I_0\left(1-e^{-\epsilon[UO_2^{++}]l_0}\right) = I_a \qquad (2)$$

where I_a is the *absorbed* light flux (in einsteins per sec per 1000 cm²).

The rate of loss of excited molecules, by fluorescence and by non-radiative (monomolecular) energy dissipation, is given, for each layer with constant concentration of these molecules, by Equation (3):

$$-\frac{d[UO_2^{++}*]}{dt} = \alpha*[UO_2^{++}*]$$

$$= (a\epsilon+k_d)[UO_2^{++}*] = \frac{[UO_2^{++}*]}{\tau} \qquad (3)$$

where
$$a\epsilon = \frac{N_A\lambda^2 10^{-3}\epsilon}{8\pi} = 2.4\times10^{19}\,\epsilon\lambda^2 = \frac{1}{\tau_0} \qquad (4)$$

The preceding equation is the universal relation between the natural lifetime of an excited state, the absorption coefficient of the spectral line that leads to this state, and its wavelength (N_A is Avogadro's number). According to Lewis and Kasha, this expression should be multiplied by a factor n^2 if the process occurs in a medium with an index of refraction n. We assumed in Equation (3) that both processes bring the excited molecules back into the ground state, and not into some long-lived metastable state, and that dissipation, like fluorescence, is a first-order process in respect to the concentration of the excited ions. The constant k_d is the monomolecular velocity constant of the radiationless dissipation process. The total monomolecular deactivation constant, $\alpha*(= a\epsilon+k_d)$, is the inverse of the *actual* mean lifetime of the excited state, τ.

The concentration of excited ions, $[UO_2^{++}*]$, present in an infinitely thin layer at depth l after an illumination time of t_f sec is obtained by integrating the difference between (1) and (3):

$$[UO_2^{++}*]_{t_f} = \left(1-e^{-\alpha*t_f}\right)\frac{\epsilon I_l[UO_2^{++}]}{\alpha*} \qquad (5)$$

By integration of Equation (5) over the depth l_0, we obtain, using (3.2):

$$\int_0^{l_o} [UO_2^{+++*}]_{t_f} \, dl = \frac{1-e^{-\alpha^* t_f}}{\alpha^*} \epsilon [UO_2^{++}] \int_0^{l_o} I_l \, d_l \tag{6}$$

$$= \frac{1-e^{-\alpha^* t_f}}{\alpha^*} I_0 \left(1 - e^{-\epsilon[UO_2^{++}]l_0}\right) = \frac{1-e^{-\alpha^* t_f}}{\alpha^*} I_a$$

where I_a is the amount of light absorbed in passage through the layer l_0.

At the beginning of illumination, as long as $t_f \ll 1/\alpha^*$, the concentration of excited ions in each layer dl increases proportional to t_f:

$$[UO_2^{+++*}]_t = \epsilon I_l t_f [UO_2^{++}] \tag{7}$$

and the same is true of the total number of excited molecules in the finite layer, l_0. When $t_f \ll 1/\alpha^*$, the concentration of excited molecules in each thin layer reaches a steady value:

$$[UO_2^{+++*}] = \frac{\epsilon I_l}{\alpha^*} [UO_2^{++}] \text{ moles/liter} \tag{8}$$

and the same is true of the total amount of excited molecules in a finite layer, l_0:

$$\int_0^{l_o} [UO_2^{+++*}]_\infty \, dl = \frac{I_a}{\alpha^*} \tag{9}$$

The momentary local intensity of fluorescence at any given time is

$$F = a\epsilon [UO_2^{+++*}] \text{ einsteins/(sec liter)} \tag{10}$$

Immediately after the beginning of illumination, therefore, we have for an optically thin layer:

$$F = a\epsilon^2 I_l t_f [UO_2^{++}] \quad \text{einsteins/(sec liter)} \tag{11}$$

and for a finite, optically dense layer l_0:

$$F_0 = \int_0^{l_o} F_l \, dl = a\epsilon I_a t_f \quad \text{einsteins/(sec 1000 cm}^2\text{)} \tag{12}$$

In the steady state, we have, for an optically thin layer:

$$F_\infty = \frac{a\epsilon^2 I_l}{\alpha^*}[UO^{+\frac{1}{2}}] \quad \text{einsteins/(sec liter)} \tag{13}$$

and for an optically dense layer:

$$F_\infty = \int_0^l F_{\infty l}\, dl = \frac{a\epsilon}{\alpha^*} I_a = \tau a\epsilon I_0 \quad \text{einsteins/(sec 1000 cm}^2) \tag{14}$$

When illumination stops, the fluorescence decays exponentially as a function of the dark time, t_d.

If the excitation period had been *long* (meaning "long enough to reach the steady state"), $t_f \gg 1/\alpha^*$, we have, for a thin layer, dl:

$$F_{t_d} = \frac{a\epsilon^2 I_l}{\alpha^*}[UO_2^{++}]e^{-\alpha^* t_d} = F_0 e^{-\alpha^* t_d} \quad \text{einsteins/(sec liter)} \tag{15}$$

or, for a dense layer, l_0:

$$F_{t_d} = \int_0^{l_0} F_{t_{d_l}}\, dl = \frac{a\epsilon I_a}{\alpha^*}e^{-\alpha^* t_d}$$

$$= F_0 e^{-\alpha^* t_d} \quad \text{einsteins/(sec 1000 cm}^2) \tag{15a}$$

where F_0 is the fluorescence intensity immediately after the cessation of illumination.

The (time) integral of the yield of fluorescence after the cessation of "long" excitation is:

$$L = \int_0^\infty F_{t_d}\, dt_d = \frac{a\epsilon^2 I_l}{\alpha^{*2}}[UO_2^{++}]$$

$$= \frac{F_0}{\alpha^*} \quad \text{einsteins/liter (for a thin layer)} \tag{16}$$

or
$$L = \int_0^{l_0} L_l\, dl = \frac{a\epsilon}{\alpha^{*2}} I_a$$

$$= \frac{F_0}{\alpha^*} \quad \text{einsteins/1000 cm}^2 \text{ (for a dense layer)} \tag{16a}$$

If the excitation was by a brief flash $t_f > 1/\alpha^*$, the fluorescence immediately after the end of the flash is:

$$F_0 = (1 - e^{-\alpha^* t_f}) \frac{a\epsilon^2 I_l}{\alpha^*} [UO_2^{++}] \quad \text{einsteins/(sec liter)}$$

(thin layer)   (17)

or $$F_0 = \int_0^{l_0} F_{0_l} \, dl$$

$$= (1 - e^{-\alpha^* t_f}) \frac{a\epsilon}{\alpha^*} I_a \quad \text{einsteins/sec 1000 cm}^2) \text{ (dense layer)}$$ (17a)

It then decays exponentially with time:

$$F_{t_d} = (1 - e^{-\alpha^* t_f}) \frac{a\epsilon^2 I}{\alpha^*} [UO_2^{++}] e^{-\alpha^* t_d}$$

$$= F_0 e^{-\alpha^* t_d} \quad \text{einsteins/(sec liter) (thin layer)}$$ (18)

or $$F_{t_d} = (1 - e^{-\alpha^* t_f}) \frac{a\epsilon}{\alpha^*} I_a e^{-\alpha^* t_d}$$

$$= F_0 e^{-\alpha^* t_d} \quad \text{einsteins/(sec 1000 cm}^2) \text{ (dense layer)}$$ (18a)

The time-integrated emission is in this case:

$$L = \int_0^\infty F_{t_d} \, d_{t_d} = (1 - e^{-\alpha^* t_f}) \frac{a\epsilon^2 I_l}{\alpha^{*2}} [UO_2^{++}]$$

$$= \frac{F_0}{\alpha^*} \quad \text{einsteins/liter (thin layer)}$$ (19)

or $$L = \int_0^{l_0} L_l \, dl = (1 - e^{-\alpha^* t_f}) \frac{a\epsilon I_a}{\alpha^{*2}}$$

$$= \frac{F_0}{\alpha^*} \quad \text{einsteins/1000 cm}^2 \text{ (dense layer)}$$ (19a)

If the flash is *very short* $(t_f \ll 1/\alpha^*)$, we have:

$$L = \frac{a\epsilon^2 I_l t_f [UO_2^{++}]}{\alpha^*} = \frac{F_0}{\alpha^*} \quad \text{einsteins/liter (thin layer)}$$ (20)

$$L = \int_0^{l_0} L_l \, dl = \frac{a \epsilon t_f I_a}{\alpha^*}$$

$$= \frac{F_0}{\alpha^*} \quad \text{einsteins/1000 cm}^2 \text{ (dense layer)} \quad (20a)$$

When k_d can be neglected (and α^* is therefore equal to $a\epsilon$, meaning 100 per cent fluorescence yield in the steady state!), we obtain, after long excitation:

$$L = \frac{I_l}{a} [UO_2^{++}] \quad \text{einsteins/liter (thin layer)} \quad (21)$$

and $\quad L = \int_0^{l_0} L_l \, dl = \frac{I_a}{\epsilon a} \quad \text{einsteins/1000 cm}^2 \text{ (dense layer)} \quad (21a)$

After a "brief" flash:

$$L = (1 - e^{-a \epsilon t_f}) \frac{I_l}{a} [UO_2^{++}] \quad \text{einsteins/liter (thin layer)} \quad (22)$$

$$L = \int_0^{l_0} L_l \, dl$$

$$= \frac{1 - e^{-a \epsilon t_f}}{a \epsilon} I_a \quad \text{einsteins/1000 cm}^2 \text{ (dense layer)} \quad (22a)$$

and after a "very brief" flash:

$$L = t_f I_l \epsilon [UO_2^{++}] \quad \text{einsteins/liter (thin layer)} \quad (23)$$

$$L = \int_0^{l_0} L_l \, dl = t_f I_a \quad \text{einsteins/1000 cm}^2 \text{ (dense layer)} \quad (23a)$$

The yield of fluorescence, measured by integrating the emission *after* a flash, can reach 100 per cent only in the third case, i.e. if $t_f \ll a\epsilon$, because then practically no absorbed energy is re-emitted during the flash. The same applies generally to the relation between the fluorescence yield in steady light and the fluorescence yield after flash illumination: the latter is generally lower, but approaches the former when the duration of the flash becomes very short compared to the lifetime of the excited state.

2. Intensity and Decay of Uranyl Fluorescence in Crystals

E. Becquerel (1872) first determined by means of a "phosphoroscope" the *duration* of light emission by illuminated solid uranium nitrate. He noted that the luminescence lasted for 3–4×10^{-3} sec after the cessation of excitation—a value which agrees well with the more recent determinations. (As will be seen below, these determinations gave values of about 3×10^{-4} sec for the "lifetime" of the excited state, i.e. the time required for the fluorescence intensity to decline by a factor of e; fluorescence remains visible—or detectable—for a considerably longer period, depending on its initial intensity and on the sensitivity of the eye or of the measuring device.)

Nichols and Howes (1919) constructed a "synchrono-phosphoroscope" to study the law of decay of luminescence in uranium compounds. They began by establishing the identity of what they called "fluorescence spectrum" with what they designated as "phosphorescence spectrum," i.e. of the spectrum of uranyl luminescence *during* excitation and that emitted at different times *after* the cessation of excitation. Sparks repeated 120 times per sec served for excitation; observation was either synchronized with excitation, or shifted to different moments in the intervals between sparks. The same seven groups of bands were found in both cases, and they had the same relative brightness. This result is in agreement with the since well-established concept that light-excited uranyl salts are capable of only *one* kind of photoluminescence, namely *a slow-decaying fluorescence*. (In other words, they exhibit no true phosphorescence.) The reason why the fluorescence of uranyl salts persists in the dark for several milliseconds (thus resembling phosphorescence), while the fluorescence of organic dyestuffs, such as fluorescein, disappears in less than a microsecond, is the low intensity of the absorption bands of the uranyl ion, as compared to the bands of organic dyestuffs and the consequent long lifetime of the excited state (cf. Equation 4). In true phosphorescence, according to the most appropriate definition of this term, delayed re-emission of absorbed light energy is caused by the conversion of the primarily excited state into another, metastable state (of somewhat lower energy), and not by the long life of the excited state itself. The emission of phosphorescent light can originate in the metastable state; in this case the phosphorescence band is displaced towards the longer waves compared to the fluorescence band (which originates directly in the light-excited state). Alternatively, emission may be caused by return of the molecule from the metastable into the original excited state, caused by thermal agitation; in this case, the phosphorescence band will coincide with the fluorescence band (cf. Fig. 3.1).

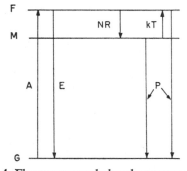

FIG. 3.1. Fluorescence and phosphorescence scheme.
A, absorption.   M, metastable state.
E, fluorescence.   NR, non-radiative transition.
F, fluorescent state.   P, phosphorescence.
G, ground state.   kT, thermal excitation.

The decay curves of luminescence of uranium salts after cessation of illumination were assumed by Nichols and Howes to follow the equation

$$\sqrt{1/F_{t_\mathrm{d}}} = \sqrt{1/F_0} + Ct_\mathrm{d} \tag{24}$$

where F_0 is the intensity of fluorescence at time zero, and C is a proportionality constant. Already before that time, when Equation (24) was applied to other phosphorescent substances, deviations from this "law" had been found by Nichols and Howes. These had been interpreted by them by assuming *two* superimposed decay processes: the decay first followed Equation (24) with the higher value of the constant, C_1, and later the same equation with a smaller decay constant, C_2. In the case of uranyl salts, an apparent change in the opposite direction was found: the constant C appeared to become *higher* as the luminescence decayed. Three increasingly steep linear sections were found by Nichols and Howes in the fluorescence–time curves ($\sqrt{1/F_{t_d}}$ as function of t_d) of several uranyl salts (Fig. 3.2). (For re-interpretation of these results see below.)

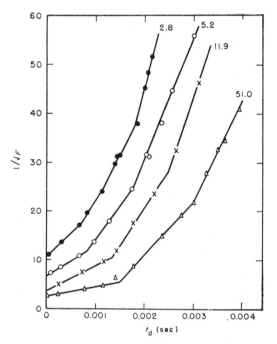

FIG. 3.2. Fluorescence decay of rubidium uranyl nitrate crystals at four light intensities (after Nichols and Howes). (Intensity is supposed to decline proportionally to t_d^{-2}.) From Vavilov and Levshin (1928).

The total periods over which the decay of uranyl salt fluorescence could be followed were found by Nichols and Howes to be of the order of 10^{-3} sec. This was noted with crystals of uranyl sulfate, ammonium uranyl sulfate, potassium uranyl sulfate, uranyl nitrate hexahydrate, and ammonium uranyl chloride. At constant intensity of illumination, the initial intensity of emission, F_0, was highest in ammonium uranyl and potassium uranyl double sulfates, and several times lower in uranyl nitrate, uranyl sulfate, and ammonium uranyl chloride. Potassium sulfate, freshly prepared in the dark, gave a much brighter fluorescence than a similar preparation exposed to light for a long time.

Simultaneous irradiation with red or infrared light, which enhances the phosphorescence of sulfide phosphors, had no effect on the luminescence of uranyl salts. This is in agreement with its interpretation as a long-lived fluorescence rather than phosphorescence. (The phosphorescence of sulfide phosphors and similar luminous solids is caused by conversion into a metastable state, in which the originally excited electron wanders away from its nucleus and is caught in a "trap," often provided by an impurity; infrared radiation liberates the electron from the trap and thus accelerates the restoration of the initial excited state and the emission of phosphorescence.)

Excitation by quartz mercury arc gave the same decay curve as excitation by a spark.

Uranium glass, although its composition invites comparison with a phosphor made luminescent by an impurity, showed a decay curve similar to that of pure uranyl salts.

Viscous uranyl phosphate did not fluoresce at all until the water content was reduced so far that it became a plastic solid; in this state the phosphate showed the same decay curve as crystalline uranyl salts.

Lowering of *temperature* from $+60°$ to $-180°C$ made the decay slower, but the effect was irregular. In the ammonium uranyl sulfate, for example, the decay was *faster* at $-180°$ than at $+20°C$.

Intensity of excitation has no effect on the shape of the decay curve. (In the interpretation of Nichols and Howes, all three consecutive decay stages were prolonged in the same proportion; the duration of each stage was found to be proportional to the logarithm of the intensity of the exciting light.)

Decay was much slower in uranyl nitrate *hydrate* than in the corresponding anhydrous salt.

Double chlorides (such as rubidium uranyl chloride) exhibited a *polarization* of the fluorescent light. The components polarized in the two perpendicular planes had the same rate of decay.

Nichols and Howes also studied the luminescence of uranyl salts excited by *cathode rays*. Its spectrum was the same as that of light-excited luminescence, but the emission lasted minutes instead of milliseconds.

To measure the duration of rapidly decaying fluorescence of organic dyestuffs, Gaviola (1927) constructed an elcctro-optical "fluoroscope" based on the Kerr effect—an instrument suitable to observe changes in light intensity occurring within 10^{-8} sec or less. He applied it also to uranium salt solutions (uranyl sulfate, in methanol or in concentrated sulfuric acid) and obtained an unexpected result: he found the mean lifetime τ to be even shorter than in dyestuff solutions—of the order of 10^{-9} sec! For a sample of uranium glass, on the other hand, he found $\tau \gg 15 \times 10^{-9}$ sec (the latter figure represented the upper limit of usefulness of his instrument). One could think at first that perhaps the fluorescence of uranyl salt *solutions* decays much faster than that of uranyl salt *crystals*, but Gaviola and Pringsheim (1927), using the same instrument, also found a value of 5.1×10^{-9} sec for the decay constant of fluorescence of *solid* uranyl nitrate. They noted the wide disagreement between this value and the decay periods found for uranyl salts by phosphoroscopic methods (10^{-4} to 10^{-2} sec) but could give no explanation of the discrepancy. Subsequent studies confirmed the observation of Becquerel and of Nichols and Howes that the visible fluorescence of uranyl salts lasts for about a thousandth of a second. The existence, in addition to this slow-decaying fluorescence, of a rapidly decaying fluorescence, such as was described by Gaviola, is very unlikely.

Two extensive investigations of the fluorescence of uranyl salts were carried out by Vavilov and Levshin (1927, 1928) and by Perrin and Delorme (1928, 1929). They studied crystals as well as solutions. (For results obtained with the latter, see Section 3.)

Vavilov and Levshin (1928) re-interpreted the above-described fluorescence measurements of Nichols and Howes by plotting the data on a semi-logarithmic scale, $\log F = f(t_d)$. In this way they obtained straight lines (Fig. 3.3), indicating that the true decay law is exponential:

$$F = F_0 e^{-t_d/\tau} \tag{25}$$

as expected for a monomolecular process. From Nichols and Howes' data, Vavilov and Levshin calculated the values of τ shown in the second column of Table 3.1.

Previous investigations by Vavilov and co-workers had shown that in dye solutions in glassy media a long-living *phosphorescence* often was superimposed on short-lived *fluorescence*, while in liquid solutions only the latter was observed. The luminescence of solid uranyl salts showed no such complexity, and because of its long duration Vavilov and Levshin (similarly to Nichols and Howes) first classified it as a *phosphorescence*. They saw a confirmation of this view in an observation that a dark interval intervened between the cessation of illumination and the beginning of emission in

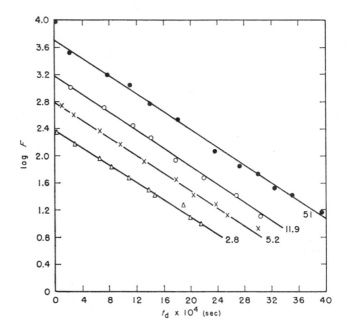

FIG. 3.3. Same data as in Fig. 3.2. replotted by Vavilov and Levshin (log *F* as function of *t*). From Vavilov and Levshin, (1928).

uranium glass—a phenomenon they had noted previously in typical phosphorescences. However, both arguments proved fallacious: the low intensity of the visible uranyl absorption bands indicates that the excited uranyl ions must have a long natural lifetime, τ_0, so that no doubts need to arise as to the fluorescent character of its emission merely because of its long duration. As to the "dark interval" (again found in Vavilov and Levshin's second investigation, in 1928, where it was determined to last, in uranyl nitrate, for about

TABLE 10.1 THE DECAY TIME CONSTANTS OF THE FLUORESCENCE OF SOLID URANYL COMPOUNDS

$$F = F_0 e^{-td/\tau}$$

Salt	$\tau \times 10^4$/sec, as observed by:									
	NH	PD	VL	RW	GHG	HD	PD (93°)	GHG (100°)	HD (77°)	HD (4°)
$UO_2(NO_3)_2$	5.6, 6.7	6.1	5.4	7.19	5.6	—	8	6.4	—	—
$RbUO_2(NO_3)_3$	—	—	—	—	—	5.0	—	—	14.3	15.8
$NH_4UO_2(NO_3)_3$	—	—	—	—	—	3.74	—	—	8.7	16.0
$MgUO_2(NO_3)_3$	—	—	—	—	—	6.5	—	—	8.2	9.2
$K_2UO_2(NO_3)_4$	—	—	—	—	—	9.7	—	—	15.8	18.5
$AgUO_2(NO_3)_3$	—	—	—	—	—	7.1	—	—	10.7	13.9
$CsUO_2(NO_3)_3$	—	—	—	—	—	5.16	—	—	14.2	20.8
UO_2SO_4	2.55*	2.5	2.6	—	—	—	3.5	—	—	—
$(NH_4)_2UO_2(SO_4)_2$	4.3	—	—	—	—	3.59	—	—	4.15	6.15
$K_2UO_2(SO_4)_2$	4.15	1.66	—	—	—	—	—	—	—	—
$Rb_2UO_2(SO_4)_2$	—	—	—	—	—	2.67	—	—	2.51	2.52
UO_2Cl_2	—	1.54	—	—	—	—	3.6	—	—	—
$(NH_4)_2UO_2Cl_4$	—	—	—	—	—	—	—	—	—	21.5
$K_2UO_2Cl_4$	4.2	—	—	—	—	3.94, 1.4	—	—	6.28, 1.5	26.2
$Rb_2UO_2Cl_4$	—	—	—	—	—	5.35, 0.92	—	—	10.25, 1.1	24.4, 2.8
$CsUO_2Cl_4$	—	—	—	—	—	5.06,† 1.56	—	—	9.07, 1.56	16.3, 2.7
$(NH_4)_2UO_2F_4$	—	—	—	—	6.3	—	—	7.0	—	—
$UO_2(ClO_4)_2$	—	—	—	—	2.6	—	—	2.6	—	—
Uranyl phosphate	—	0.5	—	—	—	—	—	—	—	—
Uranyl ammonium phosphate	—	—	—	1.42	—	—	—	—	—	—

(continued)

Salt	$\tau \times 10^4$/sec, as observed by:									
	NH	PD	VL	RW	GHG	HD	PD (93°)	GHG (100°)	HD (77°)	HD (4°)
$(NH_4)_2UO_2(CO_3)_2$	—	—	0.3	—	—	—	—	—	—	—
$UO_2(CH_3COO)_2$	—	—	—	—	1.95	3.55	—	2.6	10.1	17.8
$UO_2(CH_3COO)_3Na$	—	—	—	—	—	0.57	—	—	10.6	17.8
$UO_2(CH_3COO)_3Rb$	—	—	—	—	—	2.42, 21.2	—	—	11.7	15.2
$UO_2(CH_3COO)_3Cs$	—	—	—	—	—	2, 0.3	—	—	5.4, 1.1	14.9, 1.8
$(UO_2)_2(CH_3COO)_6Zn.7H_2O$	—	—	—	—	—	—	—	—	—	—
$UO_2(CH_3COO)_4Cd.6H_2O$	—	—	—	—	—	2.16	—	—	2.90	17.3, 1.8
Uranium glass‡	4.45	3.2–3.9	2.8–3.2§	—	—	—	—	—	—	—

Key: Heading indicates Kelvin temperature at which measurement was made.
Two values separated by comma indicate components for a two-term decay.
Two values separated by dash indicate range of values.

NH: Nichols and Howes, calculated by Vavilov and Levshin.
PD: Perrin and Delorme.
VL: Vavilov and Levshin.

RW: Randall and Wilkins.
GHG: Gobrecht, Hahn and Gretzinger.
HD: Hall and Dieke.

* Another numerical example in Nichols and Howes' monograph gave $\tau = 0.44 \times 10^{-4}$ sec.

† Other samples prepared from enriched Cl^{35}, Cl^{37}, or O^{18} gave slightly different values (up to 25 per cent different); this is natural variation from specimen to specimen rather than an isotope effect.

‡ A further decay is superimposed. Levshin and Sheremetjev (1947) found later, by photographic methods, $\tau = (2.7 \pm 0.2) \times 10^{-4}$ sec.

§ Sevchenko (1944) found values between 3.2 and 11 for a series of different composition

1×10^{-4} sec), his observation was subsequently found to be erroneous (Levshin and Sheremetjev, 1947).

The decay constant measurements by Vavilov and Levshin are shown in Table 3.1.

The shape of the decay curves found by Vavilov and Levshin for uranyl *sulfate* suggested that a second decay period, with $\tau = 0.8 \times 10^{-4}$ sec, is superimposed on the main decay period (2.6×10^{-4} sec). Similarly, the 3.2×10^{-4} sec decay period of "uranium glass 1" was

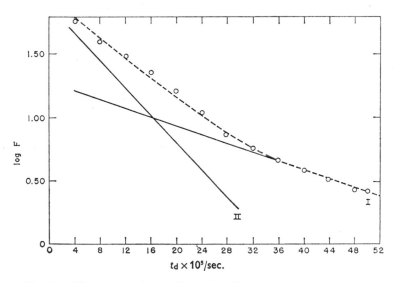

FIG. 3.4. Fluorescence decay of uranyl sulfate excited with ultraviolet light. Empirical decay data ($\bigcirc$) interpreted as superposition (— —) of two logarithmic decay curves, $\tau = 2.6 \times 10^{-4}$ sec (curve I) and $\tau = 8 \times 10^{-5}$ sec (curve II). From Vavilov and Levshin, (1928).

combined with a second decay period of 0.5×10^{-4} sec. This shorter-lived fluorescence was particularly strongly excited by far ultraviolet light (Fig. 3.4) and was absent in fluorescence excited by visible (blue) light.

Nichols and Howes' data on cathode ray-excited fluorescence indicated a very slow decay, following a complex course (cf. above, p. 194); Vavilov and Levshin suggested that this phenomenon may be similar to long-lasting *triboluminescence*, which can be observed when uranyl salt crystals are broken by a hammer.

Vavilov and Levshin found no evidence of the extremely short-lived fluorescence described by Gaviola. The same conclusion was reached by Perrin and Delorme (1928, 1929).

Contrary to Vavilov and co-workers, Perrin and Delorme interpreted the long-lived emission of uranyl salts correctly as "fluorescence of long duration." Their phosphoroscopic measurements gave, for solid uranyl salts, the values of τ listed in the second column of Table 3.1. They found that the decay required up to $2\frac{1}{2}$ times as much time in liquid air as at room temperature. This indicates that the actual lifetime of the fluorescent state is limited, or at least "co-limited," by a non-radiative energy dissipation process (i.e. that k_d in Equation (3) is *not* zero); the rate of such processes can be expected to increase with temperature.

In uranyl compounds in which fluorescence was very weak, its lifetime was distinctly shorter than in strongly fluorescent salts, but no exact proportionality, or even consistent parallelism, was observed between the lifetime for emission, τ, and the initial intensity of emission, F_0. For example, uranyl sulfate was found to fluoresce stronger than nitrate, but its fluorescence decayed faster. (Below we will quote examples of a parallelism of τ and F_0.)

Hein and Retter (1928) were concerned only with the practical problem of analytical determination of various elements by their fluorescence, and gave figures for the minimum concentration of uranyl sulfate in a powder mixture at which the uranyl fluorescence (in the light of a quartz mercury lamp) is recognizable to the eye: 1 g UO_2SO_4 in 80–100 g CuO, 25–30 g Cr_2O_3, in 2–3 g Fe_2O_3, 5–8 g HgO, or 50–70 g azobenzene.

Anderson and Bird (1928) investigated the possibility of using the fluorescence of uranium glass (as well as that of esculin or fluorescein) for measuring the relative intensities of visible fluorescence excited by various mercury lines in the ultraviolet (253.7–366 mμ), with the relative intensities of the same lines, measured by means of a thermopile. They found the two sets of values to be proportional to each other, showing that fluorescence can serve as a measure of the intensity of exciting light. [The observed proportionality *can* be considered as proof of two things: (*a*) complete absorption of exciting light, at all wavelengths used, in a thin layer of the fluorescent material; and (*b*) identical quantum yield of fluorescence at all these wavelengths.]

Gurevich and Chakhrov (1936) made a direct determination of the absolute yield of fluorescence of solid uranyl potassium sulfate [it probably was $K_2UO_2(SO_4)_2.2H_2O$]. The method used was, however, rather inexact, since it involved visual photometry of colored light. Fluorescence was excited by filtered light from a carbon arc; the exciting band was assumed to be 325–410 mμ, with a maximum of 370 mμ. It fell on a screen covered with potassium uranyl sulfate powder, and the intensity of fluorescence was measured by a visual photometer, while the intensity of exciting light was measured simultaneously by a thermoelement. The fluorescent light was reduced in intensity and changed in color by a "pink" filter (which transmitted only about 3 per cent), to permit convenient visual comparison with white light from a sheet of magnesium; the thermoelement was calibrated by a tungsten band lamp. The absorption of the exciting light in the fluorescent screen was determined by means of the same visual photometer. In this way a quantum yield of about 1.1 (quanta emitted per quantum absorbed), corresponding to an energy yield of 80 per cent (ergs emitted per erg absorbed), was calculated. Not much significance can be attached to this result in view of the crudeness of the method used, except that it indicates that the yield of fluorescence of solid potassium-uranyl sulfate is rather high.

Sevchenko (1944) investigated the *polarization of fluorescence in uranium glass*. Gaviola and Vavilov had found in this case no polarization at all, while Perrin (cf. above) had observed a polarization of up to 10 per cent. Sevchenko showed that the degree of polarization depends on the specific composition of the glass and on the wavelength of exciting light; furthermore, it changes as fluorescence decays.

Basic glasses containing uranates do not fluoresce at all. Acid glasses, which can be presumed to contain uranyl ions, fluoresce with more or less strongly polarized light, depending on the anions present. The glasses studied contained 1 per cent uranium in a boron, boron-silica, basic silica, or phosphate glass.

Excitation with the light of the ordinary quartz mercury lamp (centered around 365 mμ) gives the weakest polarization. Using a nickel arc and a monochromator, Sevchenko plotted the degree of polarization as a function of the wavelength of the exciting light. In $BaO.P_2O_5$ glass the polarization was lowest (about 10 per cent), and practically constant between 240 and 500 mμ. In acid glass (K$_2$O.7B$_2$O$_3$.10SiO$_2$) the polarization varied between 15 and 25 per cent and showed three maxima: at 240–250, 330–340, and 400–420 mμ. The same three maxima also occurred, although less pronouncedly, in other silica glass.

The degree of polarization decreased with time after excitation; this is plausible, since the ions which emit later have more time to change their orientation in the crystal. The degree of polarization and the half-time of decay were independent of the uranyl concentration in glass between 4×10^{-6} g/ml and 2×10^{-3} g/ml, showing that, in this concentration region, resonance exchange of excitation energy between ions is unimportant. The total yield of fluorescence, L, was found to be proportional to the lifetime, as it should be if the initial intensity, F_0, is the same for all glasses [cf. Equations (16), (16a), etc., where α^* is inversely proportional to τ]. Values of the actual lifetime, τ, between 0.32×10^{-3} and 1.1×10^{-3} sec were found by Sevchenko for the different glasses studied (cf. footnote to Table 3.1).

At 4×10^{-3} g/ml of [UO$_2^{++}$], polarization declined markedly (e.g. from 13 to 10 per cent), and the yield became lower (e.g. 35 instead of 43 rel. units). This may perhaps be taken as evidence of incipient resonance exchange between adjacent uranyl ions.

Sevchenko discussed whether the uranyl emission is a dipole or a quadrupole radiation. Low intensity and long duration of fluorescence suggest a quadrupole radiation. On the other hand, Vavilov's criterion of polarization indicated dipole nature. (This argument is based on comparison of uranyl glass fluorescence with fluorescence of dyestuffs in aqueous glycerol, whose dipole character is certain. In both cases, measurements of the degree of polarization as a function of angle between the electric vector of incoming light and the direction of observation gave the same maximum—about 12.5 per cent.)

Randall and Wilkins (1945) studied the photoluminescence of various solids in relation to their *photoconductivity*. Theoretically, photoconductivity is expected when light absorption liberates an electron from its atom and transfers it into a "conductivity band." An external electric field affects the motion of the electrons in the conductivity band and thus causes an electric current to flow during illumination. In uranyl salts no photoconductivity was found, confirming that the excited electron remains within the attraction sphere of its original atom (or, rather, of the triatomic group UO_2^{++}). This, too, is in agreement with the interpretation of the luminescence of uranyl salts as true fluorescence.

Figure 3.5 shows the growth and decay curve of ammonium uranyl phosphate fluorescence, excited by constant ultraviolet light, as registered by an oscilloscope. It will be noted that in this case the rate of decay appears the same at 90° and 300°K, indicating no temperature-dependent dissipation processes co-limiting the lifetime of the excited state and thus pointing to a fluorescence yield close to unity.

FIG. 3.5. Rise and decay of fluorescence in solid ammonium uranyl phosphate. Above, 90°K; below, 300°K. From Randall and Wilkins, (1945).

No time scale is given for this curve, but in phosphoroscopic measurements of Randall and Wilkins (made by means of a photo-cell rather than by visual comparison, as in the experiments from Vavilov's and Perrin's laboratories) the mean lifetime of fluorescence was found to be 1.42×10^{-3} sec for the ammonium uranyl double phosphate; for uranyl nitrate it was 7.19×10^{-4} sec (cf. Table 3.1). The precision with which the decay follows the exponential law is illustrated by Fig. 3.6. This figure also shows that the rate constant of decay is unaffected by a tenfold change in the intensity of exciting light, a result which is to be expected if both fluorescence and radiationless deactivation are monomolecular processes.

Levshin and Sheremetjev (1947) reinvestigated some topics not satisfactorily clarified in the study of Vavilov and Levshin (1928). In the first place they analyzed the apparent delay in the beginning of fluorescent emission, mentioned on p. 196. They found an (at least qualitatively) satisfactory explanation of this delay in the gradual approach of fluorescence intensity to its stationary peak value (cf. Equation 11). As shown in Section 1, the illumination time required to reach the stationary concentration of the excited atoms or molecules is greater the longer the lifetime of the latter (t_f must be $\gg 1/\alpha^* = \tau$). With such slow emitters as uranyl ions ($\tau = 5 \times 10^{-4}$ sec), fluorescence grows so slowly as to produce the

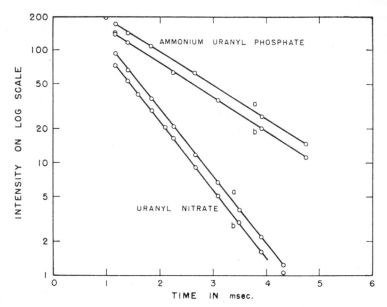

FIG. 3.6. Uranyl salt fluorescence decay curves. The exciting intensity for curves a is ten times that for curves b. Ammonium uranyl phosphate, $\alpha^* = 703$ sec^{-1}. Uranyl nitrate, $\alpha^* = 1390$ sec^{-1}. From Randall and Wilkins, (1945).

impression that it does not begin at all until 10^{-4} sec after the start of illumination. By experiments of higher precision, Levshin and Sheremetjev showed that if the beginning of uranyl fluorescence lags behind absorption at all, the lag is shorter than 3×10^{-6} sec.

Another point studied by Levshin and Sheremetjev was whether the spectral distribution of uranyl sulfate fluorescence changes in the course of its decay. Comparison of spectrophotograms made at the beginning of decay ($1-2 \times 10^{-5}$ sec after cessation of illumination) with those taken 8×10^{-4} sec later (when the intensity of fluorescence has decreased by a factor of 28) showed no difference (outside the limits of experimental error) in the relative intensity of the seven main bands, originating in the non-vibrating excited state, and of the eighth, short-wave band originating in the state with one quantum of symmetric bond vibration (cf. Chapter 1). Also no significant change was noticeable in the energy distribution within each of the eight bands. These results indicate that the thermal equilibrium distribution of excited molecules over their vibrational levels is achieved, at room temperature, within a time that is short compared to the decay time of fluorescence so that this distribution already is present, to all practical purposes, when fluorescence first becomes observable, and is maintained throughout the emission. If the fluorescence decay constants of the different vibrational states are different—which is likely—the distribution of excited molecules over these levels must be maintained during the emission by exchange of vibrational quanta in collisons. This applies to the relatively large quanta of the bond vibrations ν_s and ν_a, as well as to the smaller quanta of molecular and lattice vibrations, which determine the intensity distribution in the individual bands.

The uranyl sulfate preparation on which the decay measurements were made had a "doublet type" fluorescence spectrum; according to Chapter 1 (p. 73), it must have consisted of two types of trihydrate crystals. The relative intensity of the two doublet components also did not change during the decay, showing that the transition probabilities are not significantly different in the two types of crystals.

Levshin and Sheremetjev also measured (by photographic comparison) the relative intensity of the total fluorescence of uranyl sulfate preparations as function of water content. Table 3.2 shows the results. The anhydrous crystals are non-fluorescent, the monohydrates but weakly fluorescent. It was mentioned in Chapter 1, p. 72, that the bands of preparation I became double on drying to dihydrate and even more strongly so on conversion to monohydrate, indicating partial recrystallization to forms derivable from form II of the trihydrate.

A photographic redetermination of the decay constant of the fluorescence (determination of time needed to decrease fluorescence intensity by a factor of 4) by Levshin and Sheremetjev gave

TABLE 3.2. TOTAL INTENSITY OF FLUORESCENCE OF URANYL SULFATE
CRYSTALS IN RELATION TO WATER CONTENT

Preparation (cf. p. 72)	$UO_2SO_4.3H_2O$		$UO_2SO_4.2H_2O$	$UO_2SO_4.H_2O$	UO_2SO_4
	Non-dried	Dried at 18°C			
I+II (doublet bands)	100	91	35	1	0
I (single bands)	75	43	38	9	0

$\tau = (2.7 \pm 0.2) \times 10^{-4}$ sec, in good agreement with the earlier determinations (Table 3.1).

Temperature dependence of the luminescence, particularly of its quantum yield, has been studied by Gobrecht, Hahn, and Gretzinger (1954). They studied uranyl ammonium fluoride, uranyl perchlorate, uranyl nitrate, and uranyl acetate crystals from $-180°C$ to $+120°C$. They found no dependence of quantum yield upon excitation intensity over this entire temperature range; furthermore, they found the decay to be simple exponential at all temperatures. Some of their results are reproduced in Figs. 3.6a and b.

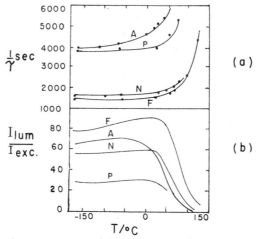

FIG. 3.6a. Decay constants of the fluorescence for uranyl acetate (A), perchlorate (P), nitrate (N), and ammonium fluoride (F) as functions of temperature. After Gobrecht, Hahn and Gretzinger (1954).

FIG. 3.6b. Quantum yield of same salts as functions of temperature. After Gobrecht, Hahn and Gretzinger (1954).

Hall and Dieke (1957) made an extensive study of fluorescence time constants and quantum yields of several uranyl double salts in powder form at room temperature, liquid nitrogen temperature, and liquid helium temperature. Their time constants are listed in Table 3.1 and their yield data in Table 3.2a, together with similar data of Sevchenko (1951). Most of the salts showed simple exponential fluorescence decay, but a few, including all the chlorides, had a second, faster decay superimposed on it. The major component covered the range from 0.05 to 1 msec at room temperature; with the notable exception of the two sulfates, all salts had lifetimes near 2 msec at 4°K.

TABLE 3.2a. FLUORESCENCE YIELDS AND DECAY TIMES OF
URANYL SALTS

Samples	τ_{77}/τ_{293}	τ_4/τ_{77}	L_{77}/L_{293}	$L_{77}\tau_{293}/L_{293}\tau_{77}$
$RbUO_2(CH_3COO)_3$	18.6	1.68	17.2	0.925
$UO_2(CH_3COO)_2.2H_2O$	1.24	—	1.0	0.807
$UO_2(NO_3)_2.6H_2O$	1.15	—	1.14	0.992
$NH_4UO_2(NO_3)_3$	2.32	1.85	1.11	0.478
$K_2UO_2(NO_3)_4$	1.63	1.17	0.775	0.475
$RbUO_2(NO_3)_3$	2.93	1.08	1.25	0.427
$CsUO_2(NO_3)_3$	2.76	1.46	1.4	0.51
$UO_2Cl_2.3H_2O$	2.2	—	2.14	0.973
$UO_2Br_2.7H_2O$			$\gg 2$	
$(UO_2)_3(PO_4)_2.nH_2O$	1.06	—	1.0	0.94
$UO_2(SO_4)_2.3H_2O$	1.04	—	1.02	0.98
$K_2UO_2(SO_4)_2.2H_2O$	1.01	—	1.02	1.01
$(NH_4)_2UO_2(SO_4)_2$	1.16	1.48	1.08	0.931
$Rb_2UO_2(SO_4)_2$	0.94	1.00	1.11	1.18

τ = Mean observed lifetime of fluorescence.
L = Fluorescence intensity for fixed quantity of absorbed exciting radiation.
All data given for hydrates were reported by Sevchenko (1951); all others by Hall and Dieke (1957).

Previously, transition probabilities in the absorption spectra had been measured, as well as relative fluorescence intensities for the strong lines of $CsUO_2(NO_3)_3$ (Dieke and Duncan, 1949). With a minor allowance (6 per cent of resonance line) for unmeasured intensity in very weak bands, Hall and Dieke estimated the entire fluorescence spectrum to be 100 times as strong as the resonance line. This, together with the transition probability for resonance line absorption, allowed them to estimate the natural radiative lifetime as $\tau_0 \approx 2.7$ msec (see Equation 4). This figure is in excellent agreement with the observed lifetimes for almost all the salts at 4°K. Hall and Dieke concluded that at this temperature virtually all of the absorbed light is re-emitted as fluorescence.

At high temperatures, excitation energy can be rapidly dissipated as lattice vibrations. For many of the salts studied by Hall and Dieke it was evident that at room temperature the lattice-ion relaxation time dictates the fluorescence lifetime. They cited the case of rubidium uranyl acetate at 293°K, for which $\tau_0(4°K) = 1.78$ msec, $\tau(293°K) = 0.0570$ msec, giving τ_r(relaxation time at 293°K) = 0.0589 msec.

The sulfates studied by Hall and Dieke had unusually short fluorescence lifetimes at 4°K, and in one—$Rb_2UO_2(SO_4)_2$—no change was seen from 4 to 293°K. It is possible that these sulfates have smaller natural lifetimes than the other salts.

Any loss of excitation energy by lattice interaction should be reflected in the fluorescence quantum yield as well as in the lifetime (i.e. L/τ should be a constant for a given sample absorbing the same amount of radiation at different temperatures). If this were strictly true, all the entries in the last column of Table 3.2a should be 1. Only meager data is available, but these divide into two groups: one containing the acetates and sulfates, which nearly obey the rule (though only the acetate values are very meaningful), and one containing the double nitrates, in which fluorescence yields increase only half as rapidly as their lifetimes. The reason is not clear. Hall and Dieke suggest that about half the excitation energy of the uranyl group might go by resonance transfer into a nitrate oscillation which happens to have nearly the same frequency as one of the uranyl vibrations, and that this oscillation may be long-lived but non-radiative; at high temperatures the uranyl and nitrate frequencies will interact so strongly that this energy is rapidly fed back into the radiative mode. More experiments are needed.

Stepanov (1951) attempted a theoretical discussion of line widths in the fluorescence of uranyl salts. He assumed that the line breadth must be related to the lifetime of an appropriate process by the Heisenberg uncertainty relationship, $\Delta\nu\Delta t = 1$. He considered five such processes: (1) fluorescence, (2) conversion of uranyl excitation energy to lattice vibrations, (3) conversion of complex vibration to lattice vibrations, (4) redistribution or propagation of local vibration energy through the lattice, and (5) intermolecular transfer of the excitation energy to other UO_2^{++} ions. He concluded that only process (4) was sufficiently fast to account for line widths in the neighborhood of 100 cm^{-1} seen at room temperature. Although his argument on this point is not compelling (must this be an "uncertainty broadening" at all?), his reasoning that the line breadths cannot be accounted for on the basis of perfectly isolated UO_2^{++} ions can be accepted.

3. Intensity and Decay of Uranyl Fluorescence in Solutions

F. Perrin (1926) first measured the duration of fluorescence of uranyl salt *solutions* and compared it with that of crystals. The former he found to be much shorter; he pointed out that this does not mean that the one is a "fluorescence" and the other a "phosphorescence," as both can be due to the same mechanism and even have the same *intrinsic* decay constants, $\alpha\epsilon$. According to Equation (2), this is possible if the *radiationless* decay constant, k_d, is higher for the liquid than for the solid state, thus increasing the *total* decay constant, α^*.

The total light emission and the initial intensity of emission after a flash must be affected in the same proportion as the duration. This relationship was first suggested by Perrin; it follows from the exponential decay law, since for an exponential function $F = F_0 e^{-\alpha t_d}$, the value of F at any given time and its integral between two given times are inversely proportional to the "decay constant," α. Perrin found that, among different uranyl salt solutions, the strongest and longest afterglow is exhibited by uranyl sulfate dissolved in concentrated sulfuric acid. Although the viscosity of sulfuric acid is only 20 times that of water, and thus much less than that of a "rigid" solvent, the lifetime of fluorescence in this solvent is as long as 5×10^{-4} sec, or one-fourth of that in solid uranyl sulfate. Perrin concluded that rigidity is not a necessary condition for long-lived luminescence, as has been often asserted before. The occurrence of long-lived luminescence of uranyl sulfate solution in sulfuric acid was one of the reasons that caused Perrin to interpret the luminescence of uranyl ions as "fluorescence of long duration" rather than phosphorescence (p. 196). Perrin realized that according to the quantum theory of light absorption, this hypothesis is only permissible if the absorption bands are very weak and he was uncertain whether the uranyl absorption bands actually *are* sufficiently weak to permit a lifetime of the order of 10^{-4} or 10^{-3} sec. Subsequent measurements of the intensity of absorption have confirmed that this is in fact the case.

TABLE 3.3. LIFETIME OF FLUORESCENCE OF UO_2SO_4 SOLUTIONS
After Perrin and Delorme (1928)

UO_2SO_4 in conc. H_2SO_4	$\tau \times 10^4$ (sec)		
	28°C	17°C	1°C
7.2×10^{-3} g in 1 ml	1.25	1.4	2.0
7.2×10^{-2} g in 1 ml	—	1.0	—
7.2×10^{-1} g in 1 ml	—	0.9	—

Perrin and Delorme (1928) gave experimental values for the lifetime of fluorescence in uranyl sulfate solutions, listed in Table 3.3. According to Table 3.3, the lifetime decreases with temperature and uranyl concentration. (The total yield of fluorescence after a flash should change in the same way.) This indicates that the rate is affected by deactivation ("quenching") processes and deactivation is accelerated by an increase in the concentration of UO_2^{2+} ions (for explanation, see below, Section 4).

Dilution of sulfuric acid with water also had a quenching effect (e.g. τ declined to 0.55×10^{-4} sec when sulfuric acid was diluted by 30 vol. per cent water).

In a second paper, Perrin and Delorme (1929) noted that the duration of fluorescence is very sensitive to small impurities, such as halogen ions, or certain organic substances. One part HCl in 30,000 parts of water reduced L and τ by 50 per cent.

Perrin and Delorme also measured the fluorescence of uranyl phosphate in metaphosphoric acid, to observe the effect of changes in viscosity. Table 3.4 gives the results.

Gaviola (1927) and Gaviola and Pringsheim (1927) used a fast Kerr-effect fluorometer (cf. p. 195) for the determination of the rate of decay of fluorescence of uranyl sulfate solutions, and found very low τ values: 1.9×10^{-9} sec for a solution in concentrated sulfuric acid, and 1.3×10^{-9} sec for a solution in methanol. As mentioned previously, the existence of such a fast-decaying uranyl fluorescence (in addition to the slow-decaying fluorescence with a lifetime of 10^{-4} to 10^{-3} sec) is very doubtful.

Independently of Perrin and co-workers, Vavilov and Levshin (1927, 1928) also noticed the comparatively long life and high intensity of uranyl sulfate fluorescence in concentrated sulfuric acid, and proceeded to study this phenomenon under a great variety of conditions.

TABLE 3.4. VISCOSITY AND LIFETIME OF URANYL FLUORESCENCE
After Perrin and Delorme (1929)

η (approx.) (cgs units)	$\tau \times 10^4$/sec
0.02	0.9
1.4	1.0
100	2.3
20,000	3.8
Paste	5.6
Glass	7.0
(pure acid)	

Since they considered the luminescence of solid uranyl compounds as a "phosphorescence" (cf. above, p. 197), they were astonished to find that the same phenomenon can be observed, with the same slow decay, also in solutions. (No "phosphorescence" was supposed at that time to occur in liquids.) They therefore made many tests to convince themselves that the systems studied were true solutions, and not colloidal suspensions.

Vavilov and Levshin measured the dependence of the decay constant, α^*, on the concentration $[UO_2SO_4]$ (Table 3.5). At all three concentrations used, the decay followed the exponential law (Fig. 3.7).

In Table 3.5, τ and L (the integrated intensity of fluorescence after "practically instantaneous" excitation by a spark) were measured directly, while F_0, the *inital intensity* of fluorescence, was calculated. In the range studied, F_0 turned out to be practically independent of concentration, as expected (cf. Equation 12), when

TABLE 3.5. FLUORESCENCE DECAY CONSTANTS OF URANYL SULFATE
IN CONCENTRATED SULPHURIC ACID*
After Vavilov and Levshin

$[UO_2SO_4]$ (g/ml)	$\tau \times 10^4$ (sec)	$L = \int_0^\infty F dt$	$F_0 = L/\tau$
0.74	0.47	0.6	1.28
0.35	0.89	1.14	1.28
0.14	1.27	1.44	1.13

* All uranyl concentrations used sufficiently high for practically complete absorption.

practically no deactivation by radiation has time to occur during the excitation period. (In other words, excitation is interrupted when the concentration of the excited ions still grows proportionally with time.) With longer excitation periods, the final steady concentration of excited ions will depend on the strength of the uranyl

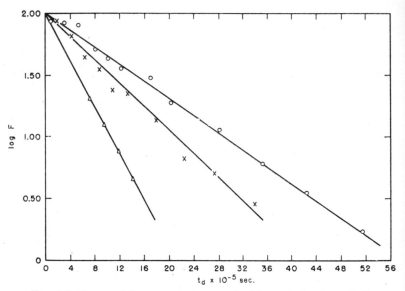

FIG. 3.7. Decay of fluorescence in uranyl sulfate solution in sulfuric acid. Three concentrations: 0.74 g/ml (triangles), $\tau = 4.7 \times 10^{-5}$ sec; 0.35 g/ml (crosses), $\tau = 8.9 \times 10^{-5}$ sec; 0.14 g/ml (circles), $\tau = 12.7 \times 10^{-5}$ sec. From Vavilov and Levshin, (1928).

solution, since the rate constant of deactivation, k_d, and with it the constant α^* ($= a\epsilon + k_d$), is increased by rise in concentration ("self-quenching").

The initial intensity, F_0, also proved to be independent of temperature in the region between 18.5 and 67°C; the explanation must be the same as in the case of variations in concentration (no measurable dissipation during the flash). On the other hand, the decay of fluorescence is accelerated by increasing temperature, and the integral yield of fluorescence is consequently decreased (Table 3.6).

TABLE 3.6. EFFECT OF TEMPERATURE ON URANYL SULFATE
FLUORESCENCE IN SULFURIC ACID SOLUTION

$t°C$	$\tau \times 10^4$ (sec)	L	$F_0 = L/\tau$
18.5	1.08	3.9	3.6
27	0.81	3.1	3.8
45	0.58	2.0	3.4
52	0.46	1.6	3.5
67	0.33	1.1	3.3

$\tau = 1/\alpha^* =$ decay time; $L =$ integrated intensity

The reason for accelerated dissipation of electronic energy at higher temperatures is (according to Franck) that the internal conversion of electronic into vibrational energy requires the co-operation of thermal agitation to bring the electronically excited molecule into a configuration identical with that of a strongly vibrating molecule in the ground state. The effect of uranyl salt concentration and temperature on the yield of fluorescence is illustrated by Fig. 3.8.

Aqueous solutions of UO_2SO_4 and $UO_2(NO_3)_2$ fluoresce too weakly for exact measurements of the mean lifetime; τ is, in any case, *shorter than* 10^{-5} *sec*. No fluorescence at all could be noticed in glycerol, alchol, and several other solvents.

UO_2^{++} solutions in ($H_2SO_4 + H_2O$) mixtures showed an increase of τ with increasing concentration of the acid (Table 3.7).

The considerable difference between the fluorescence constants in the solid state and in fluid solution naturally leads to consideration of the effect that *viscosity* may have on the yield and the rate of

TABLE 3.7. FLUORESCENCE DECAY OF URANYL IONS IN SULFURIC ACID OF
DIFFERENT CONCENTRATIONS AT 18°C
$c =$ g UO_2SO_4 in 1 ml solvent

Solvent: Aqueous sulfuric acid	$c = 5 \times 10^{-3}$	$c = 5 \times 10^{-1}$
90% H_2SO_4	1.6×10^{-4} sec	0.65×10^{-4} sec
75% H_2SO_4	1.4×10^{-4} sec	...
50% H_2SO_4	1.1×10^{-4} sec	0.20×10^{-4} sec
25% H_2SO_4	0.25×10^{-4} sec	...
0% H_2SO_4	$< 0.1 \times 10^{-4}$ sec	...

decay of fluorescence. The higher yield and slower decay in concentrated sulfuric acid, compared to pure water, as well as the enhancing effect of lower temperature, can be interpreted, at least in
part, as consequences of increased viscosity.

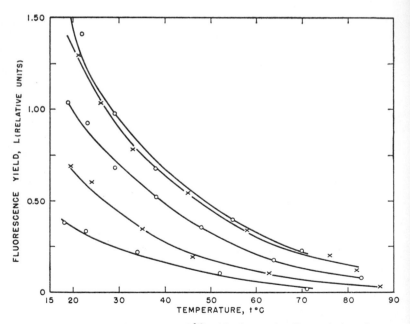

FIG. 3.8. Yield of fluorescence ($\int_0^\infty F dt$) of uranyl sulfate solutions in
sulfuric acid as function of temperature. Five concentrations (reading
from top to bottom curve): 0.1, 0.22, 0.40, 0.67, 1.0 g/ml. From
Vavilov and Levshin, (1928).

To investigate this possibility, Vavilov and Levshin re-plotted the data obtained by varying the temperature at a constant value of the concentration $[UO_2^{++}]$ as function of viscosity. (For this purpose the viscosity of solutions of uranyl sulfate had first to be determined for different concentrations and temperatures.) Figure 3.9 shows the resulting plot. The total yield of fluorescence, L, at a given concentration appears to be directly proportional to viscosity, the points obtained at different temperatures falling on the same straight lines. This can be taken as indication that the temperature effect is due entirely to changes in viscosity.

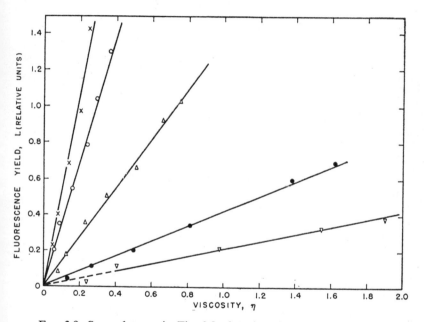

FIG. 3.9. Same data as in Fig. 3.8 plotted against viscosity. From Vavilov and Levshin, (1928).

Of course, the lines in Fig. 3.9 representing L as function of η cannot remain linear indefinitely since they must approach a finite limit for $\eta = \infty$. This is confirmed by figures in Table 3.8. At very low viscosities, too, L approaches a certain constant value and does not tend to become zero.

The effect of changing concentration can be calculated from these data, for constant temperature (and changing viscosity), or for constant viscosity (and changing temperature). The results are represented in Fig. 3.10.

TABLE 3.8. FLUORESCENCE YIELD AS FUNCTION OF VISCOSITY AT CONSTANT CONCENTRATION OF URANYL SULFATE

$t°C$	103	83	63	47	35	26	14
η	0.043	0.058	0.067	0.095	0.135	0.170	0.250
L	0.030	0.78	1.28	2.02	2.60	3.45	4.5

$t°C$	7	4	−1	−2	−6	−9	
η	0.350	0.375	0.425	0.485	0.580	0.625	
L	5.6	6.0	6.5	7.0	7.2	7.8	

TABLE 3.9. TOTAL ABSOLUTE FLUORESCENCE YIELD AS FUNCTION OF CONCENTRATION OF URANYL SULFATE

$[UO_2SO_4]$ (mg/ml)	L	$[UO_2SO_4]$ (mg/ml)	L
0.93	0.28	0.096	0.81
1.7	0.26	0.166	0.73
3.0	0.26	0.23	0.59
5.8	0.23	0.333	0.47
14.0	0.22	0.47	0.42
36	0.21	0.595	0.40
79	0.21	0.695	0.35
147	0.21	0.77	0.31
265	0.19	1.00	0.25
365	0.17		
700	0.10		

A separate set of measurements was made at *low uranyl sulfate concentrations*, from 9×10^{-5} g/ml to 1×10^{-3} g/ml. (In the previously described measurements, the concentration was so high that the absorption of the exciting light could be assumed to be complete, independently of the uranyl salt concentration.) In the low concentration region, absorption could be assumed to be proportional to concentration. Table 3.9 shows the absolute yield of fluorescence,

L, in relation to concentration, in this region. The last measurements in set 1 are affected by changing viscosity and by a deviation of absorption from proportionality with concentration.

The *yield* (quantum yield) of the fluorescence of uranyl sulfate solution in sulfuric acid was estimated by Vavilov and Levshin, for a solution containing 10^{-2} g/ml (complete absorption!) at $+10°C$,

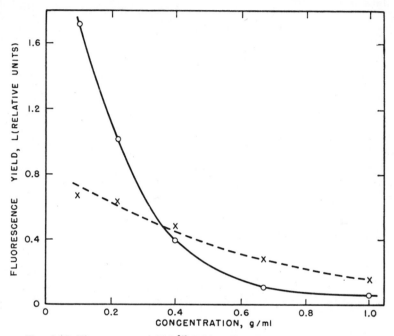

FIG. 3.10. Fluorescence yield ($\int_0^\infty F\,dt$) as function of concentration at constant viscosity, $\eta \simeq 0.3$ (solid line) and at constant temperature, 40° (dashed line). From Vavilov and Levshin (1928).

by comparing it with that of a fluorescein solution excited by the same wavelength (435 mμ). (The emission peaks are at 520 mμ in fluorescein, and at 530 mμ in uranyl sulfate.) For fluorescein, a yield of 80 per cent was found previously; for the uranyl sulfate solution, a value of about 25 per cent ($\phi = 0.25$) was estimated by comparison. Since the yield at 5°C is about one-fourth of the maximum yield (observed at liquid air temperature), the latter must be close to 100 per cent.

Vavilov and Levshin calculated fluorescence yield isothermals (similar to those given in Fig. 3.10 for concentrated uranyl sulfate solutions) for the dilute solutions also. In Fig. 3.11, the 53°C isothermal shows no dependence on concentration at all; the 18°C isothermal and the curve showing fluorescence as function of $[UO_2^{2+}]$ at constant *viscosity* (instead of temperature) are similar to those in Fig. 3.10.

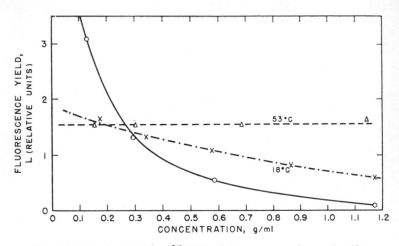

FIG. 3.11. Total yield ($L = \int_0^\infty F\,dt$) of fluorescence of uranyl sulfate solutions in water as function of concentration at constant temperature, 18° and 53°C (dashed lines) and constant viscosity (solid line). From Vavilov and Levshin (1928).

In uranyl *nitrate* solutions, isothermals ($L = f[UO_2^{2+}]$ at $t =$ const.) were horizontal even at room temperature.

Plotting the fluorescence data for dilute uranyl sulfate solutions in sulfuric acid as function of viscosity (by proper combination of temperature and concentration) again gave straight lines (Fig. 3.12).

Figure 3.13 shows a similar plot for four different uranyl salts. The curves for nitrate, sulfate, and carbonate extrapolate linearly to the same limiting value of viscosity, $\eta \simeq 0.005$, which would give $L = 0$ if the curves did not bend at low viscosities. The acetate line is curved in the opposite sense, probably because of photochemical decomposition.

The uranyl nitrate fluorescence in *nitric acid* is about as intense as in water. (The viscosities of the two solutions are similar.)

No polarization could be detected in the fluorescence of uranyl sulfate solution at various stages of decay, not even in very dilute uranyl solution in pure sulfuric acid at liquid air temperature.

Vavilov and Levshin also described experiments (made by Trapeznikov) showing that the luminescence of uranyl salts can be excited by X-rays. The decay period is $< 10^{-3}$ sec, the emission being invisible in Vavilov's phosphoroscope.

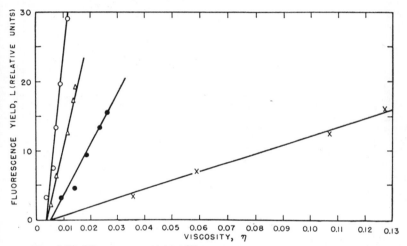

FIG. 3.12. Fluorescence yield ($\int_0^\infty F\,dt$) of uranyl sulfate solutions in water as function of viscosity. Four concentrations, counting from above: 0.13, 0.256, 0.571 and 1.15 g/ml. From Vavilov and Levshin (1928).

Vavilov and Levshin considered their experiments as establishing the luminescence of uranyl salts as a *phosphorescence*, involving a *metastable* state. They surmised that this state may be an electronic state produced by collisions of excited uranyl ions with the medium. (The monomolecular decay law excluded transient *dissociation* or *ionization* as explanation of the metastable state.) Without sufficient reason, Vavilov and Levshin rejected as "implausible" the attribution of the long-lived emission to the longevity of the original excited state itself; we have seen above that this interpretation (which we now know to be correct) was supplied by Perrin.

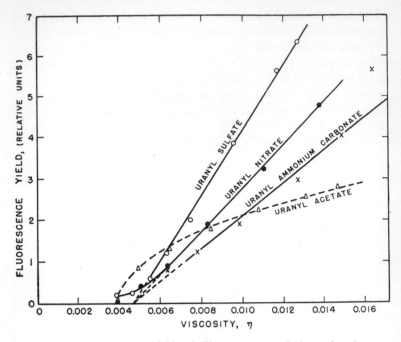

Fig. 3.13. Fluorescence yields of dilute aqueous solutions of various uranyl salts as function of viscosity. From Vavilov and Levshin (1928).

Vavilov and Levshin derived equations for the influence of concentration on uranyl fluorescence. They attributed it to deactivating encounters between normal and excited uranyl ions: $UO_2^{++*} + UO_2^{++} \rightarrow 2UO_2^{++}$.

The average interval between two such encounters (and also the average time between excitation and the first encounter) must be inversely proportional to the diffusion coefficient, and thus directly proportional to the coefficient of viscosity:

$$\tau' = \frac{C\eta}{[UO_2^{++}]} \tag{27}$$

when C is a constant. (This equation can be expected to be most satisfactory for *high* η values and low $[UO_2^{++}]$ values.) Its validity was analysed in a subsequent paper by Vavilov (1928).

The probability that an excited molecule will suffer a quenching collision between the times t_d and $t_d + dt$ is $(e^{-t_d/\tau'})dt/\tau'$; the integral of this probability from 0 to t_d is $(1 - e^{-t_d/\tau'})$; the probability of survival after this time, $e^{-t_d/\tau'}$. Without quenching, we would have:

$$F_{t_d} = F_0 e^{-t_d/\tau_0} \tag{28}$$

while with quenching we have

$$F_{t_d} = F_0 e^{-t_d \left(\frac{1}{\tau_0} - \frac{1}{\tau'} \right)} = F_0 e^{-t_d/\tau} \tag{29}$$

This gives

$$\tau = \frac{\tau_0 \tau'}{\tau_0 + \tau'} = \frac{C\eta\tau_0/[\text{UO}_2^{++}]}{(C\eta/[\text{UO}_2^{++}]) + \tau_0} \tag{30}$$

Integration of F from $t_d = 0$ to $t_d = \infty$ gives

$$L = \int_0^\infty F_{t_d}\, dt_d = \frac{F_0 \tau_0 C\eta/[\text{UO}_2^{++}]}{(C\eta/[\text{UO}_2^{++}] + \tau_0} \tag{31}$$

When $k\eta/[\text{UO}_2^{++}] \ll \tau_0$ (low viscosity, strong quenching), L becomes a linear function of viscosity, η. When η approaches ∞, Equation (31) reduces itself to $L = F_0 \tau_0$; if we call this limiting value L_0,

$$\frac{1}{L} = \frac{1}{L_0} + \frac{\tau_0 [\text{UO}_2^{++}]}{CL_0 \eta} \tag{32}$$

For large η, where $\tau' \simeq \eta/[\text{UO}_2^{++}]$ is a good approximation, L must be a linear function of $1/\eta$. This is confirmed by Fig. 3.14.

Assuming that at $\eta = \infty$ (i.e. $1/\eta = 0$), the yield of fluorescence has the maximum possible value (quantum yield 1, or energy yield 0.81, equal to the ratio of the wavelengths of the exciting light, 435 mμ, and of the fluorescent light, $\lambda = 535$ mμ, a value of 23 per cent can be derived from Fig. 3.14 for the yield at 18°C (dotted line), in agreement with Vavilov and Levshin's estimate (25 per cent). However, the assumption of a limiting quantum yield of fluorescence $\phi = 1.0$ at $\eta = \infty$ (rigid solvent) probably is incorrect. It presupposes the absence of any quenching except that caused by encounters with other uranyl ions, neglecting, for example, the quenching by internal dissipation of energy in the excited uranyl ion itself (more exactly, in the complex formed by excited uranyl ion and the solvent).

Vavilov and Levshin noted that the Equations (27) to (32) do not apply to the data obtained at high temperature and high concentration and suggested "solvate effects" as an explanation.

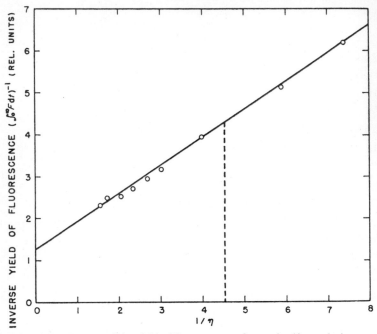

FIG. 3.14. Inverse of the yield of fluorescence of uranyl sulfate solutions in sulfuric acid as function of inverse viscosity. From Vavilov and Levshin (1928).

Vavilov (1928) attempted to calculate the concentration quenching of uranyl fluorescence theoretically from a simple molecular model of diffusion (assuming that quenching occurs whenever an excited and a non-excited ion encounter each other by diffusion). He concluded that the constant $1/C$ in Equation (32) must be equal to $8kTN/\delta\pi$, where N is the number of molecules in 1 g of the solute ($[UO_2^{++}]$ being measured in g/ml), and δ a numerical factor

$1 < \delta < 2.83$. The empirical coefficient $1/C$ (as determined in sulfuric acid at $291°K$, with $\eta = 0.22$, $\tau_0 = 4.3 \times 10^{-4}$, and $L_0 = 0.82$) turns out, however, to be only 2 per cent of the theoretical value. Vavilov attributes this difference to solvation of the uranyl ions (that slows down diffusion) and perhaps also to not every encounter being effective. (One should, perhaps, think also of the effect of the ionic charge, which makes collisions of two UO_2^{++} ions less likely than a collision between two neutral solute molecules of the same diameter.)

Alenzev (1951) described a calorimetric method of measurement of the yield of fluorescence. He used it primarily for fluorescent dyestuffs; but mentioned, without any details, that he found a figure of 63 per cent for the yield of fluorescence of a uranyl salt solution—not much lower than that he found for fluorescein (67–80 per cent).

4. Quenching of Uranyl Fluorescence in Solutions

Quenching is the decline in the probability of fluorescence of an excited molecule caused by presence of other molecules. If the quenching is caused by increased concentration of the fluorescent molecules themselves, it is called "concentration quenching" or "self-quenching."

Several different mechanisms of quenching (or self-quenching) are feasible. In the first place, one can distinguish between "chemical" and "physical" quenching, depending on whether the energy lost for fluorescence is used for chemical reaction, or is dissipated into vibrational energy (and finally converted into heat), without causing chemical change. In the second place, a distinction can be made between three mechanisms of quenching: quenching caused by *association* of the light-excited molecules with the quenching molecule preceding the excitation (quenching by *complexing*), quenching by *proximity* of the excited and the quenching molecule (quenching by *resonance transfer*), and quenching by kinetic *encounter* of the quencher with the excited molecule. (In all three cases quenching can be either chemical or physical.)

The "self-quenching" data and theoretical considerations of Vavilov and Levshin (1928) and Vavilov (1928) were presented in Section 3.

Trümpler (1915) first observed the quenching of fluorescence of uranyl solutions by *organic acids*, which he attributed to their oxidation by light-excited uranyl ions ("chemical quenching"). The quenching by formic acid was described by Trümpler as "weaker than that by oxalic acid."

The quenching of UO_2^{++} fluorescence by *inorganic* ions was first studied by West, Müller and Jette (1928) in connection with the effect of these ions on uranyl-sensitized photodecomposition of oxalate. Figure 4.7 shows the competition between fluorescence and sensitization of uranyl oxalate mixtures with different ratios of the components. Addition of Cl^-, Br^-, CNS^-, or I^- ions depresses both the fluorescence and the decomposition, both effects increasing in strength with the size of the anion, from Cl^- to I^-.

Volmar (1928) noted that solutions of uranyl sulfate, nitrate or acetate cease to be fluorescent at pH $\geqslant$ 7. The disappearance of fluorescence is followed by precipitation of a hydroxide. (The formation of insoluble hydroxide probably is preceded by that of soluble, but non-fluorescent, complex ions, of the types discussed in Chapter 2.) Uranyl *halogenides* do not fluoresce even in acid solution, because of the quenching effect of the halide ions, as first noted by Perrin (1926).

Volmar and Mathis (1933) investigated the possibility of using the quenching of uranyl fluorescence for analytical determination of the anions. Using uranyl nitrate as fluorescent material, exciting it with 350 mμ, and adding various salt solutions, they found that the strongest quenchers were the following anions: I^-, Br^-, CNS^-, $Cr_2O_7^{--}$, $Fe(CN)_6^{-4}$, As_3^{-3}, S^{--} (in decreasing order).

Other "active" anions were NO_2^-, $S_2O_3^{--}$, CrO_4^{--}, MnO_4^-.

"Inactive" were the anions F^-, ClO_3^-, BrO_3^-, IO_3^-, CN^-, NO_3^-, SO_4^{--}, SO_3^{--}, PO_4^{-3}, AsO_4^{-3}, formate, acetate, oxalate, tartrate, citrate, borate, and palmitate.

Among *cations*, only one, Ag^+, was found to quench the fluorescence of uranyl ions. All the other cations tested (Na^+, K^+, Li^+, NH_4^+, Ca^{++}, Ba^{++}, Zn^{++}, Mg^{2+}, Al^{+3}, Fe^{+3}, Bi^{+3}, Pb^{+4}, Cu^{++}, Hg^{++}) proved inactive.

Fluorescence was not affected by small changes in pH, temperature, and uranyl ion concentration.

In plotting the number of drops, n, required to produce quenching, as function of concentration, c, of the quencher in them, Volmar and Mathis were baffled not to find inverse proportionality. At a certain (low) concentration, c_0, the curve $n = f(c)$ became vertical; no complete quenching could be obtained with still lower concentrations, $c < c_0$. This result is, however, trivial. If what matters for complete quenching is not the *amount* of the quencher added, but its *final concentration*, C (which must exceed a certain value c_0), then we have (V being the initial volume of the uranyl solution and v the volume of a drop):

$$c_0 = \frac{n_0 c v}{V + n_0 v}; \qquad n_0 = \frac{c_0 V}{v(c - c_0)}$$

When c approaches c_0 (from above), the number n_0 of drops needed to quench the fluorescence in a given volume of uranyl solution approaches infinity; at $c < c_0$ complete quenching becomes impossible. This relationship indicates that the quenching of uranyl fluorescence by anions is *not* due to stable complexing, e.g. $UO_2^{++} + Cl^- \rightarrow UO_2Cl^-$. Because of the weakness of the absorption, it is also unlikely to be due to a resonance transfer of energy; the most probable mechanism of quenching is therefore by kinetic encounters. The most likely effect of these encounters is, in turn, a reversible oxidation reduction, e.g.,

$$UO_2^{++*} + I^- \rightarrow UO_2^+ + I \qquad (33a)$$

$$I + UO_2^+ \rightarrow I^- + UO_2^{++} \qquad (33b)$$

$$UO_2^{++*} \rightarrow UO_2^{++} \qquad (33)$$

Practically all quenching ions (I^-, Ag^+, $Fe(CN)_6^{-4}$, etc.) are, in fact, reductants, i.e. have a tendency to acquire electrons. The question remains open whether reaction (33a) is reversed immediately, even before the two products have separated in solution, the net result being an internal conversion of electronic energy into heat in the complex $\{UO_2^{++*} (I) H_2O)_n\}$ or whether the products react back only after a certain free life in solution, in which case partial irreversibility and net photochemical transformation become possible, e.g.

$$UO_2^{++*} + 2I^- + 4H^+ \rightarrow U^{+4} + I_2 + 2H_2O \qquad (34)$$

This, in fact, is the probable mechanism of the photochemical reaction of uranyl ions with iodine (cf. Chapter 4).

Carter and Weiss (1940) measured the quenching of fluorescence of uranyl nitrate solution by potassium iodide. Figure 3.15 shows the results. The curve is from the equation

$$I = \frac{I_0}{1 + 5 \times 10^3 [I^-]} \tag{35}$$

This indicates "half-quenching" $(F = \frac{1}{2}F_0)$ at $[I^-] = 2 \times 10^{-4}$ m/l; assuming 10^4 sec^{-1} for the rate constant of fluorescence, we obtain

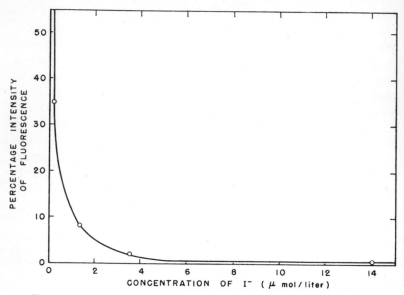

Fig. 3.15. Quenching of the fluorescence of uranium ions by iodide ions (KI). Carter and Weiss (1940).

a value of $10^4/(2 \times 10^{-4}) = 5 \times 10^7$ for the rate constant of the quenching reaction, which we may tentatively assume to be identical with the first step in the reaction of uranyl and iodide ions:

$$UO_2^{++*} + I^- \rightarrow UO_2^+ + I \quad \text{(cf. Chapter 4, p. 238)} \tag{36}$$

However, quenching could also be associated with the formation of nonfluorescent complexes $(UO_2^{++} I^-)$, an alternative which could only be excluded by more extensive and systematic measurements.

Galanin (1951) looked for a proof of resonance quenching of uranyl fluorescence. He pointed out that the long life of the excited state (which is associated with the weakness of the absorption band) makes this proof difficult, since it facilitates the quenching by encounters. To distinguish between the two quenching mechanisms, Galanin measured the lifetime of the fluorescence (which, according to Equation 14, is proportional to the yield of fluorescence as function of concentration of the quencher at different viscosities). (Increased viscosity reduces the quenching by encounters, but leaves unaffected the quenching by resonance transfer.)

Figure 3.16 shows the lifetime, τ, as function of temperature for uranyl sulfate in sulfuric acid, with potassium bichromate and chrysoidine as quenchers. The quenching by bichromate, which is complete at room temperature, almost disappears at $-185°C$, while the quenching by the dye remains strong even in liquid air (as expected for a resonance effect).

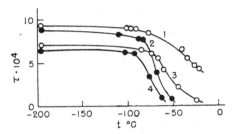

Fig. 3.16. Relation between temperature and duration of phosphorescence of a solution of uranyl sulfate in sulfuric acid. From Galanin (1951).
Curve 1: Pure solution.
Curve 2: Solution with the addition of 10% sodium chloride.
Curve 3: Solution quenched with chrysoidine ($c = 5 \times 10^{-4}$ g/ml).
Curve 4: Solution quenched with potassium bichromate ($C = 5 \times 10^{-3}$ g/ml).

Figure 3.17 represents τ_0/τ as function of the concentration of the quencher, at $-185°C$. The effect of quencher concentration [Q] (molecules/ml) can be represented by equations of the Stern–Volmer type, $\tau_0/\tau = 1 + \beta[Q]$ with $\beta = 0.2 \times 10^{-18}$ for chrysoidine and 0.04×10^{-18} for bichromate. If these constants are compared with the overlap $\bar{a}$ of the absorption spectra of the fluorescer and the quencher, $\beta/\bar{a}$ values of 5 and 57 respectively are obtained for bichromate and chrysoidine respectively. These ratios are of the same order of magnitude as found for resonance quenching of the fluorescence of dyestuffs, where the natural lifetime is of the order 10^{-8} sec (as compared to 10^{-4} sec for uranyl ions!).

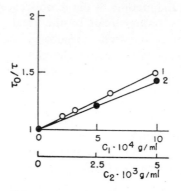

FIG. 3.17. Change of fluorescence duration (τ) of the solution of uranyl sulfate in sulfuric acid (at the temperature of liquid nitrogen) in relation to the concentration of the quencher. From Galanin (1951). Curve 1: Chrysoidine. Curve 2: Potassium bichromate.

CHAPTER 4

PHOTOCHEMISTRY OF URANYL COMPOUNDS

Introduction

Photochemistry of uranyl compounds is one of the most extensively studied and also the most confused chapters of photochemistry. One of the reasons may be that the primary photochemical reactions are slow, giving time for many different secondary thermal reactions to develop. Another reason is that much of the study in this field has been done by insufficiently precise methods. Mechanisms often were suggested to fit a given set of observations without considering whether they could be reconciled with the other sets available in the literature.

In the presentation below, some attempts have been made to establish correlations between the different studies, but much of it is tenuous and many contradictions remain unresolved. Much of the field calls for renewed experimental investigation with better research tools and more precise analysis of the results.

To understand the slow rate of photochemical reactions of uranyl ions in visible light, it must be borne in mind that the average molar absorption coefficient of non-complexed uranyl ions in the region 400–500 mμ (the absorption is negligible > 500 mμ) is of the order of 5 liters mole^{-1} cm^{-1} only (cf. Fig. 2.3). Consequently, to obtain 50 per cent absorption over a light path of 1 cm, the UO$_2^{++}$ concentration must be of the order of 0.06 mole/liter.

If a solution of this concentration, 1 cm deep, is exposed to a light flux of n einstein/(sec 1000 cm^2) and undergoes a photochemical reaction with a quantum yield of 1, it will need 0.06/n sec for half-transformation if the absorption remains constant (sensitized reaction), and somewhat less than twice this time if the absorption declines with the progress of the reaction (direct photochemical reactions of UO_2^{++}, e.g. oxidation–reductions with UO_2^{++} as oxidant). The half-decomposition time for direct reaction is therefore

about 6×10^3 sec for $n = 10^{-5}$ [6×10^{15} quanta/(sec cm²)]

about 6×10^4 sec for $n = 10^{-6}$ [6×10^{14} quanta/(sec cm²)]

about 6×10^5 sec for $n = 10^{-7}$ [6×10^{13} quanta/(sec cm²)]

Diffuse daylight (illumination of the order of 10,000 lux) corresponds to about 10^{14} quanta/(sec cm²) in the region $\lambda < 500$ mμ. A 1 cm layer of 0.06M uranyl solution, exposed to such light, and reacting with a quantum yield of 1, will consequently require about 5 days of continuous illumination for half-decomposition. In other words, an average UO_2^{++} ion will absorb, under these conditions, only one quantum every 5 days.

Many uranyl reactions, particularly those with organic acids, proceed, however, mainly or exclusively by light absorption in uranyl-anion complexes, which may absorb considerably more strongly than the free ions (cf. Chapter 2).

Remarkably enough, it seems that in several cases excitation of a complex $UO_2^{++}A^-$ is insufficient to cause a reaction of UO_2^{++} with A^- without a further encounter, $[UO_2^{++}A^-]^* + A^-$.

1. Photochemical Reactions of Uranyl Ions with Inorganic Compounds

Uranyl ions can serve in light either as *oxidants*, or as *sensitizers* for oxidation by other oxidants, particularly molecular oxygen ("autoxidation"). The results of photochemical experiments in which air was not rigorously excluded often are ambiguous because of the superposition of these two phenomena.

The best-known photochemical reactions of uranyl ions are those with organic compounds, such as formic acid, oxalic acid, and other fatty acids. Among reactions with inorganic reductants, only that with iodide has been investigated quantitatively, and even this reaction has been studied only with very crude techniques.

1.1 *Oxidation of Iodide*

Luther and Michie (1908) stated that uranyl salts "slowly precipitate iodine from potassium iodide solutions." This observation probably was made in the presence of light and air, and, most likely, refers to uranyl-sensitized photochemical autoxidation of iodide. Baur (1910), starting from a theory of the photogalvanic effect (Becquerel effect) in oxidation–reduction systems, predicted that in the absence of air, light will cause a reversible shift of the oxidation–reduction equilibrium of the couples uranyl ion–uranous ion and iodine–iodide ion; he expected this shift to produce a strong photogalvanic effect. Trümpler (1915) tried to detect the latter, but found only a very weak change of galvanic potential in light. He used a solution 0.1M in UO_2SO_4, 0.02N in I_2, 0.04N in KI and 1N in H_2SO_4. It will be noted that it contained a considerable proportion of iodine, and we will see below that the photochemical reaction of uranyl ions with iodide ions stops with the formation of a small amount of free iodine. This may explain Trümpler's negative results.

That uranyl ions do react in light with iodide, even in the absence of air, was first observed, also in Baur's laboratory, by Hatt (1918). He noted that the liberation of iodine ceased after only a few per cent of the available iodide was oxidized. The final "photostationary" concentration of iodine depended on the intensity of illumination, L, but increased much slower than proportionally with it.

Let us assume that the reaction in light is a reversible oxidation–reduction:

$$U(VI) + 2I^- \underset{\text{dark (and light?)}}{\overset{\text{light}}{\rightleftarrows}} U(IV) + I_2 \qquad (1)$$

The normal redox potential of the iodine–iodide couple is -0.535 V and is independent of pH. The empirical uranyl–uranous potentials are variable and difficult to interpret because of complex formation, and probably also because of intermediate formation of U(V) ions, but from the thermodynamic data for the free ions UO_2^{++} and U^{+4} we calculate $E_0' = -0.48 + 4 \times 0.03(\text{pH})$ volt.

Iodine molecules are thus somewhat stronger oxidants than uranyl ions at all practically significant pH values; it is therefore plausible that reaction (1) should proceed in the dark from the right to the left.

If this back-reaction occurred in the simple way indicated in reaction (1) [and not, for example, via the intermediate formation of U(V)], and if all U(IV) present in the illuminated solutions were due to the photochemical reduction of U(VI) (making the concentrations $[I_2]$ and $[U(IV)]$ identical), the rate of the back-reaction would be

$$-\frac{d[U(IV)]}{dt} = \text{const.} \times [U(IV)] [I_2] = \text{const.} \times [U(IV)]^2 \qquad (2)$$

Assuming, further, that U(VI) is present in large excess (so that the concentration $[U(VI)]$ is not markedly depleted in light) and that the concentration of $[I^-]$ is high enough to permit all excited UO_2^{++} ions to react with I^- during the excitation period, the rate of the forward reaction in (1) must be, independently of the concentration $[I^-]$:

$$+\frac{d[U(IV)]}{dt} = \text{const.} \times L \qquad (3)$$

where L is the rate of light absorption, which is proportional to the intensity of incident light.

We then have for the photostationary state (designated by an asterisk):

$$[U(IV)^*] = [I_2]^* = \text{const.} \times \sqrt{L} \qquad (4)$$

Hatt's results indicated that $[I_2]^*$ is proportional to a power of L even lower than $\frac{1}{2}$; using the empirical formula $[I_2]^* = \text{const.} \times L^{1/x}$, he obtained values of x between 3.6 and 7. Baur suggested that such a high value of x can be explained by a high order of the back-reaction. He attempted to make the latter plausible by assuming a very complicated mechanism for this reaction, involving intermediary formation of the ions U(V), their dismutation, and a final reaction involving five ions. We do not need to discuss this implausible mechanism, since it was abandoned in the next paper from Baur's laboratory. This publication, by Ouellet (1931), contained the somewhat more precise determinations of the photostationary state shown in Table 4.1.

The "calculated" $[I_2]^*$ values in Table 4.1 were derived from an empirical equation:

$$[I_2]^* = \frac{L}{A + BL} \qquad (5)$$

with the constants

$$A = 3400, \ B = 0.020 \text{ in series } 1$$

$$A = 3400, \ B = 0.0113 \text{ in series } 2$$

TABLE 4.1. PHOTOSTATIONARY STATE IN URANYL IODIDE SOLUTIONS
After Ouellet (1931)
50 ml 0.1N UO_2SO_4; [KI] = about 0.01N; no O_2. No I_2 formed in the dark after several days.

Light	Intensity (in 1000 lux)	$[I_2]^*$ obs.†	$[I_2]^*$ calc. (Eq. 5)
Artificial	1.8	9.7	—
	7.5	12.7	—
	11	14.6	—
Sun (Series 1)	170	24.8	25
	360	33.2	34
	660	40.7	40
	900	41.0	42
Sun (Series 2)	170	27.5	30
	360	36	39
	660	53	55
	900	57	59
Sun (Series 3)	465	49	—
	870	54	—
Sun (Series 4)	445	35.4	—
	850	41.5	—

† $[I_2]^*$ expressed in ml of 4×10^{-4}N $Na_2S_2O_3$ needed for titration of the solution after illumination.

Ouellet proceeded to show that an equation of type (5) can be derived from Baur's quaint theory of photochemistry as "molecular electrochemistry." According to this theory, light causes a "polarization" of the absorbing molecule, and the charges on the two "poles" are removed by reactions with cathodic and anodic "depolarizers" present in solution. For example, the reactions in the uranyl iodide solution were represented by Baur as follows:

$$U(VI) \xrightarrow{\text{light}} [U(VI)]_{--}^{++} \text{ (polarization)} \tag{6a}$$

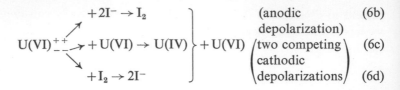

$$+2I^- \rightarrow I_2 \qquad \text{(anodic} \qquad \text{(6b)}$$

depolarization)

$$U(VI)\overset{++}{\underset{--}{\longrightarrow}} + U(VI) \rightarrow U(IV) \Big\} + U(VI) \begin{pmatrix} \text{two competing} \\ \text{cathodic} \\ \text{depolarizations} \end{pmatrix} \quad \text{(6c)}$$

$$+I_2 \rightarrow 2I^-$$

(6d)

Reaction (6d) represents "depolarization" by one of the reaction products (iodine) and, as such, should cause "self-inhibition" of the forward reaction (6b, c). This "negative auto-catalysis" accounts, according to Baur and Ouellet, for the second term in the denominator of (5), and thus for the rapid "light saturation" of reaction (1).

Replacing "molecular electrolysis" by the usual photochemical concepts, one could imitate reaction system (6a–d) by assuming that light absorbed by UO_2^{++} ions can *sensitize the back-reaction* between U(IV) and I_2. However, a simpler and more natural assumption, which leads to a similar result, is that with increasing concentration of iodine, more and more light is absorbed by the latter (instead of by the uranyl ions) and that under these conditions the back reaction in (1) becomes predominantly photochemical:

$$I_2 \overset{\text{light}}{\longrightarrow} I_2^* \text{ (or } I+I) \overset{+U(IV)}{\longrightarrow} U(VI) + 2I^- \qquad (7)$$

One is at first tempted to suggest that the dark back-reaction in (1) may be so slow that even in moderate light (1) will be practically *entirely* a photochemical reaction. Hatt has, in fact, observed that preilluminated systems containing uranyl ions, iodide and photochemically formed iodine can be left in the dark for several days without losing entirely the brown color they have acquired in light. However, kinetic analysis shows that a combination of two opposing purely photochemical reactions would lead to a photostationary state which is *independent* of light intensity. The amount of light absorbed by iodine in a mixture containing uranyl ions as competing absorbers is:

$$L_{I_2}^{abs} = \frac{\bar{\alpha}_{I_2}[I_2]L_{total}^{abs}}{\bar{\alpha}_{I_2}[I_2] + \bar{\alpha}_{UO_2^{++}}[UO_2^{++}]} \qquad (8)$$

where the $\bar{\alpha}$'s are the average absorption coefficients of the two colored species for the light used. Since we assumed UO_2^{++} to be present in excess, and $[UO_2^{++}]$ therefore to be practically constant, we have, for the photostationary state:

$$L_{I_2}^{abs*} = \frac{[I_2]^* L_{total}^{abs}}{K + [I_2]^*} \tag{9}$$

where

$$K = \frac{\bar{\alpha}_{UO_2^{++}} [UO_2^{++}]}{\bar{\alpha}_{I_2} [I_2]} \tag{10}$$

The amount of light absorbed by uranyl ions in the photostationary state is:

$$L_{UO_2^{++}}^{abs*} = L - L_{I_2}^{abs*} = \frac{KL_{total}^{abs}}{[I_2]^* + K} \tag{11}$$

If the quantum yields of the forward and the backward reaction were the same (e.g. unity), the photostationary state would be simply the state in which one half of the light is absorbed by UO_2^{++}, and the other half by I_2:

$$[I_2]^* = K \tag{12}$$

independently of light intensity.

The quantum yield of the forward reaction may be 1, since I^- is present in concentrations of the order of $10^{-2}M$, which should be enough for all excited UO_2^{++} ions to encounter I^- ions within the period of excitation. The quantum yield of the back reaction, on the other hand, may be < 1 [because of the lower concentration of U(IV), or because of primary recombination of some of the iodine atom pairs formed by the photochemical process, $I_2 \overset{h\nu}{\rightleftharpoons} I + I$]. This will make $[I_2]^* > K$, but leave it *independent of light intensity*. On the other hand, since the absorption spectra of the two colored species, UO_2^{++} and I_2, are different, the constant K, and with it the photostationary concentration of iodine, would depend on the *spectral composition* of the light used.

To sum up, if (1) were a purely photochemical reaction in both directions, the intensity of illumination, while affecting the *rate of approach* to the photostationary state, would not affect the composition of the solution once this state has been reached; the latter would, however, depend on the spectrum of the illuminating light.

Experimentally, $[I_2]^*$ is practically independent of light intensity only in strong light; it declines to zero as light becomes weaker. Assuming that this decline is real (and not due merely to a very slow approach to the equilibrium), it can be explained by assuming that the photochemical back-reaction is superimposed on a slow thermal back-reaction. The limiting value of $[I_2]^*$, reached in strong light, can be derived from the data in Table 4.1; it is of the order of 5×10^{-4}M. Inserted in (12) and (10) this gives a value of about 200 for the ratio $\bar{\alpha}_{I_2}/\bar{\alpha}_{UO_2^{++}}$. The absorption coefficients of UO_2^{++} in aqueous solution for visible light are of the order of 1–10; those of iodine are of the order of 100–1000, so that their ratio is, in fact, of the order of 10^2. More exact verification is not possible on the basis of Ouellet's results, since they were obtained in white light of unknown spectral composition. (Also, the quantum yield of the two reactions needs to be determined experimentally.)

An equation can be derived for the stationary concentration, $[I_2]^*$, as a function of light intensity, containing, as parameters, the rate constant of the thermal back reaction

$$U(IV) + I_2 \xrightarrow{k_i} U(VI) + 2I^- \tag{13}$$

and the quantum yields of the forward and the reverse photochemical reaction, γ and γ'. This equation is of the third order, even under the simplest assumptions; the primitive measurements of Ouellet do not justify an effort to analyze them by means of such an elaborate equation. It can be seen without mathematical analysis that $[I_2]^*$ will increase with $\sqrt{L}$ at low intensities (where the back-reaction is practically entirely thermal) and approach saturation in strong light, where the back-reaction is practically completely photochemical. This is in general agreement with the experiment.

If this interpretation is correct, the reaction of uranyl ions with iodide offers an interesting subject for more precise study, as a rather unusual example of an inorganic oxidation–reduction system in which visible light accelerates the reaction in both directions.

Carter and Weiss (1940) noted that the oxidation of uranous salts to uranyl salts by iodine is retarded by *acids*. (A similar observation was made in 1909 by McCoy and Bunzel in the case of oxidation of uranous salts by oxygen.) They therefore expected to find the stationary amount of iodine, produced by illumination of

$UO_2^{++}+I^-$ mixtures, to increase with acidity. This expectation was confirmed by the experimental results listed in Table 4.2.

TABLE 4.2. IODINE LIBERATION FROM IODIDE BY URANYL IONS IN LIGHT
After Carter and Weiss (1940)
0.0166M UO_2SO_4; 0.15M KI; $[I_2]$ present after one hour illumination

Acid added	$[I_2]$ (moles/liter)	[U(IV)] (moles/liter)
None	0	0
1.0M	0.125×10^{-3}	$0.15 \pm 0.05 \times 10^{-3}$
2.0M	$0.25 \ \times 10^{-3}$	$0.30 \pm 0.05 \times 10^{-3}$

The complete absence of iodine in illuminated solutions containing no added acid contradicts the above-described earlier results of Hatt and Ouellet (cf. Table 4.1). However, exact comparison would require the consideration of intensity and spectral composition of the light used in the two investigations. It will also be noted that Ouellet used a 10 : 1 excess of uranyl sulfate over iodide, while Carter and Weiss operated with a reverse ratio of the two components. This may change the character and the concentration of the complexes present in solution.

The photochemical reaction of uranyl ions with iodide ions *in the presence of oxygen* was studied quantitatively by Schneider (1935). In his paper, sensitization was attributed to "collisions of the second kind," i.e. to *energy transfer* from UO_2^{++*} to I_{aq}^-. However, the I^- ions have no excited electronic states low enough to permit the acceptance of the excitation energy of UO_2^{++*}; neither is the latter sufficient to bring about the dissociation:

$$UO_2^{++*}+I^-.H_2O \rightarrow UO_2^{++}+I+H+OH^- \qquad (14)$$

(a type of elementary photochemical process suggested by Franck and Haber). Schneider suggested that energy transfer is made possible in this case by an (at least partial) utilization of the recombination energy of the atoms H and I:

$$UO_2^{++*}+I^-.H_2O \rightarrow UO_2^{++}+HI+OH^-$$
$$(\rightarrow UO_2^{++}+H^++I^-+OH^-) \qquad (15)$$

The net chemical change in (15) is zero, and Schneider suggested that iodine liberation only occurs when the HI molecules meet an oxidant, such as molecular oxygen, before dissociating into $H^+ + I^-$. He concluded from this theory that no iodine at all should be liberated in the absence of oxygen and gave Fig. 4.1 as experimental confirmation of this prediction. However, this conclusion contradicts the results of the above-described experiments of Hatt, Ouellet, and Carter and Weiss, who have observed and measured the iodine production in oxygen-free atmosphere.

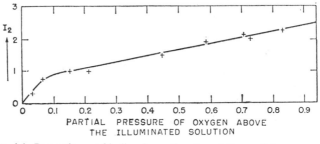

FIG. 4.1. Dependence of iodine formation (in relative units) on oxygen concentration. Solution: 0.025N KI, 0.05M UO_2SO_4. After Schneider (1935).

On theoretical grounds, the hypothesis of interim HI formation is implausible. Pringsheim (1937) pointed out that the assumption of collisions of the second kind as mechanism of quenching of UO_2^{++} fluorescence by iodide ions encounters grave difficulties (cf. Chapter 3), and Weiss (1938) suggested that Schneider's results could be much better interpreted by assuming a transfer of *electrons* (rather than a transfer of energy) from the excited molecule to the quencher. If (16a) is the primary process of quenching, the increased yield of iodine in the presence of oxygen can be explained by competition between the reoxidation of UO_2^+ by I and by O_2.

$$UO_2^{++} + I^- \xrightarrow{h\nu} UO_2^+ + I \tag{16a}$$

$$UO_2^+ \begin{cases} + I \to UO_2^{++} + I^- \\ \\ + \tfrac{1}{4}O_2 + H^+ \to UO_2^{++} + \tfrac{1}{2}H_2O \end{cases} \begin{array}{l} \text{competitive} \\ \text{reoxidation} \\ \text{of U(V)} \end{array} \tag{16b}$$
$$\tag{16c}$$

$$I + I \to I_2 \tag{16d}$$

Figure 4.2 shows the yield of iodine (in relative units) as a function of iodide concentration in 0.025M UO_2SO_4 solution according to Schneider. The two curves are for solutions with and without added acid. The effect of acid concentration is shown in Fig. 4.3, in which the yield is plotted against acidity.

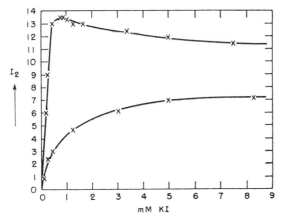

FIG. 4.2. Iodine formation (in relative units) in light in $KI + UO_2SO_4$ solution as function of iodide concentration. Upper curve: With 0.008N H_2SO_4. Lower curve: Without added acid. After Schneider (1935).

The gradual approach to [I⁻] saturation could be understood on the basis of either the electron transfer or the energy transfer theory. In the absence of acid, the rate is "half-saturated" at about 5×10^{-4}M iodide; if it is assumed that the reaction of UO_2^{++*} with I⁻ competes with fluorescence, half-saturation must be achieved when $k_\phi = k[I^-]$ (where k_ϕ is the rate constant of fluorescence, or $\sim 10^4$ sec⁻¹ for UO_2^{++}; cf. Chapter 3). This gives $k \approx 2 \times 10^7$. (A value of the same order of magnitude, $k = 5 \times 10^7$, was found by Carter and Weiss for the rate constant of quenching of uranyl nitrate fluorescence by iodide.) In the presence of 0.008N H_2SO_4 the curve rises much more steeply and, after reaching saturation, shows a slow *decline* with increasing [I⁻]. Disregarding this decrease, we estimate that the rate is half-saturated at about 2×10^{-4}M, corresponding to $k = 5 \times 10^7$. The order of magnitude of these k values ($2-5 \times 10^7$) appears at first to be incompatible with the assumption of a reaction by the first encounter between UO_2^{++*} and I^- ions: gas-kinetic methods for the calculation of collision frequencies give about 10^{-8} sec as the average interval between two collisions of heavy particles, such as UO_2^{++} and I^-, at one atmosphere partial pressure (i.e. at a concentration of about 5×10^{-2} M of each component), and thus $\tau_0 = 5 \times 10^{-10}$ sec for the average collision interval at 1M. This would mean $k = 1/\tau_0 \simeq 2 \times 10^9$ sec^{-1} for the rate constant of a reaction occurring by the first collision or a

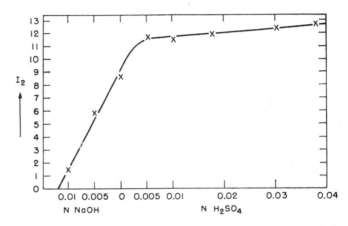

Fig. 4.3. Iodine formation (in relative units) in illuminated solution (0.02M in I_2, 0.025M in UO_2SO_4) as function of acidity. After Schneider (1935).

hundred times the experimental rate constant of both the fluorescence quenching and the iodine liberation. However, encounters in a solution, particularly between ions, probably are spaced wider than collisions in a gas of equal concentration. (This wider spacing between encounters compensates for the so-called "cage effect"—the longer average period which particles spend together once they find themselves inside a common hydration sphere.) This effect could perhaps reduce the order of magnitude of k for a first-encounter reaction between uranyl and iodide ions from 10^9 to 10^7.

The decrease in the rate of reaction with increasing pH may be due to an association of UO_2^{++} ions with OH^- or O^{--} ions (cf. Chapter 2). In this interpretation we have to assume that complex uranyl ions have less inclination than free UO_2^{++} ions to react with I^- after excitation, perhaps in consequence of more rapid energy dissipation in the complex. For example, one could imagine that, in the complex, the primary photochemical reaction causes an electron to be transferred to the anion: $UO_2^{++}OH^- \overset{h\nu}{\longrightarrow} UO_2^+OH$. The electron immediately returns back to the cation, and the excitation energy is dissipated by the coupling of this electron transfer with molecular vibrations. If this mechanism really occurs, it should be recognizable by a quenching effect of OH^- ions on the fluorescence of UO_2^{++}. Unfortunately, no reliable measurements of the yield of fluorescence of uranyl ions are available at present for *any* pH value—not to speak of a systematic study of this yield as a function of pH.

A similar suggestion could also be used to interpret the decline which the iodine formation shows (in acid solution) when $[I^-]$ becomes $> 2 \times 10^{-3} M$ (and, incidentally, to explain the difference between the results of Carter and Weiss and of Ouellet, noted above). The required assumption is, however, that in this case the reaction between UO_2^{++*} and I^- is *less likely* to occur when these two ions are associated in a complex, such as $UO_2^{++}I^-$, than when they meet in solution. This sounds paradoxical, but may be true— for example, because the primary back-reaction (electron transfer from I to UO_2^+) may have a higher probability in the complex than in a colliding and immediately separating ion pair.

At very high KI concentrations the iodine liberation increases again (Fig. 4.4), perhaps because of formation of a new kind of complex.

Qualitatively similar results were obtained by Schneider with uranyl *nitrate* in the presence of KI or LiI.

The initial *quantum yield* of iodine liberation, γ_0 (in 0.025M $UO_2SO_4 + 0.02$N KI), was found by Schneider to be somewhat smaller than 1:

λ (mμ)	γ_0
435.8	0.57
406	0.32
366	0.70

That γ_0 is smaller than 1 may be due to the above-mentioned "primary back-reaction" of UO_2^+ and I, occurring before the separation of the two reaction products by diffusion ("cage effect"). This recombination may occur not only when the ions are associated in a complex (as suggested above for $UO_2^{++}OH^-$ and $UO_2^{++}I^-$) but also—albeit with a lesser probability—when they react during a kinetic encounter. The increase of γ_0 with decreasing wavelength (between 406 and 366 mμ) can then be attributed to increased

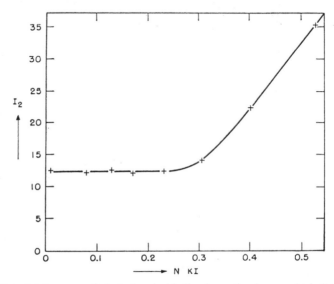

Fig. 4.4. Increase of photochemical iodine formation in uranyl + iodide solutions at high iodide concentrations. After Schneider (1935).

probability of escape from recombination when the products are formed with a higher kinetic energy (the energy of a 366 mμ quantum being larger than that of the 406 mμ quantum). The renewed increase of γ at 436 mμ requires, however, a different interpretation.

The reaction of UO_2^{++} with I^- in the presence of air was also studied by Montignie (1938), but in a rather crude way. He found that the decomposition in an open vessel is considerably more rapid than in a sealed bulb (4 per cent I_2 liberated in four days in a sealed bulb, 7 per cent in an open vessel). Montignie interpreted the reaction as oxidation of uranyl iodide by oxygen:

$$UO_2I_2 + H_2O + \tfrac{1}{2}O_2 \rightarrow UO_2(OH)_2 + I_2 \qquad (17)$$

In this scheme the uranyl salt is hydrolyzed while serving as catalyst for the oxidation of iodide by oxygen. Solid uranyl iodide is, in fact, an unstable compound, but its aqueous solutions have been described as stable (cf. Katz and Rabinowitch, 1951, pp. 595–6). Of course, it is not impossible that such solutions might be hydrolyzed in light, but there seems to be no reason why hydrolysis should be a necessary concomitant of uranyl-sensitized oxidation of iodide.

1.2. *Oxidation of Other Inorganic Reductants*

Another photochemical reaction of UO_2^{++} with an inorganic reductant was studied by Diénert and Villemaine (1934); the reductant was hypophosphate. Rosenheim and Trewendt (1922) had previously found no interaction of UO_2^{++} and hypophosphate in the dark in strongly acid solution (while a precipitate was produced in weakly acid or neutral solution). In light the formation of a green colloidal precipitate was observed by Diénert and Villemaine even in the presence of strong sulfuric acid. It was formed in 150 sec in diffuse light and in 50 sec in direct sunlight. Precipitation ceased when the vessel was again transferred into darkness.

Lipkin and Weissman (1942) made qualitative observations of the photochemical behavior of solutions of uranyl salts in the presence of various reductants. The results obtained with *inorganic reductants* are summarized in Table 4.3. The report did not make it clear whether the experiments were carried out with the exclusion of air or in its presence.

The same authors attempted to produce *internal* photochemical oxidation–reductions in crystalline salts of uranyl cations containing oxidizable anions. They obtained indications of a positive effect in *uranyl potassium ferrocyanide*, $UO_2K_2Fe(CN)_6$, but no signs of reaction in solid uranyl sulfite, phosphite, metarsenite, hypophosphite, uranate, and thiosulfate (as well as in several salts containing organic anions).

Schwab and Issidoridis (1942) found evidence of photochemical UO_2^{++} reduction in *adsorbed layers* on inorganic adsorbers, such as Al_2O_3 or ZnO; the yellow color of uranyl ions changed in light to greenish-brown. This occurred only in acid media. No change was observed with glass powder, MgO, SnO_2, SiO_2, $CdCO_3$, or uranyl aluminate as adsorber. The effect disappeared when weak oxidants were added to the solution.

TABLE 4.3. REDUCTION OF INORGANIC COMPOUNDS BY
UO_2^{++} IONS IN LIGHT
After Lipkin and Weissman (1942)

UO_2^{++} compound	Reductant	Solvent	Temp. (°K)	Fluorescence	Reduction
Sulfite	H_2SO_3	H_2SO_4	90	strong	no
Sulfite	H_2SO_3	H_2SO_4	193	weak	yes
Sulfite	H_2SO_3	H_2SO_4	293	none	yes
Sulfate	NH_2NH_2	H_2SO_4	293	none	no
$(NH_4)_2CO_3$ complex	NH_2NH_2	H_2O	293	none	yes
Bromide	$SOCl_2$	$SOCl_2$	293	none	no
Acetate	$SOCl_2$	$SOCl_2$	293	none	no

1.3. *Uranyl-sensitized Oxidation of Water by Bromate*

Uranyl ions do not oxidize water in light, i.e. illuminated aqueous uranyl salt solutions liberate no oxygen. Since excited UO_2^{++} ions have an electron affinity sufficient to discharge OH^- ions, the absence of oxygen liberation must be attributed to effective back-reaction (as suggested above on p. 239). Baur (1918) observed that oxygen is liberated from illuminated uranyl sulfate solution if *bromate* is added (0.025M UO_2SO_4, 0.025M $KBrO_3$, 0.5N H_2SO_4).

Sixty ml of oxygen were evolved from such a solution exposed to sunlight for two weeks [together with about an equal amount of nitrogen, attributed by Baur to the decomposition of $(NH_4)_2SO_4$ present as impurity in UO_2SO_4]. If oxygen in this experiment actually was the product of oxidation of water, a possible mechanism is

$$U(VI) + OH^- \overset{\text{light}}{\rightleftharpoons} U(V) \ [\text{or } \tfrac{1}{2}U(IV) + \tfrac{1}{2}U(VI)] + OH \qquad (18a)$$

$$U(V) \ [\text{or } \tfrac{1}{2}U(IV) + \tfrac{1}{2}U(VI)] + \tfrac{1}{6}BrO_3^- + H^+$$
$$\rightarrow U(VI) + \tfrac{1}{6}Br^- + \tfrac{1}{2}H_2O \qquad (18b)$$

$$4OH \rightarrow 2H_2O + O_2 \qquad (18c)$$

In other words, the reoxidation of U(V) [or U(IV)] by bromate (reaction 18b) may so successfully compete with its reoxidation by hydroxyl radicals (back-reaction in 18a) that some hydroxyl radicals will be left free for conversion to oxygen.

However, the experimental results of Baur are in need of confirmation, particularly because some gas was also obtained in his experiments by irradiation of the bromate solution without the presence of uranyl salt.

2. Photochemical Reactions of Uranyl Ions with Organic Acids

A characteristic feature of the reactions of UO_2^{++} ions with organic compounds in light is the apparent combination of *direct photochemical oxidation* of the organic material by the uranyl ion [and the concomitant reduction of U(VI) to U(IV)] with *sensitized decomposition* (usually decarboxylation) of the acid, which leaves U(VI) unchanged. Decarboxylation can be interpreted as *dismutation* (internal oxidation–reduction), in which one part of the acid is reduced, while the other part is oxidized to carbon dioxide. It can be suggested that in reactions of this type light-excited uranyl ions oxidize one part of the organic molecule and are then oxidized back to the U(VI) level by the other part, thus serving as light-activated dismutation catalysts. Reactions of both types can occur in the absence of oxygen; in the presence of the latter, a third reaction becomes possible—sensitized *autoxidation* of the organic reductant.

2.1. *Monobasic Aliphatic Acids*

(*a*) *Formic acid.* Fay (1896), in describing the photodecomposition of oxalic and other organic acids by uranyl ions in sunlight, mentioned that he could obtain no evidence of a reaction with formic acid. The reason may be the comparatively weak absorption of light by uranyl–formic acid complexes in the visible and near ultraviolet (compare the ϵ values at 300 mμ in Tables 2.2 and 2.8; the difference is probably even more pronounced at $\lambda > 300$ mμ). The first positive observation was made by Schiller (1912), in Baur's laboratory, on the occasion of a study of photogalvanic potentials (Becquerel effect). He noted that in a uranyl salt solution containing 0.025M sodium formate the electrode potential gradually grew more positive upon exposure to light, and attributed this change to the reaction

$$UO_2^{++} + 3H^+ + HCOO^- \xrightarrow{\text{light}} U^{+4} + CO_2 + 2H_2O \qquad (19)$$

This slow, irreversible reaction formed the background for a more rapid, reversible change, which caused a shift of the electrode potential in the opposite direction for the duration of illumination. (Under the most favorable conditions, this shift was as wide as 0.6 V, e.g. from -0.33 to $+0.26$ V; cf. below, the section on photogalvanic effect.)

The irreversible reaction (19), which was very slow in the light of a Nernst burner, became much more rapid in the light of a mercury lamp. The reaction product was pure carbon dioxide; no formation of carbon monoxide was observed.

Courtois (1913) prepared solid uranyl formate (yellow crystals, which he identified as $UO_2(COOH)_2.H_2O$ and dehydrated at 150°C) and found dilute solutions of this compound to be unstable, particularly in light. In the presence of air, a 2 per cent solution exposed to light rapidly formed a violet U_3O_8 hydrate; an abundant precipitate of basic uranyl formate was formed simultaneously.

In the absence of air, the precipitate was initially white, and the solution became green. Later, gas bubbles appeared. After two weeks' exposure, the precipitate was green and the solution colorless, but the gas evolution continued slowly. The gas contained both carbon dioxide and carbon monoxide, with an excess of the former.

Müller (1915) described the photochemical sensitivity of *solid* uranyl formate: The intensely yellowish-green crystals acquired dark green or even black color upon illumination by a mercury arc. In aqueous or alcoholic solution of the same salt, U_3O_8 hydrate was precipitated upon illumination.

Hofmann and Schumpelt (1916) confirmed that uranyl formate is very sensitive to light. Yellow aqueous solutions of this salt became dark green in sunlight, and a black powder was precipitated. Distillation of the mixture after exposure indicated the presence of some formaldehyde (identified by violet coloring with morphine), an observation which caused Hofmann to speculate on the possible similarity of this reaction to photosynthesis.

A more systematic investigation of the uranyl–formic acid reaction in light was carried out, in Baur's laboratory, first by Hatt, and later by Ouellet.

Hatt (1918) confirmed Schiller's finding that the reaction of UO_2^{++} ions and HCOOH in light gives pure carbon dioxide and no carbon monoxide (contrary to the findings of Courtois). He illuminated uranyl sulfate solution in dilute sulfuric acid in the presence of formic acid with the light of a mercury arc. Air was excluded by sealing off the reaction tubes under carbon dioxide. The progress of reaction was determined by U(IV) titration with permanganate. The following are some of the results obtained by Hatt:

Effect of UO_2^{++} concentration. The formation of U(IV) was found to begin with almost the same velocity at two different UO_2^{++} concentrations, one twice as high as the other. This indicates that the rate of light absorption was approximately the same in both cases (probably, absorption was practically complete even in the more dilute solution). However, the reaction approached completion more rapidly in the more concentrated solution. The suggestion that this may be due to a competition for light quanta between UO_2^{++} and the newly formed U^{+4} (which, at a given value of U^{+4}, will be the less effective the higher the concentration of UO_2^{++}) was rejected by Hatt because of his inability to explain, on this basis, the shape of the curves of reaction velocity as function of time. Hatt suggested that the cause of the slowing down of the reaction with time is an anticatalytic action of the reaction products, specifically, U(IV)—an effect which for some reason is the more effective the lower the U(VI) concentration.

Effect of light intensity. The initial velocity of the reaction proved to be proportional to light intensity.

Effect of additions. The following additions were found to retard the reaction strongly:

Cl^-: 0.01N KCl reduced the initial velocity to about $\frac{1}{4}$.

I^-: This ion had an even stronger effect than Cl^-.

Fe^{+3}: 0.004N FeCl$_3$ reduced the initial velocity by 95 per cent.

U(IV) and U(V) compounds: These compounds retarded the reaction only when present in concentrations of the same order of magnitude as U(VI). This effect may be due to competition for light quanta rather than to anticatalytic inhibition.

HSO_3^- ions: Sulfite ions had no strong effect on the rate.

Quantum yield. Hatt, using published data for the intensity of the mercury arc, and assuming complete absorption, calculated a quantum yield of 0.4 for the initial velocity of formate oxidation by uranyl ions. In a subsequent publication from Baur's laboratory, Büchi (1924) mentioned 0.7 as the quantum yield of the same reaction, but it was not explained why this higher value was substituted for Hatt's value of 0.4. (Still later, cf. below, Ouellet estimated that, under most favorable conditions, the quantum yield should be near 1.0.)

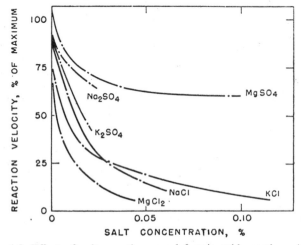

FIG. 4.5. Effect of salts on the uranyl–formic acid reaction. After Berger (1925).

The influence of various salts on the rate of photochemical reaction between UO_2^{++} and $HCOOH$ also was investigated by Berger (1925), whose point of view was quite different from that of Baur and his co-workers. Berger considered this effect as related to the effect of salts on the rate of ordinary chemical reactions between ions (Brönsted's theory). With this concept in mind, he studied the salt effect in more dilute solutions than those used by Hatt (e.g. 0.0674N $COOH^-$, 0.00795N UO_2^{++}, 0.0599N free $HCOOH$). He illuminated the solutions at 10°C with a mercury lamp in the presence of varying amounts of KCl, NaCl, KBr, $MgCl_2$, $MgSO_4$, Na_2SO_4, and K_2SO_4. Fig. 4.5 shows the effect of six of these salts on the initial rate of CO_2 liberation.

Berger stated that the observed salt effects can be interpreted if the "reaction complex" is assigned the composition $\{UO_2^{++} + H^+ + 3HCOO^-\}$, and if the influence of ionic strength on the equilibrium concentration of this complex is calculated by means of Brönsted's equation. The proportionality between the calculated concentrations of the reaction complex, [C], and the observed relative rate of reaction, v_{rel}, was best in the case of KCl (Table 4.4).

TABLE 4.4. EFFECT OF POTASSIUM CHLORIDE ON PHOTO-OXIDATION OF
FORMIC ACID
After Berger (1925)

[KCl] (moles/liter)	0.01	0.02	0.05	0.10
v_{rel} (interpolated)	0.44	0.33	0.18	0.09
[C] (calculated)	0.43	0.31	0.19	0.10

However, Berger did not inquire whether the equilibrium concentration of the postulated pentamolecular complex can be high enough to account for the high observed *absolute* yield of decomposition. Since the latter has a quantum yield of the order of 1, Berger's hypothesis is improbable. Subsequent investigations indicated that a much simpler, binary complex probably accounts for much of the reaction.

Baur (1929, 1932) saw in the inhibition of the uranyl formate reaction by salts (including the effects observed by Berger) a confirmation of his "depolarization" theory. He thought that to prove this it was sufficient to show that the inhibition can be represented by an equation of the type

$$v = av_0/(1 + b[c]) \qquad (20)$$

where $[c]$ is the concentration of the inhibitor, and a and b are constants. This equation ("Stern–Volmer equation"), however, is valid for *all* cases of competition between a monomolecular and a bimolecular reaction (cf. discussion below), and can therefore not be used to support a specific mechanism.

In applying Equation (20), Baur mainly used the elaboration of Hatt's results in a more detailed investigation by Ouellet. Ouellet (1931) used white light, with ultraviolet and infrared filtered out; a reaction vessel without inhibitor served as an actinometer for the determination of relative light intensity. The UO_2SO_4 solution was excluded in the same way as by Hatt (cf. above), and the $KMnO_4$ titration method again was used for the determination of U(IV).

The effect of the following additions on the time curves of the photochemical reduction of U(VI) to U(IV) was measured:

Strong Inhibitors: Hydroquinone, $Cr_2O_7^{--}$, NO_2^-, Fe^{++} (according to Hatt, Cl^-, I^-, Fe^{+3} belong to the same class).*

Medium Strong Inhibitors: Ag^+, CN^-, Hg^{++} (according to Hatt, also V_2O_5 and VO).

Weak Inhibitors: NO_3^-, Co^{++}, Cr^{+3}, Cu^{++}, Mn^{++}, F^- (also HSO_3^-, according to Hatt).

No Effect: Na_3PO_4, $MgSO_4$, NH_4COOCH_3.

Of those inhibitors, Ag^+ and Hg^{++} are themselves reduced (to metallic silver and Hg_2^{++} respectively). Cr_2O^{--} changes color, but others, such as the halide ions, ferrous sulfate and hydroquinone, appear to act as true anti-catalysts. With chromate and the vanadium compounds, induction periods were observed, during which the added compound probably served as oxidant, instead of the U(VI).

Effect of [HCOOH]. The rate of photoreduction was found by Ouellet to increase with increasing concentration of formic acid until a "saturation" was reached somewhere above 10 per cent; practically no difference in rate was observed between 12.5 per cent and 50 per cent acid. Ten per cent HCOOH corresponds to about 2M; this is a very high concentration to be required for the "saturation" of a photochemical process if this process were to occur by the first kinetic encounter between light-excited ions and the acid molecules (cf. discussion below, p. 251). The effect of inhibitors ($FeSO_4$ was used as an example) was found to decrease with increasing concentration of formic acid.

Effect of [UO_2^{++}]. The rate of formation of U(IV) increased with increasing concentration of UO_2^{++}, reached a maximum in the neighborhood of 0.16M, and then declined again.

Quantum yield. Ouellet pointed out that Hatt's quantum yield estimate was made at a suboptimal concentration of formic acid (0.1N). Multiplication of his value ($\gamma = 0.4$) by the ratio found by

---

* Ouellet mentions only Fe^{++}, but Hatt's experiments explicitly referred to $FeCl_3$. It is possible that the effects first attributed to Fe^{+3} were later decided to have been due to Fe^{+2} contamination.

Ouellet between the rate in 0.1N acid, and the maximum rate, gave for the maximum quantum yield

$$\gamma = 0.97 \simeq 1$$

Analytical expression. Ouellet found that (in agreement with Baur's expectation) the inhibiting effect of various "desensitizers" can be expressed by Equation (20), in which [c] is the concentration of the inhibitor. The values of the constants a and b are given in Table 4.5. These analytical formulations apply to *initial* velocities. As U(IV) is formed, it acts as an additional "auto-inhibitor"; its effect, too, can be represented by an equation of the type (20).

TABLE 4.5. EFFECT OF INHIBITORS ON PHOTO-OXIDATION OF
FORMIC ACID BY URANYL IONS
After Baur

Inhibitor	Constants in Equation (20)	
	a	b
Cl^-	1.27	430
Fe^{++}	0.89	5000
Hydroquinone	1.1	4520
Co^{++}	0.66	66
Mn^{++}	1.07	21

Discussion. The mechanism of the uranyl formate reaction has not been fully clarified by the investigations of Ouellet, which had the typical quantitative and theoretical shortcomings of the (qualitatively often valuable) work from Baur's laboratory.

The spectroscopic studies described in Chapter 2 (Section 2.2) make it probable that the reaction occurs not—or not mainly—by kinetic encounters between free excited uranyl ions and free formate ions (or formic acid molecules) in solution, but either partially or exclusively by the excitation of preformed complexes of both reactants. The high concentration of formic acid (about 2N) required to obtain the maximum quantum yield supports the assumption that light absorbed by free UO_2^{++} ions does not contribute significantly to the reaction. The natural lifetime of excited UO_2^{++} ions, calculated from the integrated intensity of the absorption band, is of the order of 10^{-3} sec; the good fluorescence yield indicates that this lifetime is abridged by less than a factor of 10 in consequence of radiationless energy dissipation. Even a lifetime of 10^{-4} sec should be sufficient for every free UO_2^{++*} ion to encounter, during the excitation period, an HCOOH molecule (or a $COOH^-$ ion), at formate concentrations of the order of, say, $10^{-3}M$ (cf. p. 239 for similar calculation for UO_2^{++} and I^- encounters), while the maximum quantum yield is obtained only at concentration of the acid a thousand times higher. One could suggest that reaction between UO_2^{++*} and formate requires thermal activation energy in addition to the excitation energy of the uranyl ion, but this is not very plausible. It seems much more likely that "saturation" of the uranyl–formic acid reaction with formic acid occurs when all uranyl ions are complexed with formate. Determining what kind of complexes are responsible would require a special spectroscopic and kinetic investigation. Offhand, one would attribute the reaction mainly or exclusively to the simplest binary complex, $\{UO_2^{++}HCOO^-\}$. According to its estimated equilibrium constant (cf. Table 2.7), this complexing should approach completeness in about $1M$ formic acid, the same concentration region in which the reaction with uranyl reaches its full rate. However, the relative importance of higher complexes cannot be estimated until (*a*) their existence and equilibrium constants are known, and (*b*) their absorption curves have been determined. The higher complexes, studied by Ahrland (cf. Chapter 2), with other anions (e.g. acetate) have, in general, increasingly intense absorption, particularly at the longer waves. Therefore, a comparatively small number of these complexes may absorb a disproportionately high fraction of incident light, particularly in certain wavelength regions, and thus account for a disproportionately large fraction of photochemical change.

The large photogalvanic effect observed in the system $UO_2^{++}+$ $HCOO^-$ (cf. p. 246) indicates that the primary effect of light is the reversible formation of high-energy products—probably free radicals, e.g.

$$\{UO_2^{++}.HCOO^-\} \underset{\text{dark}}{\overset{\text{light}}{\rightleftharpoons}} \{UO_2^{++}.HCOO\} \rightleftharpoons UO_2^+ + HCOO \quad (21)$$

where braces refer to a complex. Liberation of carbon dioxide may require the interaction of two HCOO radicals:

$$HCOO + HCOO \rightarrow HCOOH + CO_2 \qquad (22)$$

in competition with the back-reaction in (21).

In this picture, the inhibiting effect of the "desensitizers," studied by Hatt, Berger, and Ouellet, can be due either to their influence on the *equilibrium concentration* of the complex, or to their effect on the *kinetics* of photo-oxidation. Since the complex contains at least one, and probably two, ions, an electrostatic "salt effect" on its equilibrium concentration is inevitable, and exact determinations of the equilibrium constant should take it into account. It is, however, unlikely that this effect can be strong enough to explain the inhibition. Foreign *anions* could affect the equilibrium concentration of the complex more effectively and in a more specific way—namely, by displacing the formate anion from the complex. However, the fact that the strongest "desensitizers" are either oxidants or reductants suggests that *kinetic* phenomena may be more important than equilibrium effects. Kinetic inhibition can have two reasons: the added ions may either *retard* the *forward* reactions, or *accelerate* the *back*-reaction.

When UO_2^{++*} and $COOH^-$ react by kinetic encounters, the effect of oxidizable inhibitors could consist in their direct competition with formic acid as oxidation substrate in the photochemical process, e.g.

$$UO_2^{++*} + \begin{cases} HCOO^- \rightarrow UO_2^+ + HCOO \text{ (main reaction)} & (23a) \\ I^- \rightarrow UO_2^+ + \tfrac{1}{2}I_2 \text{ (competing reaction with} \\ \qquad\qquad\qquad\qquad\qquad \text{inhibitor)} & (23b) \end{cases}$$

With constant $[HCOO^-]$, the effect of increased iodide concentration would then obey an equation of the type (20).

If, however, $HCOO^-$ and UO_2^{++} react when they are combined in a complex, the interference of an inhibitor with the photochemical forward reaction appears unlikely; in this case, "kinetic" inhibition may be due to a catalytic effect of the inhibitor on the back reaction. For example, the back-reaction in (21):

$$UO_2^+ + HCOO \rightarrow UO_2^{++} + HCOO^- \qquad (24)$$

could be catalytically accelerated by iodide (or other *oxidizable* compounds) in the following way:

$$HCOO + I^- \rightarrow HCOO^- + I \text{ (or } \tfrac{1}{2}I_2) \tag{25a}$$

$$I \text{ (or } \tfrac{1}{2}I_2) + UO_2^+ \rightarrow UO_2^{++} + I^- \tag{25b}$$

An easily *reducible* inhibitor—such as Hg^{++}—also may act catalytically on the back-reaction by reacting in the reverse order, first with the reductant, and then with the oxidant:

$$UO_2^+ + Hg^{++} \rightarrow UO_2^{++} + Hg^+ \tag{26a}$$

$$Hg^+ + HCOO \rightarrow Hg^{++} + HCOO^- \tag{26b}$$

Curves showing the overall rate as function of $[I^-]$ or $[Hg^{++}]$, derived from mechanisms (21), (22), (25) or (21), (22), (26), are more complicated than those based on Equation (20) (because the catalytic back-reactions compete with reaction (22), which is of second order in respect to [HCOO]), but have the same general characteristics—initial linearity and ultimate "saturation." A choice between these relationships and Equation (20) could be made only on the basis of much more precise measurements than those of Baur and co-workers.

The dependence of the yield on the concentration $[UO_2^{++}]$, with its peculiar maximum at about 0.16M, offers another interesting problem. The initial increase of the yield undoubtedly is due to increased light absorption, which gradually becomes complete. (An additional cause of increase may be the gradual concentration of the light absorption in a thin layer near the entrance wall of the vessel, which leads to a higher density of primary photoproducts—such as free radicals—and thus increases the probability of bimolecular reactions of these radicals relative to the probability of their practically monomolecular "deactivation." If this factor is important, it should be possible to produce similar effects by an increase in light intensity; in other words, the quantum yield should be higher in stronger light.) The decline of the yield at the higher values of $[UO_2^{++}]$ is more difficult to explain.

Ouellet interpreted this decline as evidence of "self-desensitization" of uranyl ions. The mechanism of desensitization proposed by him is unsatisfying, but the effect itself is probably real and is paralleled by many similar observations on different sensitizers. An increase in the concentration of the light-absorbing species beyond a certain limit very often leads to a decline in the yield of the photochemical reaction. One explanation of this effect is *dimerization* (or, more generally, polymerization) of the absorbing molecules and a more efficient dissipation of excitation energy in the dimer or polymer (as revealed by the disappearance of fluorescence). Sometimes, however, the decline in the photochemical yield (and the "self-quenching" of fluorescence) are observed at concentrations where the absorption spectrum does not reveal any changes one might expect to find in case of polymerization. Förster (and others) suggested that, in such cases, a very small (and therefore spectro-scopically unidentifiable) proportion of dimeric or polymeric molecules suffices to accelerate substantially the dissipation of excitation energy, because energy exchange between resonating molecules occurs with high efficiency, even across several molecular layers of the solvent. The excitation energy consequently performs a kind of "Brownian movement" through the solution. If, in this migration, the excitation visits a dimeric or polymeric molecule, it is promptly dissipated, and quenching and deactivation result. Other interpretations of self-quenching and decline in photochemical yield at high concentrations of the absorbing species, also based on the energy transfer concept, have been suggested by Vavilov and by Franck. Vavilov simply postulated a certain probability of energy dissipation in each transfer; Franck suggested that dissipation occurs when the excitation energy visits a "hot" molecule, i.e. a molecule in which many vibrations are excited.

It will be noted that only one photochemical reaction—the *photo-oxidation* of formate to carbon dioxide, with reduction of U(VI) to U(IV) (Equation 19)—was postulated in the system uranyl+formate. No observations exist which would suggest the simultaneous occurrence of *sensitized decomposition* (dismutation) of HCOOH, which would lead to H_2 and CO_2 (while analogous reactions are common with the higher aliphatic acids).

The reasons can be sought in the difference between the reactions

$$HCOOH \rightarrow H_2 + CO_2 \qquad (27)$$

$$\text{and} \quad RCOOH \rightarrow RH + CO_2 \qquad (28)$$

In the first case, an H—C bond must be broken and an H—H bond formed; in the second, a C—C bond is broken (which is about

20 kcal weaker than the H—C bond), and a C—H bond is formed (which is only $\sim$ 5 kcal weaker than the H—H bond). Consequently, the second reaction requires 15 kcal less energy than the first one. As suggested, the two steps in the sensitized dismutation may be (*a*) photochemical oxidation of the carboxyl group by excited uranyl ions and (*b*) reduction of the alkyl group by the reduction product of uranyl ions, e.g. in the form of UO_2^+:

$$RCOOH \text{ (or } RCOO^- + H^+) + UO_2^{2+} \underset{}{\overset{light}{\rightleftharpoons}} RCOOH^+$$
$$\text{(or } RCOO + H^+) + UO_2^+ \qquad (27a)$$

$$UO_2^+ + RCOOH^+ \text{ (or } RCOO + H^+) \rightarrow UO_2^{2+} + RH + CO_2 \qquad (27b)$$

Because of the above-mentioned higher energy requirement, the UO_2^{2+} ion may be incapable of reacting in a similar manner with HCOOH:

$$UO_2^{2+} + HCOOH \text{ (or } HCOO^- + H^+) \underset{}{\overset{light}{\rightleftharpoons}} UO_2^+ + HCOOH^+$$
$$\text{(or } HCOO + H^+) \qquad (28a)$$

$$UO_2^+ + HCOOH^+ \text{ (or } HCOO + H^+) \rightarrow UO_2^{2+} + H_2 + CO_2 \qquad (28b)$$

Consequently, the only reaction actually occurring is that resulting in the reduction of U(VI) and oxidation of formic acid.

It could further be suggested that photo-oxidations generally result from reactions with a (uranyl + acid) complex, while sensitized decompositions occur by kinetic encounters; the absence of sensitized decomposition in the case of formic acid could then be correlated with the apparent exclusive role of complexes as reactants in this case. With other organic acids, in which photo-oxidation and sensitized dismutation both occur, photochemical reactions appear to be brought about both by light absorption in uranyl–acid complexes, and by encounters of excited uranyl ions with acid molecules (or their anions). In the reaction with acetate, the correlation between complex formation and photo-oxidation seems to be that suggested above for formic acid (cf. p. 262), but in the reaction with oxalate, it seems to be reversed (at least according to the data of Pitzer, Gordon, and Wilson, p. 287), with sensitized decomposition occurring by internal oxidation–reduction in the complex, and uranyl reduction to uranous salt by reactions involving free excited uranyl ions. However, the interpretation is very uncertain in both cases, and the very assumption of a correlation between the type of reaction and the absorbing species is at present only a working hypothesis.

(*b*) *Acetic acid.* In uranyl salt–acetic acid solutions, both *photo-oxidation* and *photocatalytic decarboxylation* are known to occur. The conditions governing the relative rates of these two reactions are not yet well understood, as the following chronological review of the experimental investigations will show.

The earliest observations were concerned with the formation of a precipitate in illuminated uranyl acetate solutions. Bach (1893, 1894, 1898) believed that he had proved that this precipitate— which consisted of the hydroxide of an oxidation stage lower than U(VI) (probably $U_3O_8.2H_2O$)—was formed only in vessels through which a stream of carbon dioxide was conducted, and concluded that he had succeeded in achieving a photochemical reduction of carbon dioxide, thus imitating the photosynthesis by green plants. He then made experiments in which dimethyl aniline was added to the uranyl acetate solution prior to exposure to light and found that only when the solution was traversed by a stream of carbon dioxide did a blue coloration appear. He saw in this a proof of the formation of formaldehyde by photochemical reduction of carbonic acid. Euler (1904) showed, however, that the acceleration of U_3O_8 hydrate precipitation in light by carbon dioxide was due simply to the removal of air [which reoxidizes U(IV) to U(VI)] and that the same effect could also be obtained by bubbling nitrogen through the vessel. He was unable to confirm Bach's observations with dimethyl aniline. Bach later (1904, 1906) acknowledged the correctness of Euler's criticisms and retracted his original claims.

Fay (1896) was the first to pay attention to gas liberation which occurs during the photochemical decomposition of uranyl acetate. He found it to be very slow, acetic acid occupying an intermediate position between propionic acid, which he found to be rapidly decomposed by UO_2^{++} in light, and formic acid, which he was unable to decompose in this way at all. (However, we have seen above that HCOOH *can* be decomposed, under favorable conditions, with a quantum yield close to 1; we noted there that Fay's observations can be explained by the fact that the absorption bands of the uranyl–formate complex lie at shorter wavelengths than those of the uranyl–propionate complex. A similar explanation can be suggested for the intermediate behavior of acetic acid (cf. Table 2.8). Fay could obtain measurable quantities of gas only from a mixture of 15 ml glacial acetic acid and 5 ml of a "concentrated" uranyl acetate solution; after 6 weeks of exposure to the sun, 13.4 ml gas were collected, consisting of equal volumes of CO_2 and CH_4. This composition indicated sensitized decarboxylation (dismutation) without simultaneous oxidation–reduction [which could be expected to produce primarily CH_3COO radicals and UO_2^+ ions, and, ultimately, oxidation products of acetic acid, such as $C_2H_6 + CO_2$, and reduction products of U(VI), such as U(IV) or U_3O_8].

Aloy (1900, 1901) noted that the precipitation [which indicates partial reduction of U(VI)] is made much more rapid by the addition, to aqueous uranyl acetate solution, of ether (or aldehyde, or glucose) or by the use of 90 per cent alcohol as solvent. A voluminous precipitate was obtained within a few minutes under these conditions; after several washings with boiling water it was free of acetate and consisted of pure U_3O_8 hydrate. A reaction that is completed so rapidly must be a thermal chain reaction of UO_2^{2+} with the organic compound, in which only the initial step is photochemical.

Zehenter (1900) noted that solutions of the double acetates, $KUO_2(COOCH_3)_3$ and $NaUO_2(COOCH_3)_2$, are practically photo-stable, in contrast to that of simple uranyl acetate, $UO_2(COOCH_3)_2$.

C. Neuberg (1908) found *glyoxalic acid* among the products of acetate photolysis sensitized by uranyl salts.

Baur (1908) predicted that photodecomposition of acetate by uranyl ions should give H_2 and CO_2 as the main products. In a subsequent experimental investigation (1918) he could not confirm this prediction; neither could he repeat Fay's observation of the predominant formation of CH_4 and CO_2. Instead, he found $CO_2 + C_2H_6$ as the main products, together with "a little hydrogen." (One hundred ml of a 0.08M solution of uranyl acetate, containing 2 moles/liter of free acetic acid, gave, in 2 days, 84 ml of gas, of which 54.3 ml proved to be CO_2, 24 ml C_2H_6, 2.4 ml was thought to be H_2, and 1.1 ml O_2.)

Baur formulated the reaction, in his peculiar electrochemical notation:

$$(U^{+6}) \pm \begin{cases} +CH_3COO^- \to \tfrac{1}{2}C_2H_6 + CO_2 \\ +H^+ \to \tfrac{1}{2}H_2 \end{cases} + U^{+6} \qquad (29)$$

Translated into the language of photochemistry, the reaction sequence (29) implies that the photoxidation of acetic acid, e.g.

$$UO_2^{++*} + CH_3COO^-$$
$$\rightarrow UO_2^+ + CH_3COO \rightarrow UO_2^+ + \tfrac{1}{2}C_2H_6 + CO_2 \quad (29a)$$

is followed by reoxidation of U(V) by water:

$$UO_2^+ + H^+ \rightarrow UO_2^{++} + \tfrac{1}{2}H_2 \qquad (29b)$$

Reaction (29b) could explain the liberation of hydrogen—if it actually does take place, which is doubtful. The main reaction, leading to ethane and carbon dioxide, certainly is not *sensitized decomposition* of acetic acid into $\tfrac{1}{2}H_2 + \tfrac{1}{2}C_2H_6 + CO_2$ (as Baur assumed), but its photochemical *oxidation* to C_2H_6 and CO_2 without the formation of hydrogen but with the reduction of an equivalent quantity of U(VI) to U(IV), as expressed in Equation (30):

$$UO_2^{++} + 2H^+ + 2CH_3COOH \xrightarrow{\text{light}} C_2H_6 + 2CO_2 + 2H_2O + U^{+4} \quad (30)$$

Baur and Rebmann (1922) later found that Fay had observed correctly, and that methane in fact *can* be produced by the photo-decomposition of acetic acid. In other words, in addition to the oxidation–reduction (30), sensitized decarboxylation:

$$CH_3COOH \xrightarrow[\text{light}]{UO_2^{++}} CH_4 + CO_2 \qquad (31)$$

also occurs in varying proportion.

The reaction products obtained in this investigation were mixtures of CO_2, CH_4 and C_2H_6; the proportion of ethane increased with an increase in the concentration of acetate relative to that of UO_2^{++} (brought about by the addition of free acetic acid, or of sodium acetate, to uranyl acetate solution).

Hydrogen was not regularly present, although "traces" were sometimes observed, and its previous identification as reaction product by Baur was now attributed to confusion with carbon monoxide.

Typical compositions of reaction gases are given in Table 4.6. Addition of Cl^- or Hg^{++} was found by Baur and Rebmann to inhibit the reaction; addition of $FeSO_4$ or $HCOOH$ was found to prevent

TABLE 4.6. PRODUCTS OF URANYL-SENSITIZED PHOTOCHEMICAL
DECOMPOSITION OF ACETIC ACID
After Baur and Rebmann (1922)

A

U(VI) acetate (%)	Free acetic acid (%)	Products (%)			
		CO_2	O_2	CH_4	N_2
6.8	12	18.6	0.9	43.8	12.0
4.6	40	56.3	0	43.9	0*
2.3	54	42.0	0.5	43.4	4.6†

* After 13 days.　† After 20 days.

B

U(VI) acetate (%)	Na acetate (%)	Acetic acid (%)	Products (%)					
			CO_2	O_2	CH_4	N_2	CO	C_2H_6
1.6	1.4	0	40.1	0.4	43.5	14.0	0	1.9
1.6	2	10	45.4	1.8	10.9	2.7	3.6	27.4*
7.4	1.6	37.7	27.0	1.6	47.0	11.4	0	5.0†

* After 2 days.　† After 6 days.

it completely (in the second case, without decomposition of formic acid!). This "negative catalysis" can occur by any of the four "static" or "kinetic" mechanisms suggested above for a similar inhibition in the system uranyl salt + formic acid, such as displacement of acetate from the complex with uranyl, deflection of the oxidative action of activated UO_2^{2+} ions to the inhibitor (the photo-oxidation of which is later reversed in the dark), e.g.

$$UO_2^{2+} + Fe^{++} \underset{\text{dark}}{\overset{\text{light}}{\rightleftharpoons}} UO_2^{+} + Fe^{+3} \qquad (32)$$

or catalytic acceleration of back-reactions, which prevents the stabilization of the primary oxidation products of acetic acid:

$$UO_2^{2+*} + CH_3COOH \rightarrow UO_2^{+} + CH_3COOH^{+} \text{ (primary}$$

$$\text{forward reaction)} \qquad (33a)$$

$$\text{CH}_3\text{COOH}^+ \begin{cases} +\text{CH}_3\text{COOH} \rightarrow \text{C}_2\text{H}_6 + 2\text{CO}_2 + 2\text{H}^+ \text{ (secondary} \\ \qquad\qquad\qquad\qquad\qquad \text{forward reaction)} \qquad (33b) \\ +\text{Fe}^{++} \rightarrow \text{CH}_3\text{COOH} + \text{Fe}^{+3} \end{cases}$$

$$\text{Fe}^{+3} + \text{UO}_2^+ \rightarrow \text{Fe}^{++} + \text{UO}_2^{++} \qquad\qquad\qquad \left.\begin{matrix} \text{(catalytic} \qquad (33c) \\ \text{back-} \\ \text{reaction)} \qquad (33d) \end{matrix}\right.$$

Substitution of (33b) for (33a), followed by (33c), leads to complete restoration of the original composition.

In some experiments, Baur and Rebmann also found small amounts of carbon monoxide, which they attributed to intermediate formation of glyoxalic acid, suggested earlier by Neuberg and Bacon:

$$\text{CH}_3\text{COOH} \xrightarrow[-2\text{H}]{+\text{O}} \text{OCH.COOH} \xrightarrow{-2\text{H}} \text{CO} + \text{CO}_2 \qquad (34)$$

Aloy and Rodier (1922) again studied the photo-oxidation of acetate in the presence of ether. The precipitated product was found to be U_3O_8 (aq.). It dissolved in acetic acid, giving a mixture of U(VI) and U(IV) acetates.

Aloy and Valdiguié (1923, 1925) extended the study of the reaction as it occurs in the presence of organic additives, by the observation of solutions in which *glucose* and *methylene blue* were added to uranyl acetate. They noted that uranyl acetate had no effect on glucose or methylene blue in the dark, even at elevated temperatures, but that it rapidly catalyzed, in light and in the absence of air, the oxidation of glucose by methylene blue.

Phenols, although easily oxidizable, did not react with uranyl acetate and methylene blue in light; admixture of phenol also prevented the oxidation of glucose. Hydroquinone, too, acted as a "protector."

As in the case of inorganic ions, protecting substances can be conceived either as substituting for acetate in the role of oxidation substrates, or as acting as catalysts in the back-reaction between the primary oxidation and reduction products.

Later, Aloy and Valdiguié (1925) found that decoloration of methylene blue by light in the presence of uranyl acetate also occurs if aldehydes and unsaturated hydrocarbons (ethylene, amylene, acetylene, and certain cyclic compounds) are provided as reductants instead of glucose.

Most of these experiments can be repeated with uranyl sulfate (instead of acetate); we will therefore return to them later. It is not clear from the description whether in these experiments the possibility of a direct photochemical action on methylene blue was eliminated. (This could have been done by showing that no decoloration occurs in the absence of uranyl salts.)

Courtois (1923) described some new observations on the decomposition of stoichiometric uranyl acetate solutions in light. A yellow precipitate was formed after several days' exposure to diffuse illumination; the precipitate was identified as basic U(VI) acetate. In direct sunlight, on the other hand, a violet precipitate of U(VI, IV) hydroxide was obtained in the presence of ether and air. Without air, the decomposition is slowed down; the solution becomes opaque, but no precipitate appears. Without ether, but in the presence of air, the violet precipitate is formed rather rapidly if the solution is concentrated. The sluggish gas evolution produces carbon dioxide and methane.

The question of whether the uranyl acetate reaction occurs by light absorption in a complex or by encounter of excited uranyl with acetate molecules or ions was first raised by the spectroscopic observations of Henri and Landau (1914). Their results—indicating the existence of a complex—were given in Table 2.6; Table 2.8 showed those of a somewhat more extensive study of Ghosh and Mitter (1928), while Figs. 2.8d and 2.8e illustrated the more recent and precise spectroscopic determinations of the complexing constants by Ahrland (1951). The latter lead to a value of 240 (moles/liter)$^{-1}$ for the first association constant of UO_2^{++} and CH_3COO^-, 2.3×10^4 (moles/liter)$^{-2}$ for the second one, and 2.2×10^6 (moles/liter)$^{-3}$ for the third one (20°C, ionic strength 1.0).

Since photosensitized decarboxylation, according to Baur and Rebmann, increases with decreasing ratio [acetate]/[uranyl], a possible working hypothesis is that photo-oxidation [e.g. reaction (30)] occurs when light is absorbed by uranyl acetate complexes, and sensitized decarboxylation [reaction (31)] when light is absorbed by free uranyl ions (which then react by encounters with acetic acid molecules). This agrees with the conclusion (cf. preceding section) that in the reaction with formic acid, where only complexes seem to react, oxidation–reduction is the only observed reaction (cf., however, the apparently different relationship in the case of oxalate, below). A quantitative test of the hypothesis that photo-oxidation results from light absorption by complexes has been made possible by Ahrland's determinations of the complexing constants, but has not yet been attempted. The relative role of the binary and the higher complexes also could be evaluated from Ahrland's data; the photochemical importance of the higher complexes may be out of proportion with their relative concentration, if the light used is absorbed by them much more strongly than by the free ions or simpler complexes.

(c) *Higher monobasic acids.* Only incidental observations are available on the reaction of UO_2^{++} in light with *propionic, butyric,* and *valeric* acid.

Prince L. L. Bonaparte (1842, 1843) noted that a solution of uranyl *valerate*, exposed to sunlight in a closed bottle, decomposes into violet uranium oxide or U(IV) valerate, and gaseous oxidation products of valeric acid.

Wisbar (1891) exposed to sunlight a solution of *butyric acid*, C_3H_7COOH, to which $UO_2(NO_3)_2$ had been added, and observed a decomposition accompanied by liberation of gas. Analysis of the latter showed 32 per cent CO_2. The remainder, made oxygen-free by phosphorus, contained 5 per cent N_2 (obviously, air was not effectively excluded). The other 63 per cent was a combustible gas; its combustion gave a threefold volume of CO_2, indicating that it was propane. The decomposition thus probably occurred according to the equation:

$$C_3H_7.COOH \xrightarrow[\text{light}]{UO_2} C_3H_8 + CO_2 \qquad (35)$$

The fact that some CO_2 was "missing" (32 per cent instead of 50 per cent) was attributed by Wisbar to losses of this gas by dissolution in water.

Fay (1896) investigated butyric as well as isobutyric acid and found both to decompose readily in sunlight in the presence of uranyl nitrate. Gas analysis confirmed the observations made by Wisbar with n-butyric acid. The liberated gas contained 50 per cent CO_2 and 50 per cent of a hydrocarbon, the combustion of which gave the volume change expected for C_3H_8. A viscous, green liquid or a light-green precipitate was formed.

Similar experiments with *propionic acid* gave about 50 per cent CO_2 and approximately 50 per cent of a hydrocarbon (for confirmation see Bacon, 1907). The combustion of the latter gave a volume change corresponding to $n = 2.38$ in C_nH_{2n+2}—possibly C_2H_6.

Butyric, propionic, and isobutyric acid decomposed at approximately the same rate. (As mentioned before, the cause of differences in the rate of photochemical decomposition of mixtures of UO_2^{++} with different aliphatic acids, noted by earlier observers, probably lies in the different intensity of light absorption in the visible and near ultraviolet by the complexes formed by these acids with uranyl ions.)

Courtois (1914, 1923) found dilute uranyl *propionate* and *butyrate* solutions to be "very stable" in darkness and in diffuse light. In sunlight, both solutions decomposed in the same way, in the presence as well as in the absence of air. A violet U_3O_8 hydrate was precipitated during the first day, without appreciable gas evolution; on the second day, gas evolution began. The gas proved to be $CO_2 + C_nH_{2n}$, with combustion experiments giving $n = 1.84$ for propionate (C_2H_6?). In the case of butyrate, Courtois found "a mixture of hydrocarbons."

In saturated propionate solution, the reduction of uranyl to U_3O_8 is complete after a month of exposure to sunlight; it is accelerated by the presence of ether, even in dilute uranyl salt solution. In methanol solution the precipitation is rapid, giving violet $U_3O_8.2H_2O$.

Isobutyrate, valerate, and isovalerate behave similarly; the decomposition becomes more rapid with increasing molecular weight of the acid.

2.2. *Dibasic Aliphatic Acids*

The acids studied were oxalic acid and its higher homologues—malonic acid, succinic acid and pyrotartaric acid. By far the most extensive work was carried out with oxalic acid.

(*a*) *Oxalic acid.* Ebelmen (1842) noted that a hydrated uranium oxide can be prepared by decomposition of a uranyl oxalate solution in light. The clear solution became turbid when exposed to light; a brownish-violet precipitate, which Ebelmen identified as a U_3O_8 *hydrate* (cf. Katz and Rabinowitch, 1951, Chap. 11), was formed, while a mixture of *carbon monoxide* and *carbon dioxide* escaped into the atmosphere. Nièpce de Saint-Victor and Corvisart (1860) reported that a solution containing 1 per cent uranyl nitrate and

4 per cent oxalic acid could be boiled for 40 hr in the dark without visible reaction, but evolved a combustible gas immediately upon exposure to light, even at 0°C. Similar results were obtained when U(VI) oxide was used instead of nitrate. Seekamp (1862), too, found that a solution containing 5 per cent oxalic acid and 1 per cent uranyl nitrate evolved gas bubbles in light; the solution became green and then discharged a green precipitate of *uranous oxalate*, $U(C_2O_4)_2$. The total gas produced consisted of 43 per cent carbon monoxide and 57 per cent carbon dioxide, but the ratio of the two components changed with the progress of the reaction. The residual solution was colorless, acid, and contained no oxalate ions; the products of its distillation with sulfuric acid indicated the presence of *formic acid*. (At first, in 1862, Seekamp thought that formic acid was a secondary product, due to a photochemical reaction between carbon monoxide and water; later, in 1865, he suggested direct formation of formic acid by decarboxylation of oxalic acid, $HOOC.COOH \rightarrow CO_2 + HCOOH$, which is much more plausible.)

Bolton (1866) observed that uranyl–potassium fluoride solutions react with oxalic acid in light, giving a mixture of a brownish-red with a green precipitate (the first one probably was identical with Ebelmen's uranium hydroxide, the second one with Seekamp's uranous oxalate).

Fay (1896) first described the work done by H. C. Jones, confirming the formation of carbon dioxide, carbon monoxide and formic acid by photochemical decomposition of uranyl oxalate. Jones varied the concentrations of uranyl oxalate and of free oxalic acid and found that one molecule of carbon dioxide was always formed when one molecule of oxalic acid was decomposed ($\Delta CO_2 = -\Delta C_2H_2O_4$), but that the relative quantities of carbon monoxide and formic acid, ΔCO and $\Delta HCOOH$, depended on the specific conditions of the experiment, and that the sum ($\Delta CO + \Delta COOH$) usually was slightly smaller than ΔCO_2. These observations are consistent with the assumption that the main reaction was the *sensitized decomposition* of oxalic acid, either by the reaction:

$$COOH.COOH \xrightarrow[UO_2^{++}]{light} CO_2 + CO + H_2O \qquad (36)$$

or by the reaction:

$$COOH.COOH \xrightarrow[UO_2^{++}]{light} CO_2 + HCOOH \qquad (37)$$

[Reaction (37) could be the first step of reaction (36).] The observed slight excess of CO_2 conceivably could be due to a third sensitized reaction:

$$COOH.COOH \xrightarrow[UO_2^{++}]{light} 2CO_2 + H_2 \qquad (38)$$

but the above-mentioned formation of uranous oxalate and of U_3O_8 hydrate (which was also noted by Jones) makes it much more likely that the excess carbon dioxide originated in *photochemical oxidation* of oxalic acid by uranyl ions:

$$COOH.COOH + UO_2^{++} + 2H^+ \xrightarrow{light} 2CO_2 + U^{+4} + 2H_2O \qquad (39)$$

By gradually depleting the photocatalyst, reaction (39) limits the amount of oxalic acid that can be decomposed photocatalytically by a given amount of uranyl ions.

The composition of the precipitate was found by Jones to depend on the ratio $x = $ [oxalic acid]/[uranyl]. When this ratio was high, the precipitate consisted of a mixture of green crystals with an amorphous green mass; when it was lower, the precipitate consisted mainly of the green mass, which gradually became purplish-brown. The latter product was obtained also by photodecomposition of a uranyl oxalate solution without added oxalic acid.

Continuing Jones' work, Fay tried to separate the two components of the precipitate. First he isolated the greenish crystalline precipitate and found it to be uranous oxalate hexahydrate, $U(C_2O_4)_2.6H_2O$ (thus confirming Seekamp's observations). Then he prepared the purplish-brown, amorphous product by photochemical decomposition of uranyl oxalate without added oxalic acid. No gas evolution was observed in this experiment. (Perhaps carbon dioxide was tied up, under these conditions, by the formation of U(IV) carbonate, which can effectively compete with the formation of oxalate when no excess oxalate ions are present.) Upon drying, the product became yellow; in this state, it contained from 1 to 1.5 per cent carbon. Fay therefore considered the purplish-brown precipitate as the salt of an organic acid, rather than as a hydroxide (as suggested by Ebelmen). Ebelmen's analysis was, however, confirmed by Aloy and Rodier (1920) and Courtois (1923). The latter found that the purplish-brown U_3O_8 hydrate, precipitated by light from uranyl oxalate solution, is transformed, by washing with cold water, into yellow $UO_3.2H_2O$. This oxidation can already occur during the photochemical reaction before the sedimentation of the precipitate.

Obviously, when U(IV) ions are formed by reduction of UO_2^{++} ions in a solution that contains hydroxyl and oxalate anions, and in which carbon dioxide and formic acid are produced at the same time, a competition must ensue between hydrolysis [i.e. association of U(IV) cations with hydroxyl ions, and subsequent precipitation of a hydroxide] and the complexing of the same cations with oxalate, carbonate or formate anions, and ensuing precipitation of basic or neutral U(IV) salts by reactions (40a) and (40b).

$$U(IV) + HOOC.COOH \rightarrow U(IV) \text{ oxalate} \tag{40a}$$

(green precipitate)

$$U(IV) + CO_2 + H_2O \rightarrow U(IV) \text{ carbonate} \tag{40b}$$

The composition of the precipitate actually formed must therefore depend on the pH of the solution and on the relative concentrations of oxalate, carbonate and formate ions at the time of precipitation.

An additional complication arises from the possibility of precipitation of U(VI) together with U(IV), e.g., in the form of a U_3O_8 hydrate. Formally, this precipitation can be interpreted as resulting from the capacity of U(VI) derived *anions*, such as $[UO_2^{++}(OH^-)_4]$, to enter into competition with other anions for the U(IV) cations, e.g.

$$U^{+4} + 2H_4UO_6^{--} \rightarrow U(H_4UO_6)_2 \; (= U_3O_8.4H_2O) \text{ (brown-}$$

$$\text{violet precipitate)} \tag{41}$$

Another possible mechanism of U_3O_8 precipitation is via the UO_2^{++} ions that had been hydrolyzed according to the Equation (42a):

$$2UO_2^{++} + H_2O \rightleftharpoons (UO_2\text{—}O\text{—}UO_2)^{++} + 2H^+$$

$$(= U_2O_5^{++} + 2H^+) \tag{42a}$$

$$U_2O_5^{++} + U^{+4} + 6OH^- \rightarrow U_3O_8.3H_2O \tag{42b}$$

Fay checked whether formic acid can be formed from water and carbon monoxide in light in the presence of UO_2^{++} ions and obtained negative results, confirming Seekamp's second interpretation (cf. above, p. 265). This formic acid produced by photochemical reaction of uranyl and oxalate must thus be a direct decomposition product of oxalic acid.

Bacon (1907, 1910) also measured the rate of decomposition of oxalic acid (in sunlight) in relation to the concentrations $[UO_2^{++}]$ and $[H_2C_2O_4]$. He found a "saturation" in respect to $[UO_2^{++}]$ (probably due to complete absorption of the light used) at 0.2 g uranyl acetate in 100 ml in the presence of 0.5 g oxalic acid. Saturation with respect to $H_2C_2O_4$ occurred between 0.3 g and 1.0 g oxalic acid in 100 ml, in the presence of 0.1 g UO_2^{++} (i.e. > 10 mole oxalate per mole uranyl; see below). Addition of acid or alkali had no effect on the rate as long as the solution remained acid. Uranyl nitrate gave the same results as uranyl acetate, and ammonium oxalate the same as free oxalic acid. Phenol, aniline, malachite green, methyl violet and fluorescein were found to act as inhibitors. Temperature changes (30–100°C) had no influence. Only very little formic acid was found by Bacon among the products of decomposition.

These early experiments have clearly established the complex character of the photochemical reaction of uranyl ions with oxalate. This reaction obviously includes:

1. *Photochemical oxidation of oxalic acid by uranyl* [reaction (39)], followed by various association and precipitation reactions of U(IV), such as (40a), (40b) or (41);

2. *Uranyl-sensitized decomposition of oxalic acid* (dismutation, decarboxylation), described by Equations (36) and (37), and probably also:

3. *Sensitized auto-oxidation*, in consequence of reoxidation of U(IV) in air:

$$U(VI) + HOOC.COOH \xrightarrow{\text{light}} U(IV) + 2CO_2 + 2H^+ \xrightarrow{+\frac{1}{2}O_2}$$
$$U(VI) + 2CO_2 + H_2O \quad (43)$$

Subsequent investigators have attempted to establish the mechanism of the various reactions and the conditions under which the one or the other predominates, but the picture is still far from complete.

Bruner and Kozak (1911) were interested in photocatalytic reactions. They took it for granted that photocatalytic auto-oxidations caused by uranyl salts are due to reaction sequences of type (43);

but found it more difficult to explain *photocatalytic decompositions* (decarboxylations) of type (36) and (37), which appear to involve no intermediate reduction of uranyl to uranous ions. In the hope of clarifying the mechanism of the reactions, they studied the kinetics of the formation of formic acid in uranyl-sensitized photodecomposition of oxalic acid, i.e., reaction (37).

Bruner and Kozak found that in a solution containing 0.5 g oxalic acid and 0.1 g uranyl nitrate in 20 ml, as much as 26–29 per cent of decomposed oxalate was converted to formic acid. When the concentration of uranyl nitrate was raised from 0.03 to 0.4 g, the proportion of formic acid increased. Increase of oxalate concentration, up to $[H_2C_2O_4] = 0.2$ g in 20 ml, caused an increase in the total rate of decomposition; from there on (in agreement with the earlier findings of Bacon) the reaction appeared "saturated" with oxalic acid (cf. below). A "saturation curve" was also obtained with varying $[UO_2^{2+}]$ (again confirming Bacon's findings); the rate reached its limiting level at about 0.5 g uranyl nitrate in 20 ml, corresponding to about 0.07M, much higher than was found by Bacon. However, if saturation is due to total light absorption, the level at which it occurs will depend on the thickness of the absorbing layer and the spectral composition of the light used. As in Bacon's experiments, temperature changes (4–80°C) had no noticeable effect on the decomposition rate.

Bruner and Kozak's experiments on the effect of wavelength and light intensity were too primitive for valid conclusions.

In contrast to Bruner and Kozak, Boll (1913) could find no formic acid at all in the products of uranyl-sensitized photodecomposition of oxalic acid $[10^{-3}M \ UO_2(NO_3)_2 + 10^{-3}M \ H_2C_2O_4]$; the conductivity of the solution after the reaction was negligible. He made the first attempt to determine the *quantum yield* of the uranyl-sensitized oxalate decomposition and found very high values, > 500. He concluded that this reaction does not obey Einstein's law of photochemical equivalency, but is a "catalytic" reaction in which light acts as a catalyst. These results were not confirmed by subsequent investigators.

Mathews and Dewey (1913) gave time curves of the photodecomposition of oxalic acid in the presence of varying amounts of uranyl nitrate. They noted that substitution of sulfate or acetate for nitrate left the results unchanged.

Henri and Landau (1914) compared the absorption spectra of uranyl nitrate, sulfate, chloride, and oxalate solutions, with and without the addition of oxalic acid. The results (cf. Table 2.6) indicated the formation of uranyl–oxalate complexes with enhanced absorption. Complexing appeared to be strong, but not quite complete, in stoichiometric uranyl oxalate solution. After this conclusion had been reached, much of the study of the mechanism of the uranyl–oxalate reaction was directed toward the understanding of the roles played in this reaction by various complex and non-complex molecular and ionic species. Unfortunately, no study of the uranyl oxalate system by spectrographic or potentiometric methods has yet been carried out that would take into consideration incomplete acid dissociation, uranyl ion hydrolysis, ionic strength effects, and the possibility of formation of higher complexes—in the same way as this was done by Ahrland for the uranyl acetate, thiocyanate, formate and other systems (Chapter 2). As a result, interpretation of the kinetics of the most important photochemical reaction of the uranyl ion still is mostly based on inadequate spectroscopic studies of Henri and Landau (1914), and of Ghosh and Mitter (1928) (cf. Chapter 2).

Baur (1919) began his studies of the uranyl oxalate reaction by discussing it from the point of view of his concept of "photolysis as molecular electrolysis" (cf. p. 233). By analogy with macroscopic electrolysis of oxalic acid, which produces glyoxylic acid (CHO. COOH), and also glycolic acid at the cathode, he proposed the reaction scheme:

$$[U(VI)]^{++} \begin{cases} + CHO.COOH \rightarrow CO + CO_2 + 2H^+ & \text{(44a)} \\ + COOH.COOH \rightarrow \\ \quad CHO.COOH + H_2O + 2H^+ & \text{(44b)} \end{cases} + U(VI)$$

in which glyoxylic acid appears as an intermediate product (produced by "cathodic depolarization" and consumed by "anodic depolarization").

Baur and Rebmann (1922) then undertook an experimental study. They asked whether the glyoxylic acid—which, according to scheme (44a, b), should occur as intermediate—could be made to accumulate by replacing it in the upper half of the process by another reductant ("anodic depolarizer"), such as KI, $FeSO_4$, HCOOH, or hydroquinone; however, efforts to prove the accumulation of glyoxylic acid in the presence of these reductants had no success. In this study, the effect of certain additions on the rate and character of decomposition was noted. For example, addition of 10 ml saturated $HgCl_2$ solution (to a mixture of 25 ml 0.5N oxalic acid + 5.5 ml saturated UO_2SO_4 solution + 10 ml 0.5N H_2SO_4 + 150 ml H_2O) increased the proportion of carbon dioxide in the gaseous products from 35–40 to 50–55 per cent, decreasing correspondingly the proportion of carbon monoxide. Calomel was formed. This observation was explained by the reaction scheme:

$$[U(VI)]^{++}_{--} \begin{cases} + C_2O^{--} \rightarrow 2CO_2 \\ + 2HgCl_2 \rightarrow Hg_2Cl_2 + 2Cl^- \end{cases} + U(VI) \tag{45}$$

with $HgCl_2$ acting as "cathodic depolarizer." As usual, Baur's "polarization" and "depolarization" reactions can be replaced by reduction and reoxidation of the sensitizer, e.g.

$$U(VI) + C_2O_4^{--} \xrightarrow{\text{light}} 2CO_2 + U(IV) \tag{46}$$

$$U(IV) + 2HgCl_2 \rightarrow U(VI) + Hg_2Cl_2 + 2Cl^- \tag{47}$$

The effect of potassium iodide was found to be similar to that of calomel, but somewhat weaker (the proportion of CO_2 was increased only slightly, from 40 to 46 per cent); some iodine was formed. Since iodide is a reductant, it was postulated that it acts as "anodic depolarizer" in competition with oxalate:

$$[U(VI)]^{++}_{--} \begin{cases} + 2I^- \rightarrow I_2 \\ + U(VI) \rightarrow U(IV) \end{cases} + U(VI) \tag{48}$$

$$[U(VI)]^{++}_{--} \begin{cases} + C_2O_4^{--} \rightarrow 2CO_2 \\ + I_2 \rightarrow 2I^- \end{cases} + U(VI) \tag{49}$$

This combination of "polarizing" and "depolarizing" reactions is equivalent to a primary photo-oxidation of I^- to I_2 by excited uranyl ions, followed by a uranyl-sensitized oxidation of $C_2O_4^-$ to CO_2 by iodine.

Addition of ferrous sulfate (2.5 g $FeSO_4$ in 40 ml, containing some Fe^{+3}) strongly increased the formation of carbon dioxide in light (from 51 to 72 per cent); the solution became green in consequence of U(IV) formation. The total yield of decomposition increased. These effects could be explained in the same way as those of iodide, with Fe^{+2} and Fe^{+3} substituting for I^- and I_2 respectively in Equations (48) and (49) (or in equivalent equations not using Baur's "electrochemical" notation). Sodium sulfite, despite its reducing properties, had no effect.

Addition of *formic acid* led to simultaneous decomposition of both $H_2C_2O_4$ and HCOOH.

Organic reductants, such as *pyrogallol* (7.3 g) or *hydroquinone* (19 g in 50 ml water), added to 100 ml solution containing 5 g sodium uranate and 5 g oxalate, produced effects similar to those of iodide or ferrous sulfate.

In a *neutral* solution of sodium diuranate ($Na_2U_2O_7$) and uranyl oxalate, light also caused the production of carbon dioxide; the latter was formed in excess of the amount corresponding to catalytic decomposition into HCOOH and CO_2, indicating some photo-oxidation.

In another paper, Baur (1922) described the results of experiments made in his laboratory by Haggenmacher, in which the yield of formic acid was determined by distillation instead of by oxidation with $HgCl_2$ in the reaction mixture (the method used by Bruner and Kozak), because in the latter procedure U(IV) also can be oxidized, making the results unreliable whenever photoxidation accompanies catalytic decomposition.

The formation of formic acid was qualitatively confirmed, but only small quantities of this acid were found. The amount of CO_2 formed was somewhat higher than that of CO; the excess decreased with the decreasing ratio $x = [H_2C_2O_4]/[UO_2SO_4]$ (Table 4.7). This could be due either to formic acid formation (Equation 37) or oxidation–reduction (Equation 39); for an argument in favor of the first explanation see below.

A new investigation of the uranyl–oxalate reaction in light was carried out in Baur's laboratory by Büchi (1924). His aim was to

TABLE 4.7. $\Delta CO_2/\Delta CO$ RATIO IN THE DECOMPOSITION PRODUCTS OF
OXALIC ACID
After Baur (1922)

0.5M $H_2C_2O_4$ (ml)	0.77M UO_2SO_4 (ml)	$\Delta CO_2/\Delta CO$
8.5	2	1.20
8.5	4.2	1.23
8.5	11.0	1.05
8.5	18.0	1.03

decide whether the decomposition takes place by encounters between free, excited UO_2^{++} ions and $(COOH)_2$ molecules (or oxalate ions), or by internal rearrangement in a complex of the two reactants. In favor of complex formation, Büchi quoted the cryoscopic observations of Dittrich, who found that UO_2SO_4 is less strongly dissociated into ions than UO_2Cl_2 or $UO_2(NO_3)_2$, the fact that the conductivity of uranyl oxalate solutions is much lower than that of uranyl sulfate solutions, and Henri and Landau's spectroscopic observations.

He considered the latter as proving the existence of a 1 : 1 complex, $UO_2C_2O_4$, in solution. The enhanced solubility of $UO_2C_2O_4$ in the presence of oxalic acid can be considered as indicating the formation of complexes with more than one oxalate ion (or oxalic acid molecule) per uranyl ion.

In Büchi's experiments, mixtures containing 0.06M UO_2^{++} salt and from 0.0004 to 0.13M $H_2C_2O_4$ were illuminated in a 2.7 cm deep vessel by a 1500 W incandescent lamp. With 0.03M $H_2C_2O_4$, the rate of decomposition remained constant until 35 per cent of the oxalate was used up. Exclusion of air had no influence. Doubling of all concentrations increased the rate by only 15 per cent.

Change in oxalate concentration (at constant $[UO_2^{++}]$) had a strong effect on the overall rate (cf. Table 4.8).

The "saturation" of the reaction with oxalic acid occurred under these conditions in the neighborhood of $x =$ [oxalate]/[uranyl] $= 1$ (Table 4.9). This is a result which Büchi considered as indicating the formation of a stable complex of one uranyl ion and one oxalate ion.

The yield of U(IV) was < 1 per cent of that of decomposed oxalic acid, except in the presence of much excess acid ($H_2C_2O_4$ or H_2SO_4),

TABLE 4.8. EFFECT OF OXALATE CONCENTRATION ON RATE OF
URANYL–OXALATE DECOMPOSITION IN LIGHT
After Büchi (1924)
[Uranyl] = 0.06M

x = [Oxalate]/[Uranyl]	Δ[Oxalate]/Δt (M/hr)
8	0.086
0.25	0.022

TABLE 4.9. EFFECT OF AVERAGE OXALATE/URANYL RATIO (x) ON
RATE OF URANYL SENSITIZED OXALATE DECOMPOSITION
After Büchi (1924)

$\bar{x}$	7.2	2.0	1.43	0.84	0.43	0.27
Relative yield	1.05	1.00	0.97	0.83	0.48	0.27

where it reached 2–3 per cent. Addition of formic acid did not increase the U(IV) formation, indicating that U(IV) does not arise through secondary oxidation of formate.

Effect of additions. 0.6M H_2SO_4 ($6H_2SO_4$ to $1H_2C_2O_4$) decreased the decomposition rate by 34 per cent, a result which was attributed by Büchi to the displacement of oxalate from its complex with the uranyl ion by the sulfate.

The effect of hydrochloric acid (0.06M) was similar, yielding a 12 per cent decrease in rate. An equivalent quantity of *formic* acid had no effect on the rate of decomposition of oxalic acid. In contrast to Baur and Rebmann, Büchi found formic acid to be protected from photochemical decomposition by the presence of oxalate. He suggested that this may explain why considerable quantities of this acid can be found among the decomposition products of oxalic acid. (The relative yields of the decomposition of the two acids may depend not only on their relative concentrations, but also on wavelength, since the absorption spectra of the two complexes are different.) Büchi confirmed Bruner and Kozak's findings that the proportion of formic acid in the product increases with decreasing ratio [oxalate]/[uranyl], as well as with increased acidity (cf. Table 4.10); this explains the findings of Baur and of Bacon, who worked

in 0.5M H_2SO_4 and in 5 per cent oxalic acid respectively. The formation of U(IV), on the other hand, *increases* with acidity, but not
enough to compensate for the decrease in formic acid production.

TABLE 4.10. FORMIC ACID PRODUCTION BY SENSITIZED OXALATE
DECOMPOSITION AS FUNCTION OF OXALATE/URANYL RATIO, x, AND OF
ACIDITY
After Büchi (1924)

	[Oxalate]/[Uranyl]			[Oxalate]/[Uranyl] = 2	
	1	2	8	with 0.06M HCl	with 0.6M H_2SO_4
% formic acid	40	36	26	7	6

The decomposition of uranyl oxalate solution without added
oxalic acid proceeds in an apparently different way. Formic acid is
formed in this case as well, but much more reduction to U(IV)
takes place.

In discussing these results, Büchi used the generally accepted ideas
of photochemistry, rather than Baur's "electro-photochemical"
concepts. The fact that he found oxalate saturation near $x = 1$, led
him to assume that the reaction occurs in a stable 1 : 1 complex
(UO_2^{++} + oxalate). If one assumes that this complex is practically
undissociable, its concentration must increase linearly between
$x = 0$ and $x = 1$, and then become constant.

If the light absorption by free uranyl ions is entirely ineffective,
the curve showing reaction rate (quantum yield γ) as function of x
also should show, at $x = 1$, a break between a linearly ascending
and a horizontal branch.

This, of course, cannot be *strictly* true. The association constant
cannot be *infinitely* large; complete association, therefore, must be
approached asymptotically. For 1 : 1 association, the proportion
of UO_2^{++} bound in a complex with oxalate is determined by the
equations:

$$K[UO_2^{++}] \times [\text{oxalate}] = [\text{complex}] \tag{50a}$$

$$[UO_2^{++}] + [\text{complex}] = [UO_2^{++}]_0 \tag{50b}$$

$$[\text{oxalate}] + [\text{complex}] = [\text{oxalate}]_0 \tag{50c}$$

where $[UO_2^{++}]_0$ and $[oxalate]_0$ are the total amounts of the two reaction components. (In this formulation, the distribution of free oxalate between neutral molecules, monovalent ions, and divalent ions is neglected; cf. below.) Equations (50a–c) lead to a quadratic equation for [complex] as function of x ($x = [oxalate]_0/[UO_2^{++}]_0$), which can be formulated so as to contain either the total uranyl concentration, $[UO_2^{++}]_0$, or the total oxalate concentration, $[oxalate]_0$, as parameter.

$$[\text{complex}] = \frac{K[UO_2^{++}]_0(1+x)+1}{2K}$$
$$-\sqrt{\left(\left[\frac{K[UO_2^{++}]_0(1+x)+1}{2K}\right]^2 - x\left[UO_2^{++}]_0\right]^2\right)} \quad (51)$$

(or a similar equation with $[UO_2^{++}]_0$ replaced by $[oxalate]_0$, and x replaced by $1/x$).

If $K[UO_2^{++}]_0 \gg 1$, Equation (51) simplifies, as expected, to $[\text{complex}] = x[UO_2^{++}]_0 = [oxalate]_0$; if $K[oxalate]_0 \gg 1$, the corresponding equation with $[oxalate]_0$ as parameter simplifies to $[\text{complex}] = (1/x)[oxalate]_0 = [UO_2^{++}]_0$.

If we assume that the rate of decomposition is equal to the number of quanta of light absorbed in unit time by the complex (and if oxalate itself does not absorb in the spectral region used), we obtain for the quantum yield:

$$\gamma = \frac{\alpha_c[\text{complex}]}{\alpha_c[\text{complex}] + \alpha_f[UO_2^{++}]}$$
$$= \frac{\alpha_c[\text{complex}]}{(\alpha_c - \alpha_f)[\text{complex}] + \alpha_f[UO_2^{++}]_0} \quad (52)$$

where α_c and α_f are the absorption coefficients of complexed and free uranyl ions, respectively. If either $[\text{complex}] \gg [UO_2^{++}]$ (meaning practically complete complexing), and α_f is *not* $\gg \alpha_c$, or $\alpha_c \gg \alpha_f$, and $[UO_2^{++}]$ is not $\gg [\text{complex}]$, the quantum yield tends to unity. If the two terms in the denominator of (52) are of the same order of magnitude, an expression for γ as function of x can be obtained by insertion of (51) into (52). However, the resulting equation will contain $[UO_2^{2+}]_0$ or $[oxalate]_0$ as separate parameters, and not merely their ratio, x; γ will be a function of x alone only if the complex is stable, namely:

$$\gamma = \frac{\alpha_c x}{\alpha_c x - \alpha_f (x-1)} = \frac{\alpha_c}{(\alpha_c - \alpha_f) + (\alpha_f/x)}$$

$$\simeq \frac{1}{1 + \alpha_f/x\alpha_c} \text{ (if } \alpha_c \gg \alpha_f) \text{ for } x < 1 \tag{53}$$

$$\gamma \simeq 1 \text{ for } x > 1 \tag{54}$$

The alternative collision mechanism of reaction gives, for the probability of an encounter between an excited UO_2^{2+} ion and an oxalate molecule or ion, the "Stern–Volmer type" equation: Equation (20). If each encounter results in reaction, the same equation applies also to the quantum yield of the decomposition of oxalate:

$$\gamma = \frac{v_2 [oxalate]_0}{v_1 + v_2 [oxalate]_0} = \frac{[oxalate]_0}{v_1/v_2 + [oxalate]_0} \tag{55}$$

where v_2 is the bimolecular rate constant of the reaction of excited uranyl ions with oxalate, and v_1 the monomolecular rate constant of the deactivation of excited uranyl ions by fluorescence and energy dissipation.

According to Equation (55), γ must approach unity asymptotically with increasing [oxalate]. An important difference between the two mechanisms is that in the first one, for a given value of $[oxalate]_0$, γ depends on x, i.e. on $[UO_2^{2+}]_0$, while in the second case γ does not depend on $[UO_2^{2+}]$, but only on the oxalate concentration.

Büchi gave Fig. 4.6 as proof of the actual occurrence of a break in the yield vs. x curve at $x = 1$. He pointed out that if the experimental results in the range below $x = 1$ are used to determine the parameters in Equation (55), a quantum yield of $\gamma = 0.23$ is calculated for $x = 1$ while the experimental value is close to 1.0. This was derived by Büchi from four γ determinations with white light filtered through crystal violet and rhodamine; assuming $\bar{\lambda} = 420 \, m\mu$, he obtained $\gamma = 1.03-1.15$ (see, however, below for recent redeterminations of the quantum yield, which gave γ values < 1).

The initial slope of the curve in Fig. 4.6 is determined by the ratio of the absorption coefficients of the free (or sulfate-complexed) uranyl and the oxalate-complexed uranyl; Büchi calculated for this ratio a value of 1 : 1.3 (cf. Table 4.8).

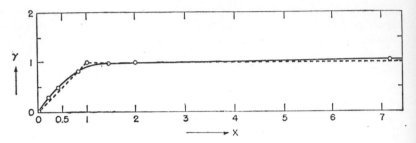

FIG. 4.6. Quantum yield of uranyl-sensitized oxalate decomposition as function of the ratio $x = $ [oxalate]/[uranyl]. After Buchi (1924).

Baur (1924) supplemented Büchi's result by an "interpretation" in the electrochemical language. His original mechanism with glyoxalic acid as intermediate (Equation 44a,b) required two quanta, or $\gamma = 0.5$; to explain Büchi's value of $\gamma = 1$, Baur now wrote

$$U(VI)^{+}_{-} \begin{Bmatrix} + {}^{-}OOC \rightarrow CO_2 \\ | \\ + {}^{-}OOC + 2H^{+} \rightarrow CO + H_2O \end{Bmatrix} + U(VI) \qquad (56)$$

for the reaction in presence of much H^{+}, and

$$U(VI)^{+}_{-} \begin{Bmatrix} + {}^{-}OOC \rightarrow CO_2 \\ | \\ + {}^{-}OOC + H^{+} \rightarrow HCOO^{-} \end{Bmatrix} + U(VI) \qquad (57)$$

for reaction in less acid solution, using the same molecule of oxalate both as "anodic" and as "cathodic" depolarizer!

Equivalent interpretations in ordinary photochemistry are:

$$U(VI)^{*} + {}^{-}OOCCOO^{-} \rightarrow U(IV) + OOCCOO$$
$$\xrightarrow{+2H^{+}} U(VI) + H_2O + CO + CO_2 \qquad (58a)$$

$$U(VI)^* + {}^-OOCCOO^- \rightarrow U(IV) + OOCCOO$$

$$\xrightarrow{+H^+} U(VI) + HCOO^- + CO_2 \qquad (58b)$$

Anderson and Robinson (1925) discussed the use of the oxalic acid–uranyl system in an actinometer for ultraviolet light. Using mercury light of very high intensity (up to 10^{18} quanta absorbed per second), they obtained, in solutions containing from 2×10^{-5} to 2×10^{-2}M uranyl nitrate, and 0.1N in oxalic acid, quantum yields between 1/24 and 1/557. In a single experiment with monochromatic light (365 mμ, 5×10^{16} quanta/sec), a value of $\gamma = 1/37$ was found. The interpretation of the results was even less plausible than the numerical values. (For example, it was suggested that radioactivity of uranium may be responsible for its sensitizing properties; light absorption by UO_2^{2+} ions was treated as incidental, or even as inhibiting the decomposition of oxalic acid, etc.)

Bowen and Watts (1926) used the Anderson–Robinson "radiometer" but redetermined the quantum yield. In 0.01M $UO_2SO_4 + 0.1$N oxalic acid, in the total light of a quartz lamp and assuming $\bar{\lambda} = 313$ mμ, they obtained, in three experiments, $\gamma \simeq 1.0$.

West, Müller and Jette (1928) discussed the relation between inhibition of a photochemical reaction and quenching of fluorescence of the light-absorbing species, using as examples the effect of anions such as Cl^-, Br^-, CNS^-, I^- on the decomposition of oxalate and on the fluorescence of uranyl salt solutions.

Both effects increase in the above series, from Cl^- to I^-. This order was compared by West *et al.* with the order of ionic deformabilities; comparison with the order of electron affinities would be more pertinent, if one assumes quenching to be due to *electron* transfer (rather than *energy* transfer) from the excited uranyl ion to the quencher.

Numerical data on the quenching of UO_2^{2+} fluorescence and inhibition of sensitized oxalate decomposition were given in an accompanying paper by Müller (1928). Figure 4.7 shows the antiparallelism of decomposition rate and fluorescence. It will be noted that, in contrast to Büchi's findings, $H_2C_2O_4$ saturation is reached here asymptotically, at about $[H_2C_2O_4]/[UO_2^{2+}] = 1.5$, rather than sharply at $x = 1$. The fluorescence becomes too weak for measurement above $x = 1$.

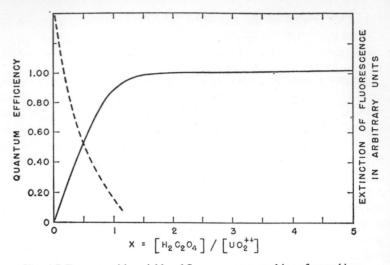

FIG. 4.7. Decomposition yield and fluorescence quenching of uranyl ions by oxalic acid. After Müller (1928).

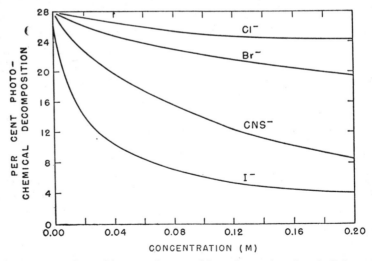

FIG. 4.8. Effect of ions on decomposition of uranyl oxalate in light. After Müller (1928).

The effect of ions on the rate of oxalate decomposition is shown in Fig. 4.8 for $[UO_2^{++}] = 0.01M$, and $[H_2C_2O_4] = 0.1M$.

Comparing the observations of different investigators, we obtain Table 4.11 for the values of x and for the absolute concentrations, $[oxalate]_0$, at which "oxalate saturation" was observed.

TABLE 4.11. "SATURATION" OF THE URANYL–OXALATE REACTION WITH OXALATE

Observer	Saturating value:	
	x	$[oxalate]_0$
Bacon (1907, 1910)	~ 10	0.3 g in 100 ml (0.05M)
Bruner and Kozak (1911)	—	0.2 g in 20 ml (0.14M)
Büchi (1924)	1	— (0.06M)
Müller (1928)	~ 1.5	—
Pringsheim (1937)*	> 1	(> 0.02M)

$x = [oxalate]_0/[uranyl]_0$
* Complex saturation from spectral data (cf. Table 2.10).

Pierce (1929) compared the kinetics of uranyl-sensitized decomposition of oxalic acid with that of the decomposition of malonic acid (cf. below, p. 297). He found the *temperature coefficient* to be substantially 1 for oxalic acid (3–73°C) (confirming the results of Bruner and Kozak, and Bacon), as against 1.13 ± 0.02 for malonic acid. A quantum yield $\gamma = 0.25$ was found by Pierce, Leviton, and Noyes for malonic acid decomposition (in 0.05M solution), as compared to $\gamma \cong 1$, given by Büchi for oxalic acid (in 0.06M oxalic acid). (More recent measurements, to be described below, gave $\gamma \simeq 0.6$ for oxalic acid decomposition.)

Discussing the relative merits of the "complex formation" theory (Büchi) and the "kinetic encounter" theory, Pierce favored the former, again quoting conductivity data (Dittrich) and spectroscopic evidence (Henri and Landau; Ghosh and Mitter). He submitted that the observed rate saturation in respect to oxalic acid concentration (Table 4.11) supports the complexing theory and contradicts the encounter theory "unless a very long life of $[UO_2^{++}]*$ is assumed." [However, this lifetime in fact is long—of the order of 10^{-4} sec. Calculations show that for a lifetime of this duration the probability of an encounter with a reactant present in a concentration $> 0.05M$ (Table 4.11) must be high.]

As a counter-argument supporting the encounter theory, Pierce quoted first the fact that the equilibrium constants calculated by Ghosh and Mitter, however high, are not high enough to assume complete complexing under the conditions of Büchi's experiments, which gave $\gamma = 1$. More specifically, with the value given in Table 2.7 ($K = 115$) complexing should be about 2/3 complete in a mixture of $0.06M$ UO_2^{2+} and $0.06M$ oxalic acid; if complexes alone were assumed to react, a quantum yield of 1 could be expected under these conditions only if the absorption by the complex were very much stronger than that by the free ions; Pierce thought that experimental data do not confirm this suggestion. This is, however, not true for near ultraviolet and visible light; furthermore, according to more recent data, the quantum yield is closer to 0.5 than to 1.0. The complex theory thus seems to be adequate to explain the results. However, Pierce pointed out that the complex theory is also less suitable than the encounter theory to explain the observed absence of a temperature coefficient, and the parallelism between the effects of ions on UO_2^{2+} fluorescence and on the sensitized decomposition of oxalate, illustrated in Fig. 4.8. The second argument, in particular, is not easily answered (cf. below). Pierce therefore suggested that perhaps free ions and complexes both take part in the reaction.

Leighton and Forbes (1930) studied the uranyl-sensitized oxalate reaction from the point of view of precision actinometry. They enumerated the advantages of the reaction: absence of dark reaction; a wide absorption band; "zero order" light reaction; temperature coefficient of practically unity; small effect of additions (?); ease of analysis (by means of permanganate titration of oxalate). Pointing out the wide discrepancies of previous quantum yield determinations (from $\gamma = 0.04$ according to Anderson and Robinson, through $\gamma = 1$ according to Bowen and Watts, and Büchi, to $\gamma \simeq 500$ according to Boll), Leighton and Forbes proceeded to systematic redetermination of γ in monochromatic ultraviolet light. The yields were determined from 255 to 490 mμ, under the following conditions:

(a) $0.01M$ UO_2SO_4; $0.05M$ $H_2C_2O_4$; $25°C$

(b) $0.01M$ UO_2SO_4; $0.05M$ $H_2C_2O_4$; $9.8°C$

(c) 0.001 to $0.01M$ UO_2SO_4; 0.01 to $0.05M$ $H_2C_2O_4$; $25°C$

The results of experiment (*a*) and of one series in experiment (*c*) are shown in Fig. 4.9. It indicates that quantum yields are $\simeq 0.6$ at all wavelengths, but that an unmistakable minimum of γ occurs at 366 mμ. Variations of [UO_2^{++}] have little effect on γ, as long as

$$x = \frac{[H_2C_2O_4]}{[UO_2SO_4]} > 5$$

Addition of sodium sulfate or sodium hydroxide was found to enhance light absorption; the latter was decreased by sulfuric acid.

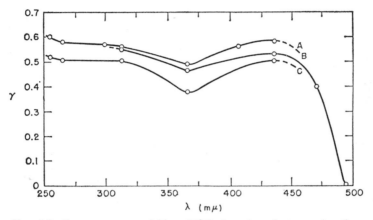

FIG. 4.9. Gross quantum yield at 25°C plotted against wavelength. Curve A summarizes experiment (a). Curve B, same solution, unstirred. Curve C, a stirred solution 0.02M in UO_2SO_4 and 0.04M in $H_2C_2O_4$.

All three additions, particularly sulfuric acid, decreased the quantum yield. An attempt was made to correct the quantum yields by apportioning the light absorption between free UO_2^{++} ions and uranyl oxalate complexes on the assumption that $\alpha_{complex}$ is the maximum absorption coefficient obtainable when [acid] $\gg$ [uranyl].

Related to total absorption, the quantum yields declined slightly —from 0.59 at $x = [H_2C_2O_4]/[UO_2^{++}] = 50$, to 0.52 at $x = 1$; they became practically constant ($\gamma = 0.57$ to 0.59) when related to the (calculated) absorption by a 1 : 1 complex alone. This somewhat improved constancy was considered as an argument for a 1 : 1 complex as the only carrier of the reaction.

The authors suggested that the parallelism of quenching and inhibition (Müller), which appears to favor the encounter theory (cf. above) could be explained by deactivating collisions of excited complexes with the inhibiting ions, or by displacement of oxalate ions from their complexes with uranyl by CNS^-, Br^-, or I^- ions. The first hypothesis requires that the time between light absorption and reaction in a complex should not be small compared to the lifetime of excitation of a free atom or ion, while one would expect a reaction in a complex to follow excitation within a much shorter time—roughly the period of one or a few molecular vibrations (10^{-12} sec). The second hypothesis is feasible, but requires quantitative checking by spectroscopic or other measurements of the several complexing constants.

Checks on the temperature dependence of the reaction, made by Leighton and Forbes, indicated the need of determining the light absorption separately at each temperature; otherwise values > 1 may be obtained. For example, if the yield at $9.8°C$ is compared with that at $25°C$ without regard to changes in absorption, a temperature coefficient of 1.13 is calculated.

In concluding, the authors recommended a system containing $0.01M$ uranyl sulfate and $0.05M$ oxalic acid, at $25°C$, as best suitable for photometric purposes.

The uranyl–oxalate system was used by Heidt and Daniels (1932) as test system for a monochromator. They obtained the quantum yields listed in Table 4.12. The quantum yield appears to be independent of the anion. Addition of $1M$ H_2SO_4 had no effect on the yield. The quantum yield found by Heidt and Daniels ($\gamma \simeq 0.5$) is in satisfactory agreement with the results of Leighton and Forbes.

TABLE 4.12. QUANTUM YIELDS IN URANYL–OXALATE SYSTEM
Heidt and Daniels (1932)

Composition			Absorption (%)	Average quantum yield
UO_2^{++} salt	conc. (M)	$H_2C_2O_4$ (M)		
$UO_2C_2O_4$	0.0005	0.0045	72 (2 cm cell)	0.64
$UO_2C_2O_4$	0.0017	0.0330	86 (1 cm cell)	0.46
UO_2SO_4	0.0017	0.0330	86 (1 cm cell)	0.59
$UO_2(NO_3)_2$	0.0017	0.0330	86 (1 cm cell)	0.53

313 mμ at 25°C

TABLE 4.13. QUANTUM YIELDS IN THE URANYL–OXALATE SYSTEM
After Brackett and Forbes (1933)

λ (mμ)	$[UO_2^{++}]$ (M)	$[H_2C_2O_4]$ (M)	γ	Probable error
278	0.01	0.04853	0.59	± 0.01
253	0.01	0.04967	0.63	± 0.03
208 (28°)	0.01	0.04967	0.48	± 0.01
208 (28°)	0.03	0.04995	0.55	± 0.01
208 (28°)	0.02	0.01963	0.53	± 0.01
208 (28°)	0.00	0.05058	0.02	± 0.01

Brackett and Forbes (1933) redetermined the quantum yields at 278 and 253 mμ, and added a measurement at 208 mμ (using a Zn spark as light source). Table 4.13 shows the results. The gross quantum yield at 208 mμ was distinctly (20 per cent) smaller than at the longer waves (Fig. 4.10). It was natural to ascribe this to light absorption by oxalic acid. The following equation was used for correction:

$$\gamma_{corr} = \frac{\gamma_{gross} - \gamma_{(H_2C_2O_4)}(\alpha_a c_a / \Sigma \alpha c)}{(\Sigma \alpha c - \alpha_a c_a)/\Sigma \alpha c} \tag{59}$$

where $\gamma_{(H_2C_2O_4)}$ is the quantum yield of direct photochemical decomposition of oxalic acid; the α's designate extinction coefficients, and the c's concentrations; the subscript a refers to free oxalic acid. The corrected curve (Fig. 4.10) shows a steady *increase* of γ between 400 and 208 mμ, which could be attributed to decreasing "cage" effect (diminishing chance for the primary photochemical products to react back before their separation; the escape is faster when the products are formed by larger quanta and therefore with higher kinetic energies). The renewed increase of γ at $\lambda > 400$ mμ requires a different explanation.

It will be noted that in the figure corrections are made in two alternative ways—by assuming that the photochemical reaction occurs in complexes containing either one or two C_2O_4 groups (in other words, the concentration of free oxalic acid is calculated by deducting, from the total oxalate concentration, either one or two equivalents of the uranyl present). The experiments do not add new arguments for (or against) the assumption of complexes as reaction carriers.

Forbes and Heidt (1934) made additional measurements at ten times lower concentrations than before (0.001M [UO_2^{2+}] and 0.005M [$H_2C_2O_4$]) in order to minimize the direct photochemical decomposition of oxalic acid (the absorption by oxalic acid decreased, in consequence of this change of concentration, much more strongly than the absorption by uranyl ions). The quantum yields remained the same as before, at 313, 279, 254, and 220 mμ (a slight drop, to $\gamma = 0.50$, occurred at 208 mμ). Even at 0.005M $UO_2SO_4 + 0.0025$M

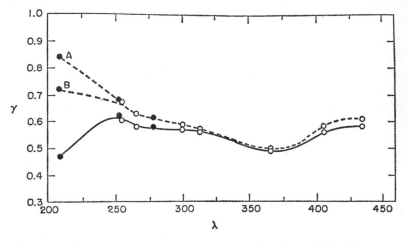

FIG. 4.10. ——— gross yield; – – – corrected yield. A, if $UO_2C_2O_4$ is the complex; B, if $UO_2(C_2O_4)_2$ is the complex. For a solution 0.05M in $H_2C_2O_4$ and 0.01M in UO_2SO_4. ○, Leighton and Forbes; ●, Forbes and Brackett; temp., 25°C. A and B practically coincident at 255 mμ and above.

oxalic acid, the quantum yields were unchanged at 254, 279, and 313 mμ. This result seems to be incompatible with the assumption of a 1 : 1 complex as the *only* reaction carrier, since the contribution of free UO_2^{2+} ions to the total absorption at 254–313 mμ is unlikely to be quite negligible compared to that of an at least four times smaller amount of the complex.

Pitzer, Gordon, and Wilson (1936) were interested in the factors affecting the ratio of photocatalytic and direct photochemical reaction. They measured the yield of U(IV) formation as function of the composition of the reaction mixture.

Figure 4.11 shows the proportion of direct oxidation–reduction for an initial composition $[UO_2^{++}] = [C_2O_4^{--}]$ (i.e. $x = 1$).

The curve indicates that a rapid reduction of U(VI) began when the oxalic acid concentration had become smaller than that of uranyl ($x < 1$). [The increase in $\Delta CO_2/\Delta CO$ ratio with increasing x observed by Baur (cf. Table 4.7) must therefore be attributed to enhanced formation of formic acid, and not oxidation–reduction.]

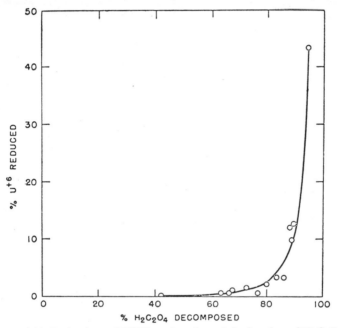

FIG. 4.11. Reduction of U(VI) as function of the fraction of $H_2C_2O_4$ decomposed. After Pitzer, Gordon, and Wilson (1936).

Protection of uranyl from reduction by excess oxalic acid is most easily understood if one assumes that light absorbed by uranyl–oxalate complexes causes sensitized decomposition of oxalate into CO, H_2O, and CO_2 (or CO_2 and HCOOH), while light absorbed by free UO_2^{++} ions (or a different kind of complexes, cf. below) causes oxidation–reduction. (It will be recalled that in the case of acetate, we have reached the reverse conclusion, namely, that light absorption in a complex produces oxidation–reduction, and light absorbed in free ions produces sensitized decomposition. This reversal is hardly credible, although there is no gainsaying that different anions and different complexes may behave in a different way.)

Pitzer *et al.* discussed the most probable composition of the reactive complex. Büchi had suggested $UO_2C_2O_4.H_2C_2O_4$, dissociating into $2H^+ + UO_2(C_2O_4)_2^{--}$. Leighton and Forbes assumed that neutral $UO_2C_2O_4$ is the reaction carrier. The occurrence of complex U(VI) *anions* was demonstrated by Dittrich (1899), who showed that in solutions containing $Na_2C_2O_4$, uranium moves towards the anode. Pitzer and co-workers followed Büchi in the assumption that the associated group is $UO_2C_2O_4.H_2C_2O_4$, dissociating into $2H^+$ and a complex anion, $UO_2^{++}(C_2O_4^{--})_2$, which can also be interpreted as the second association complex of UO_2^{++} and $C_2O_4^{--}$ ions. Since the ionic dissociation constant of $UO_2C_2O_4$ is small [10 per cent in saturated (0.0156M) solution, a value derived from the freezing point depression of water; a similar figure follows from Dittrich's conductivity measurements], "free UO_2^{++}" must be present mostly—up to 90 per cent—in the form of neutral $UO_2C_2O_4$ molecules. If sensitized decomposition of oxalic acid, ascribed above to "complexes" in general, is attributed, more specifically, to complex *anions*, oxidation–reduction may perhaps be ascribed to neutral molecules, $UO_2C_2O_4$, rather than to free uranyl ions. Such hypotheses are bound to remain guesses, until a systematic study of the products and the kinetics of the uranyl–oxalate reaction is coupled with the investigation of the composition of the reacting solutions by spectroscopic and electrochemical methods, leading to the knowledge not only of the relative concentration of the different molecular and ionic species, but also of their relative role in the absorption of light of different wavelengths.

In corroboration of their theory, Pitzer and co-workers quoted the observation that addition of uranyl oxalate increases the acidity of oxalic acid, instead of decreasing it (the usual effect of neutral salts on acids containing the same anion). The effect becomes understandable if a stronger complex acid is formed by association of $UO_2C_2O_4$ with $H_2C_2O_4$. Estimation of acid strength of the complex from the measured pH indicates complete dissociation (0.02 moles H^+ from 0.1 mole $UO_2C_2O_4 + 0.1M$ $H_2C_2O_4$). This gives (for 25°C):

$$K = \frac{[UO_2C_2O_4]\,[C_2O_4^{--}]}{[UO_2(C_2O_4)^{--}]} = 1.23 \times 10^{-5} \qquad (60)$$

At very high values of the ratio $[H_2C_2O_4]/[UO_2^{++}]$ (such as 10 : 1) a still higher complex may be formed; a potassium salt of the acid $H_6(UO_2)_2(C_2O_4)_5$ has been described in the literature.

Weiss (1938) discussed the uranyl–oxalate reaction from the point of view of the electron transfer theory. He pointed out that only this theory (as contrasted to the energy transfer theory) can account for the parallelism between the quenching of fluorescence and the inhibition of oxalate decomposition by ions described by Müller (cf. p. 279). This consideration seems offhand to apply to kinetic encounter mechanisms only, but Weiss suggested that complex formation between sensitizer and substrate does not change the situation, since electron transfer phenomena can occur within the excited complex in the same way as between excited uranyl ions and other partners in an encounter. This, however, is not quite correct, because, as mentioned above, the time between excitation and electron transfer within a complex should be much shorter where transfer does not have to await a kinetic encounter. Furthermore, this time must be independent of the concentration of the electron donor (oxalate), so that the extent of inhibition should depend only on the concentration of the quenching ions. The effect of the concentration of oxalic acid on the yield and (if the inhibitor acts by displacing the substrate from the complex, and not by kinetic encounters) also the effect of the concentration of the inhibitor, must be different in the two mechanisms. Closer kinetic studies are needed to decide whether the quenching and inhibition phenomena can be brought into accord with the hypothesis of complexes as exclusive reaction carriers.

The mechanism of sensitized oxalate decomposition is, according to Weiss, as follows (neglecting the complex formation):

$$UO_2^{++*} + HC_2O_4^- \rightarrow UO_2^+ + HC_2O_4 \text{ (electron transfer)} \quad (61a)$$

$$HC_2O_4 \rightarrow CO_2 + HCOO \quad (61b)$$

or $$HC_2O_4 \rightarrow CO_2 + CO + OH \quad (61c)$$

$$\left. \begin{array}{l} HCOO + UO_2^+ \rightarrow HCOO^- + UO_2^{++} \\ \text{or} \quad OH + UO_2^+ \rightarrow UO_2^{++} + OH^- \end{array} \right\} \begin{array}{l} \text{back} \\ \text{reactions} \end{array} \quad \begin{array}{l} (61d) \\ (61e) \end{array}$$

Net reaction: $$HC_2O_4^- \rightarrow CO_2 + HCOO^- \quad (61)$$

or $$HC_2O_4^- \rightarrow CO_2 + CO + OH^- \quad (61A)$$

This scheme shows how sensitized decomposition, (61) or (61A), can result from an initial oxidation–reduction, (61a): U^{+6} oxidizes the oxalate anion, $HC_2O_4^-$, to a radical, HC_2O_4; the latter decomposes (into CO_2, and either the radical HCOO, or the radical OH and the molecule CO); the radicals reoxidize U^{+5} to U^{+6}, and are themselves converted into stable ions, $HCOO^-$ and OH^-.

[A similar scheme can be devised by assuming reversible reduction of U(VI) to the U(IV) instead of the U(V) level.]

Weiss suggested that the retardation of the oxalate decomposition by strong acids (p. 274) could be due to decreasing ionization of oxalic acid. He postulated that only the ions, $HC_2O_4^-$, and not the neutral molecules, $H_2C_2O_4$, can serve as electron donors in reaction (61a).

In the presence of I^- ions the fluorescence of UO_2^{2+} may be completely quenched, but the photodecomposition of $H_2C_2O_4$ still goes on (cf. below). Weiss attributed this to the capacity of iodine atoms (or iodine molecules) formed in the quenching process to carry out the chemical oxidation of oxalic acid (in competition with the back-reaction, which is the reoxidation of U(IV) by I_2).

Carter and Weiss (1940) proceeded with an experimental reinvestigation of the reaction, especially of the influence of fluorescence quenchers on the ratio of the two products, CO and HCOOH (cf. Baur and Rebmann, p. 270). They suggested that such an influence would be incomprehensible from the point of view of the energy transfer theory (Schneider), as well as from that of the reaction in a stable complex (Büchi), but could be explained if mechanism (61) is assumed. The same they also thought to be true of the explanation of the pH effect on the rate of decomposition.

In a series of measurements Carter and Weiss determined ΔCO, $\Delta H_2C_2O_4$, $\Delta U(IV)$ and $\Delta HCOOH$. Oxygen was excluded; oxalic acid was used (with or without H_2SO_4 addition), as well as $Na_2C_2O_4$ (pH 5).

The results obtained with oxalic acid in the presence of potassium iodide were similar to those of West (p. 279), but their meaning was somewhat clearer because West did not exclude oxygen.

Iodide concentrations of the order of $10^{-3}M$, while decreasing considerably the yield of fluorescence, were without influence on the rate of sensitized decomposition of oxalic acid. In the presence of $0.033M$ $H_2C_2O_4$, as much as $0.1M$ KI was found to be needed to reduce the rate of decomposition by 38 per cent; approximately the same is true of an equivalent $Na_2C_2O_4$ solution. In the presence of $0.01M$ H_2SO_4, the inhibiting effect is somewhat stronger (26 per cent inhibition by $0.05M$ I^-). Table 4.14 shows the inhibitions by $0.01M$ I^- observed in oxalic acid solutions of different acidity.

TABLE 4.14. INHIBITION OF URANYL–OXALATE REACTION BY IODIDE
After Carter and Weiss (1940)

	H_2SO_4 (M)			
	0	0.01	0.1	1
Inhibition by $0.01M$ I^-	-2.7 per cent	-4.6 per cent	-20 per cent	-19 per cent

The results listed in Table 4.15 were found in the study of the effect of composition on the proportion of CO and HCOOH in the products.

TABLE 4.15. PRODUCTS OF URANYL–OXALATE REACTION
After Carter and Weiss (1940)

Composition of the photolyte	ΔCO (per cent)	ΔHCOOH (per cent)
$H_2C_2O_4$	51	44*
$H_2C_2O_4 + I^-$ (0.1M)	42	42
$H_2C_2O_4 + Br^-$ (0.1M)	44	43
$Na_2C_2O_4$	23	72
$Na_2C_2O_4 + I^-$ (0.1M)	18	56
$H_2C_2O_4 + H_2SO_4$ (0.01M)	56	38
$H_2C_2O_4 + I^-$ (0.1M)	38	34
$H_2C_2O_4 + I^-$ (0.01M)	54	36
$H_2C_2O_4 + H_2SO_4$ (0.1M)	76	14
$+ H_2SO_4 + I^-$ (0.01M)	75	11
$+ H_2SO_4$ (1M)	53	0
$H_2C_2O_4 + H_2SO_4 + I^-$ (0.01M)	34	0

* The rest is $U(IV) + CO_2$.

The two notable results of these experiments are, *first*, the wide discrepancy between the concentrations of I^- which quench fluorescence, and the (much higher) concentrations of this anion needed to inhibit the reaction of uranyl ions with oxalic acid; and, *second*, the influence of composition (acidity, presence of iodide) on the *proportion* of the two reaction products, carbon monoxide and formic acid (rather than on the *total yield* of decomposition; cf., however, Fig. 4.8).

To explain the results, Carter and Weiss used scheme (61) complemented by the assumption of the acid–base equilibria

$$UO_2^+ + 4H^+ \rightleftharpoons U^{+5} + 2H_2O \tag{62a}$$

$$UO_2^+ + 2H^+ \rightleftharpoons U^{+5} + 2OH^- \tag{62b}$$

which stabilize the UO_2^+ ions and thus retard the back-reactions (61d) and (61e). As a consequence, the stationary concentration of the radicals COOH and OH becomes higher with increasing acidity, and the probability of the reaction between them

$$OH + COOH \rightarrow CO_2 + H_2O \tag{63}$$

increases. This reaction eliminates the partners with which U(V) must react in the back-reactions (61d) or (61e) and leads to a net reduction of UO_2^{2+}. This mechanism can explain why the relative yield of UO_2^{2+} reduction (compared to the yield of sensitized decomposition of oxalic acid) increases with increasing acidity (as found by Büchi).

The inhibiting effect of H^+ ions on the overall yield of decomposition is understandable if $HC_2O_4^-$ is the electron donor, as assumed in (61a), since the ionic dissociation of $H_2C_2O_4$ declines with increasing $[H^+]$.

The fact that I^- ions can completely quench fluorescence without reducing the yield of sensitized decomposition was attributed by Carter and Weiss to capacity of the iodine atoms formed by the quenching reaction

$$UO_2^{2+} + I^- \rightleftharpoons UO_2^+ + I \tag{64}$$

to carry the reaction sequence further by themselves oxidizing oxalic acid [reaction (65)]. When the concentration of oxalic acid is low, the probability of the back-reaction in (64) compared to that of the forward reaction

$$I + HC_2O_4^- \rightarrow I^- + HC_2O_4 \rightarrow I^- + COOH + CO_2 \qquad (65)$$

is high, and the yield of photo-oxidation is small. However, this does not explain why the yield of photo-oxidation increases at higher I^- concentrations, since the latter should not change the relative probabilities of the two reactions. Furthermore, it seems from earlier experiments (cf. above) that very high $[I^-]$ concentrations inhibit the photochemical reaction of I^- with oxalate.

When $[I^-]$ is high, the yield of CO and HCOOH must decrease and more U(IV) must be produced, because the reactions

$$COOH + I \rightarrow CO_2 + HI \qquad (66)$$

and $$C_2O_4^- + I_2 \rightarrow 2CO_2 + I^- + I \qquad (67)$$

which "snatch away" the radicals needed for regeneration of UO^{++}, become important. The latter reaction is known from photo-oxidation of oxalate by iodine.

McBrady and Livingston (1946) investigated the formation of tetravalent uranium by reaction of uranyl ions with oxalate using Leighton and Forbes' actinometer. Under anaerobic conditions, this side reaction amounted to about 1 per cent of the main one.

The determinations were made by measuring the absorption of a weak "scanning" beam of light at 650 mμ (where the absorption by UO_2^{++} is negligible) while illuminating with strong light from a mercury arc at right angle to the scanning beam. The extinction curves of uranyl and uranous ions were determined over the range 400–700 mμ by means of a Beckman spectrophotometer.

With 0.01M UO_2SO_4 and 0.05M oxalic acid, in a vessel which was previously evacuated and filled with carbon dioxide, U(IV) was formed in light at a steady rate of 1.5×10^{-7} moles/liter/sec. When the concentration of oxalic acid was lowered, the yield of U(IV) formation decreased (Table 4.16). The influence of acidity is shown by Table 4.17. It was found that the quantum yield of formation of U(IV) could be represented by the equation

$$\gamma = \frac{0.0136\,[H^+]}{0.0455 + [H^+]} + \frac{0.63\,[U^{+4}]}{[H^+]} \qquad (68)$$

When the concentration of oxalic acid is not smaller than that of uranyl sulfate ($x > 1$), the quantum yield of U(IV) formation is a function of [H$^+$] (or of the total concentration of oxalic acid) represented adequately by the first term in Equation (68), but when the concentration of oxalic acid is small, only the initial rate of reaction obeys the simplified formula, the rate becoming auto-catalytically accelerated as U(IV) is formed. It increases approximately linearly with [U(IV)] [second term in Equation (68)]. In this case the formation of U(IV) continues for a while in darkness.

TABLE 4.16. QUANTUM YIELD, γ, OF U(IV) FORMATION IN
URANYL + OXALIC ACID REACTION
After McBrady and Livingston (1946)
[UO$_2$SO$_4$] = 0.1M

[H$_2$C$_2$O$_4$] (M)	$\gamma \times 10^3$
0.2	8.6
0.1	7.7
0.05	6.0*
0.025	4.3
0.01	2.3†

* Measured at two light intensities—about 4×10^{15} and 2×10^{16} quanta absorbed/ml/sec.
† Initial rate, increasing autocatalytically with formation of U(IV).

TABLE 4.17. QUANTUM YIELD OF U(IV) FORMATION
After McBrady and Livingston (1946)
[UO$_2$SO$_4$] = 0.01M   [H$_2$C$_2$O$_4$] = 0.05M

Medium	$\gamma \times 10^3$
0.04M H$_2$SO$_4$	7.4
0.02M NaOH	5.9*
0.04M NaOH	5.7*

* Initial rate; autocatalytically accelerated.

When air is admitted, U(IV) is reoxidized. An illumination of uranyl sulfate solution in the presence of air therefore causes only a passing appearance of the U(IV) bands.

Attempts were made to detect the presence of U(V) in the irradiated solution by using green light (510–600 mμ) for scanning (it has been reported that U(V) salts are red). However, no reversible increase in absorption in the green was noted during the illumination period.

In the discussion of these results, McBrady and Livingston pointed out that in the experiments of Büchi, and of Leighton and Forbes, the quantum yield of UO_2^{++} sensitized decomposition of oxalic acid was found to be practically independent of oxalic acid concentration if the latter was equal to or higher than that of uranyl ($x > 1$). The (small) yield of U(IV) formation increased in the same region with increasing $[H_2C_2O_4]$; this increase is forecast by Equation (68), which, however, relates it to a change in $[H^+]$, rather than in $[H_2C_2O_4]$ (assuming the first dissociation of oxalic acid to be complete, the second negligible). This also permits a single equation to cover the results of experiments with 0.04M H_2SO_4.

McBrady and Livingston assumed that the light-absorbing species is the complex $[UO_2^{++}(COOH)_2]$, or, more exactly, its monopositive ion,

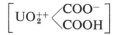

Here again the assumption is made that the first acid ionization is complete, the second negligible; the alternative is to assume that the second ionization, too, is complete, because the complex probably is a much stronger acid than free oxalic acid. The first assumption is used because it fits the experimental results somewhat better (but not decisively so).

When the initial concentration of oxalic acid is low ($\leqslant 0.025$M), or when the acid is neutralized by NaOH, or $\geqslant 70$ per cent of the initial oxalic acid has been decomposed, the autocatalytic effect of U(IV) becomes apparent, and the addition of the second term in equation (68) becomes necessary. Under the same conditions an "after-effect" becomes noticeable—formation of U(IV) by a first-order dark reaction from a colorless "precursor" formed in light.

McBrady and Livingston gave a sequence of reaction which could account for the observed regularities. The essential steps are

$$UO_2C_2O_4 \text{ or } (UO_2HC_2O_4^+) \underset{\text{dark, } k_2}{\overset{h\nu}{\rightleftharpoons}} UO_2C_2O_4^* \qquad (69a)$$

$$UO_2C_2O_4* \xrightarrow{k_3} X \text{ [metastable molecule, or two radicals}$$

$$\text{such as } UO_2^+ \text{ and } C_2O_4^-] \quad (69b)$$

$$X \begin{cases} +H_2O \xrightarrow{k_4} UO_2(OH)_2+CO_2+CO \text{ (sensitized} \\ \qquad\qquad\qquad\qquad\qquad\qquad \text{decomposition)} \\ \\ +H^+ \xrightarrow{k_5} UOOH^+ +2CO_2 \qquad\qquad\qquad\qquad (69c) \\ \\ \xrightleftharpoons{K_6} UO_2+H^+ +2CO_2 \text{ (reduction to U(IV))} \\ \\ +UO_2 \xrightarrow{k_6} A \rightarrow 2UO_2+2CO_2 \text{ (U(IV) catalysis)} \end{cases}$$

The metastable intermediate X can react in (69c) either by decomposition of oxalate to CO_2 and CO and regeneration of U(VI), or by H^+ catalysed internal oxidation–reduction, yielding U(IV) and CO_2, or with U(IV) to bring about "autocatalytic" formation of more CO_2 and U(IV).

The species of the molecules used in these equations are tentative. The reaction leading to UO_2 is formulated so as to explain the stimulation of the oxidation–reduction by acidity.

Equations (69a, b, c) give for the steady rate of the reaction (i.e. the rate established after the concentrations of all intermediates have approximately become constant),

$$\gamma_{\text{steady state}} \simeq \left(\frac{k_3}{k_3+k_2}\right) \left\{ \frac{[H^+]}{\dfrac{k_4}{k_5}+[H^+]} + \frac{k_6 K^{[UOOH^+]}}{k_4[H^+]} \right\} \quad (70)$$

in formal agreement with the empirical Equation (68).

The long-lived intermediate A is introduced to account for the "after-effect" in the dark.

The mechanism suggested is also consistent with the results of Leighton and Forbes; it is still, however, general and uncertain in most details.

(b) *Higher dibasic acids. Malonic acid* (COOH.CH₂.COOH). Fay (1896) attempted to study the photochemical decomposition of uranyl malonate but found that $UO_2(OOC)_2CH_2.3H_2O$, which he prepared from hot concentrated solutions of malonic acid and uranyl nitrate, was almost insoluble in water. This compound dissolves, however, in malonic acid or potassium malonate solution. Both solutions proved to be stable in sunlight. A dilute solution of uranyl oxalate and malonic acid decomposed in sunlight, but very slowly.

The decomposition of malonic acid by uranyl ions in light was later noted by Berthelot and Gaudechon (1913).

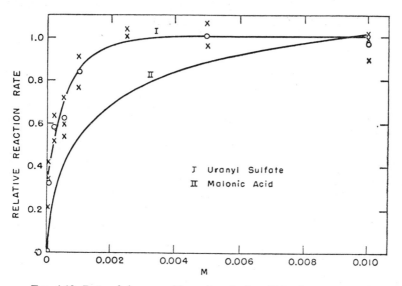

FIG. 4.12. Rate of decomposition of malonic acid in the presence of uranyl sulfate. After Pierce, Leviton, and Noyes (1929). Curve I: Rate as function of $[UO_2^{++}]$ at 0.05M malonic acid. Curve II: Rate as function of [malonic acid] at 0.01M UO_2SO_4.

Pierce, Leviton, and Noyes (1929) noted that addition of uranyl sulfate to 0.05M malonic acid, in a quartz vessel exposed to the full light of a quartz mercury arc, increased considerably (e.g. from 12.6 ml to 55 ml) the amount of liberated gas. (In the absence of the sensitizer, gas was produced by direct photochemical decomposition of malonic acid.) In both direct and sensitized decomposition, 95–96 per cent of the gas was carbon dioxide. Results were similar with Pyrex-filtered light ($\lambda > 300$ mμ). Figure 4.12 shows the effects on the rate of increased concentration of uranyl ions, observed at constant malonic acid concentration (0.05M), and of increased malonic acid concentration observed at constant uranyl concentration (0.01M). Curve II will be further discussed below; curve I shows saturation with respect to $[UO_2^{++}]$ to occur (in a vessel 5 mm deep, in 0.05M malonic acid) below 2.5×10^{-3}M; above 5×10^{-3}M the yield of decomposition fell off slightly. This can hardly be attributed to complete absorption of incident light. With $[UO_2^{++}] = 2.5 \times 10^{-3}$M, for the absorption in a 0.5 cm deep vessel to exceed 90 per cent, the average absorption coefficient, $\bar{a}$, must be $> 10^3$. According to Table 2.8, this is the case for the uranyl–malonic acid complex only below 270 mμ, while $\bar{\lambda}$ has been estimated by Pierce and co-workers to be, in their experiments, 290 mμ without the Pyrex filter, and 320 mμ with the Pyrex filter. It thus seems that "uranyl saturation" must be attributed in this case not to complete light absorption, but to energy dissipation by $UO_2^{++}* + UO_2^{++}$ interaction. The decline of the yield above 10^{-2}M UO_2^{++} is in agreement with this hypothesis.

In four runs, lasting 5–7 hr each, with no $[UO_2^{++}]$ added (3 per cent light absorption), the quantum yield of direct decomposition of malonic acid (0.5M) was found to be 0.68, 0.71, 0.73, and 0.81 respectively. In the presence of 5×10^{-3}M uranyl sulfate, the experimentally determined absorption was 27.6 per cent (confirming the above estimate that it must be incomplete); the quantum yields (averaged for 3.5–7.3 hr runs) were 0.25–0.27 in quartz ultraviolet light ($\bar{\lambda} = 290$ mμ) and 0.24–0.27 in Pyrex-filtered light ($\lambda = 320$ mμ).

Addition of 5×10^{-3}M H_2SO_4 had no effect on the quantum yield, indicating that acid dissociation of malonic acid was irrelevant.

According to Ghosh and Mitter, the concentration of the complex at 0.01M UO_2SO_4 is $x = 80(0.01 - x)(0.01 - x) = 0.0035$, corresponding to only 35 per cent complexing. If this were the explanation of the fact that the maximum quantum yield is only 0.27, further increase in malonic acid concentration should increase the yield. Since this was not found to be the case, it appears that reaction can occur not only by light absorption in the complex, but also by absorption in a free uranyl ion and its subsequent encounter with a malonic acid molecule, and that the low quantum yield is due to causes other than incomplete complexing, such as primary recombination ("cage effect") (cf., however, the later results of Pierce, given below).

In an attempt to analyze the relation between UO_2^{++} concentration and yield, Pierce *et al.* first used a simple equation

$$-\frac{d\,[\text{malonic acid}]}{dt} = k_1 I_0\left(1 - 10^{-k\,[UO_2^{++}]d}\right)$$

$$+ k_2 I_0\, 10^{-k\,[UO_2^{++}]d} \qquad (71)$$

where the first term represents the uranyl-sensitized, and the second term, the direct decomposition of malonic acid. The best approximation could be achieved by assuming $k_1 I_0 = 1.00$, $k_2 = 0.327$ and $kd = 0.64$ (d = 2 cm, $[UO_2^{++}]$ in millimoles/liter). The value of k [320 (moles/liter)$^{-1}$ cm^{-1}] seems somewhat high (cf. Table 2.8), but much of the light used was < 330 mμ.

Equation (71) does not explain the decline of the rate at high $[UO_2^{++}]$ values. To account for this it was assumed that uranyl–malonic acid complexes can be deactivated by collisions with UO_2^{++} ions. The resulting equation required, however, a more rapid decline than was actually observed.

The effect of acid concentration on the rate could be explained by collision theory more satisfactorily than by the complex formation theory, but the simple collision formula [Stern–Volmer, Equation (20)] did not fit the data exactly. The fit could be improved by adding a factor $[UO_2^{++}]/([UO_2^{++}] + [\text{acid}])$ accounting for deactivation of excited UO_2^{++} ions by encounters with non-excited uranyl ions.

Pierce (1929) found that, in contrast to the similar reaction with oxalate, the photodecomposition of malonic acid sensitized by uranyl sulfate has a marked temperature coefficient ($Q_{10} = 1.13 \pm 0.02$) between 3° and 73°C.

He corrected the statement of Pierce, Leviton, and Noyes that no enhancement of absorption is noticeable in uranyl–malonate mixtures; this is only true at the longer waves, while marked increase in absorption occurs at 220–320 mμ, as noted in the earlier observations by Ghosh and Mitter (1928) (cf. Table 2.8).

Pierce also made new experiments on the dependence of rate on UO_2^{++} concentration and confirmed the previous observation that (at 0.05M malonic acid, in the presence of 0.0528M NaOH, in a 1.5 cm deep vessel) the rate reached saturation at $[UO_2SO_4] > 0.0025$M. New measurements also were made on the effect of variations in malonic acid concentration at constant $[UO_2^{++}]$ (Table 4.18).

Table 4.18 extends curve II in Fig. 4.12 and shows that saturation had been far from reached at 0.01M (the limit of the earlier experiments). It is, however, not clear whether the absolute rate (quantum yield) exceeded in this experiment the maximum value of 0.27, found in the preceding investigation.

The results can be interpreted on the basis of the complex theory by using the complexing constant ($K = 80$) given by Ghosh and Mitter. The practical equality of rates at $[UO_2^{++}] = 0.025$M and 0.01M, for 0.05M acid is then understandable, because UO_2^{++} complexing is 87 per cent complete in the first case and 83 per cent complete in the second one, while absorption is practically complete in both cases. The effect of increased acid concentration can also be explained by progressive complexing, e.g. in Table 4.18 complexing (with $K = 80$) must have been 34 per cent complete at [malonic acid] = 0.0046 and ~ 95 per cent complete at [malonic acid] = 0.046M.

TABLE 4.18. RATE OF SENSITIZED MALONIC ACID DECOMPOSITION
After Pierce (1929)
$UO_2^{++} = 0.0116$M; NaOH = 0.528M

[Malonic acid]	0.0046	0.0092	0.023	0.046
Relative rate	0.45	0.55	0.67	0.90

Succinic acid ($COOH.CH_2CH_2.COOH$). Seekamp (1865) noted that succinic acid decomposes in sunlight, in the presence of uranyl nitrate, into carbon dioxide and propionic acid; a green precipitate [U(IV) succinate?] is also formed. Fay (1896) attempted to prepare uranyl succinate to study its decomposition in light, but the compound obtained by evaporation of a solution of uranyl nitrate and acid sodium succinate proved to be insoluble in water; its solution in dilute succinic acid was photostable. The experiments were not pursued any further.

Neuberg and Peterson (1914) found no increase in alkalinity of a solution containing 1 per cent potassium succinate and 0.1 per cent uranyl sulfate upon a 17-day exposure to sunlight (while marked changes were observed in analogous experiments with malic, citric, lactic and tartaric acid).

The photodecomposition of succinic acid by uranyl ions was studied in some detail only in a system containing, in addition to uranyl ions as sensitizers, also methylene blue (MB) as ultimate oxidant. Ghosh, Banerjee, and Bhatta (1936) investigated the behavior of this system in ultraviolet light from a mercury arc (λ 366 mμ, isolated by filter). They found that no change in [MB] occurs upon exposure to this light of a mixture of 0.32M uranyl nitrate and 4×10^{-4}M methylene blue, or of a mixture 0.1M in succinic acid and 4×10^{-4}M in methylene blue, but that the dyestuff was bleached (i.e. presumably reduced to the leuko base) upon having been exposed to light under exclusion of air in the presence of both uranyl ions *and* succinic acid.

The rate of bleaching was found to be independent of *acidity*. Therefore the observed effect of changes in the *concentration of succinic acid* could not be a pH effect. The reciprocal of the rate proved to be a linear function of the reciprocal of succinic acid concentration (Fig. 4.13), as expected for competition between monomolecular deactivation of excited uranyl ions and their bimolecular reaction with succinic acid:

$$
\left.
\begin{aligned}
v &= \frac{d\,[\text{MB}]}{dt} = \frac{ka\,[\text{succinic acid}]}{b + a\,[\text{succinic acid}]} \\[2mm]
\text{or} \qquad \frac{1}{v} &= c_1 + \frac{c_2}{[\text{succinic acid}]}
\end{aligned}
\right\}
\tag{72}
$$

The observed dependence of the rate on uranyl concentration was attributed to the combined effects of changes in light absorption and of "self-deactivation," caused by encounters between excited and normal uranyl ions. The light absorption by uranyl ions is given approximately by the equation

$$
A_1 = I_0 \left[1 - e^{-(\epsilon_1 c_1 + \epsilon_2 c_2)l} \right] \frac{\epsilon_1 c_1}{\epsilon_1 c_1 + \epsilon_2 c_2}
\tag{73}
$$

where the indices 1 and 2 refer to uranyl and methylene blue respectively (assuming that the acid does not absorb any of the light used). As an example, with $\bar{\epsilon}_1 = 17$ and $\bar{\epsilon}_2 = 2500$, $[\text{UO}_2^{++}] = 0.32$ and $[\text{MB}] = 4 \times 10^{-4}$M, the absorption by the (mostly complexed) UO_2^{++} was 85 per cent of the total absorption.

Equation (74), which accounts for self-deactivation by the second term in the denominator, was found to fit the experimental data well (cf. Table 4.19):

$$v = -\frac{d\,[MB]}{dt} = \frac{2.08 \times 10^{-3} A_1 \times 10^{-11}}{1 + 17\,[UO_2^{++}]}\ \text{moles/(sec cm}^2) \qquad (74)$$

Here, A_1 is the energy absorbed by UO_2^{++}, expressed in ergs/(sec cm²).

TABLE 4.19. KINETICS OF BLEACHING OF METHYLENE BLUE IN
MIXTURE WITH URANYL SALT AND SUCCINATE
After Ghosh *et al.* (1936)
$k_0 = 2.08 \times 10^{-3}$; [succinic acid] $= 0.1$M;
$[MB] = 4 \times 10^{-4}$M; $I_0 = 2732$ ergs/(sec cm²)

$[UO_2^{++}]$	A_1 ergs/(sec cm²)	$\Delta MB/\Delta t \times 10^{11}$ (moles/liter × sec)		Quantum yield (observed)
		Observed	Calculated (Equation 74)	
0.16	1676	0.93	0.94	0.018
0.12	1426	0.88	0.96	0.020
0.08	1083	0.88	0.95	0.026
0.04	624	0.77	0.77	0.040
0.01	175	0.33	0.31	0.061

Both the observed dependence on [succinic acid] [Equation (72)] and that on $[UO_2^{++}]$ [equation (74)] agree with those to be expected on the basis of the reaction mechanism:

$$UO_2^{++} + h\nu \underset{k_2}{\overset{k_1}{\rightleftharpoons}} (UO_2^{++})^*\ \text{(excitation and fluorescence)} \qquad (75a)$$

$$UO_2^{++*} + \begin{cases} UO_2^{++} \overset{k_3}{\rightarrow} 2UO_2^{++}\ \text{(self-quenching)} & (75b) \\[2ex] \text{succinic acid} \overset{k_4}{\rightarrow} UO_2^+ + \text{oxidation products} & (75c) \end{cases}$$

$$UO_2^+ + MB \rightarrow UO_2^{++} + \text{reduced MB (restoration of the}$$
$$\text{sensitizer)} \qquad (75d)$$

which leads to theoretical Equation (75), which includes (73) and (74) as special cases:

$$-\frac{d\,[MB]}{dt} = \frac{A_1 k_4\,[\text{succinic acid}]}{(k_2 + k_3)\,[UO_2^{++}] + k_4\,[\text{succinic acid}]} \tag{75}$$

From Vavilov's self-quenching experiments on uranyl solutions it appears that $k_3 = 99\,k_2$. The ratio k_4/k_3 was assumed to be unity in a similar investigation with mandelic acid as reductant (p. 319), but had to be assumed to be about 0.5 to account for the empirical value of the constants in Equation (75). At a given acid concentration,

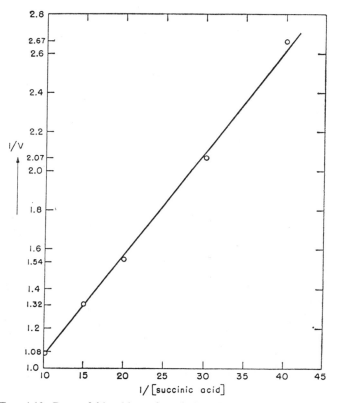

FIG. 4.13. Rate of bleaching of methylene blue in methylene blue–succinate–uranyl mixture as function of succinate concentration. After Ghosh, Banerjee, and Bhatta (1936).

the quantum yields of the MB reduction by mandelic acid were correspondingly higher (by a factor of 1.6). The ratio k_4/k_2 appeared to be $\simeq 50$.

In the above discussion, as on several similar occasions, Ghosh discussed the kinetics of the photochemical process without reference to the complex formation from uranyl ions and the organic photo-lyte, although earlier measurements by Ghosh and Mitter had indicated the extent of this association. The application of the reaction system (75a–d) to a largely associated system is somewhat doubtful—first, because it presumes that a complex, such as $\{UO_2^{++}.\text{succinic acid}\}$, only reacts if it encounters, after excitation, another molecule of the acid; and second, because the concentration of this acid is assumed to be equal to the total concentration added, while it may be that only the *free*, unassociated acid molecules should be counted. [It is, however, not impossible that for geo-metrical reasons the UO_2^{++*} ion in a complex can react with free acid molecules, and with acid molecules in other complexes, but *not* with the acid molecule in its own complex.]

2.3. *Halogenated Acids*

Uranyl salts of halogenated aliphatic and aromatic acids, first prepared by Lobanov, were studied by Křepelka and Résö (1938) for their reaction to light. In solution, all of them (uranyl α-chloro-propionate, uranyl β-chloropropionate, uranyl α-bromopropionate, uranyl β-bromopropionate, uranyl p-bromobenzoate) were found to decompose in ultraviolet and, more slowly, in visible light, showing changes in color and precipitation. A little ether was added as a catalyst to accelerate the decomposition. The aliphatic compounds gave U(IV) and carbon dioxide; aromatic compounds liberated no carbon dioxide and formed no basic salts, but instead decomposed into the corresponding hydroxy compounds (salicylates) and hydrogen chloride. In visible light (in the presence of a little ether), the decomposition of the halogenated propionates was complete in 4–6 weeks; in ultraviolet light, it reached 50–70 per cent after 1–2 days but then appeared to stop. The chlorobenzoate was more stable in light than the aliphatic compounds; β-substituted compounds were more stable than the α-substituted compounds.

Ghosh and Ray (1936a) investigated the oxidation of *mono-chloracetic acid*, $CH_2Cl.COOH$, by potassium permanganate in the presence of uranyl sulfate in monochromatic light (436 mμ and 366 mμ Hg lines isolated by filters). No reaction occurred in light with only two components present, or with all three components in the absence of light. The disappearance of KMnO$_4$ was followed by observing the absorption at 540 mμ. In 366 mμ light [2650 ergs/(sec cm²)] at 30°C in a 5 mm thick vessel containing 5.1×10^{-4}M KMnO$_4$, 0.1M CH$_2$Cl.COOH, 0.1M UO$_2$SO$_4$, and 2.5N H$_2$SO$_4$, permanganate was bleached at a constant rate of 1.5×10^{-11} (moles/liter)/(sec cm²) for 2½ hr. At 436 mμ [930 ergs/(sec cm²)] in a solution containing 4.2×10^{-4}M KMnO$_4$, 0.03M CH$_2$Cl.COOH, 0.1M UO$_2$SO$_4$ and 3N H$_2$SO$_4$, the rate of disappearance of permanganate was 0.33×10^{-11} (moles/liter)/(sec cm²). The rate in ultraviolet light remained constant even after over one-half of the initial quantity of KMnO$_4$ had disappeared, indicating that the reaction was sensitized by uranyl ions, and not brought about by direct excitation of KMnO$_4$. (The amount of light available to the uranyl ions did not change with time because the reduction products of KMnO$_4$ proved to have an unchanged absorption capacity in the ultraviolet.) The rate of light absorption by UO$_2^{++}$, designated as A_1, was calculated by multiplying the total absorption, A_{total}, by the factor

$$\bar{\epsilon}_{\text{UO}_2^{++}} [\text{UO}_2^{++}] / (\epsilon_{\text{MnO}_4^-} [\text{MnO}_4^-] + \bar{\epsilon}_{\text{UO}_2^{++}} [\text{UO}_2^{++}])$$

where $\bar{\epsilon}_{\text{UO}_2^{++}}$ is the (natural) absorption coefficient of uranyl ions determined *in the presence of chloracetic acid*, i.e. complexed to a certain extent (see Chapter 2) with chloracetate anions or molecules ($\bar{\epsilon} = 10$ at 366 mμ, $\bar{\epsilon} = 6.5$ at 436 mμ). The (natural) absorption coefficients of KMnO$_4$ at the same wavelengths are 2000 (366 mμ) and 10 (436 mμ).

The effect on the yield of the substrate concentration, [CH$_2$Cl.COOH], is shown by Table 4.20. It shows that the reaction rate is not "saturated" with respect to the substrate even at 0.2M; at that concentration, the quantum yield is still below 0.1. According to Chapter 2, complexing of UO$_2^{++}$ should be practically complete under the conditions of Table 4.20; the reaction thus does not occur after each absorption act in the complex, but appears to require encounters of excited uranyl ions (or their complexes) with free acid anions.

TABLE 4.20. URANYL-SENSITIZED OXIDATION OF $CH_2Cl.COOH$ BY $KMnO_4$
After Ghosh and Ray (1936a)

[$CH_2Cl.COOH$] (M)	0.033	0.05	0.1	0.2
$-\dfrac{d[KMnO_4]}{dt} \times 10^{11}$	0.34	0.43	0.57	0.66
Quantum yield	0.038	0.048	0.063	0.073

$[KMnO_4] = 4.2 \times 10^{-4}$M; $[UO_2SO_4] = 0.087$M
$[H_2SO_4] = 3$N; $t = 29°C$; $\lambda = 436$ mμ
$I_0 = 1030$ ergs/(sec cm²), of which 250 ergs/(sec cm²) are
absorbed by UO_2SO_4

The effect of the concentration of the sensitizer, $[UO_2^{2+}]$, was
studied in the presence of 0.1M $CH_2Cl.COOH$ and 4.2×10^{-4}M
$KMnO_4$, in 3N H_2SO_4, at 29°C. Table 4.21 gives the results.
The observed decrease in quantum yield with increasing $[UO_2^{2+}]$
can be represented by the empirical equation

TABLE 4.21. QUANTUM YIELD OF URANYL-SENSITIZED OXIDATION OF
CHLORACETIC ACID BY PERMANGANATE
After Ghosh and Ray (1936a)

[UO_2SO_4] (M)	(No. of quanta absorbed per sec cm²) $\times 10^{-13}$	$-\dfrac{d[KMnO_4]}{dt} \times 10^{11}$ obs.	calc.	Quantum yield (γ)
\multicolumn{5}{c}{(a) Incident intensity = 1030 ergs/(sec cm²) at $\lambda = 436$ mμ}				
0.0218	1.57	0.26	0.24	0.10
0.0436	3.0	0.38	0.40	0.077
0.0653	4.3	0.47	0.49	0.067
		$k_0 = 4.1 \times 10^{-3}$		
0.0871	5.5	0.57	0.57	0.063
0.1511	8.3	0.68	0.65	0.05
0.2267	11.9	0.70	0.70	0.036
\multicolumn{5}{c}{(b) Incident intensity = 3360 ergs/(sec cm²) at $\lambda = 336$ mμ}				
0.0218	5.3	1.02	0.94	0.12
0.0436	10	1.47	1.50	0.09
0.0653	14	1.89	1.88	0.082
		$k_0 = 3.9 \times 10^{-3}$		
0.0871	18	2.05	2.12	0.07
0.1511	28	2.29	2.40	0.05
0.2267	36	2.45	2.45	0.042

$$\frac{d\,[KMnO_4]}{dt} = \frac{-k_0 A_1}{1+9.08\,[UO_2^{++}]} \tag{76}$$

where A_1 is the amount of light energy absorbed by uranyl ions. The cause of self-deactivation may be sought, as before, in deactivation by encounters of $(UO_2^{++})^*$ ions with normal UO_2^{++} ions (or in the formation of dimeric uranyl ions).

Incident light intensity (at 366 mμ) was varied between 2650 and 4190 ergs/(sec cm²) and found to have no influence on the quantum yield. The temperature coefficient was slightly > 1 (1.02 and 1.04 between 30° and 40°C, in 0.067 and 0.0335M UO_2SO_4 respectively).

As a probable mechanism of the sensitized reaction, Ghosh and Ray suggested—in agreement with the concepts used elsewhere in this chapter—primary photo-oxidation of chloracetic acid by excited uranyl ions, followed by reoxidation of reduced uranyl [in the U(IV) or U(V) state] by permanganate. To account for the decrease of the quantum yield at higher uranyl concentrations, a deactivation reaction between $(UO_2^{++})^*$ and UO_2^{++} was assumed. The set of reactions

$$UO_2^{++}+h\nu \underset{k_2}{\overset{k*I}{\rightleftharpoons}} (UO_2^{++})^* \tag{77a}$$

$$UO_2^{++*}+UO_2^{++} \overset{k_3}{\rightarrow} 2UO_2^{++} \tag{77b}$$

$$UO_2^{++*}+CH_2Cl.COOH \overset{k_4}{\rightarrow} U(V)+\text{oxidation products} \tag{77c}$$

$$U(V)+KMnO_4 \rightarrow UO_2^{++}+\text{reduction products} \tag{77d}$$

leads to the rate equation

$$\frac{d\,[KMnO_4]}{dt} = \frac{-A_1 k_4\,[CH_2Cl.COOH]}{N h\nu\,(k_2+k_3)\,[UO_2^{++}]+k_4\,[CH_2Cl.COOH]} \tag{78}$$

where $1/Nh\nu$ is the number of einsteins in one erg of the light used (A_1 was measured in ergs). From Vavilov's experiments on the self-quenching of uranyl fluorescence, the authors take $k_3 = 99 k_2$. If reactions (77b) and (77c) occur after the first, or, more generally, after the same number of collisions, $k_4 \simeq k_3$, and thus k_4 also $\simeq 99\,k_2$. Transformation proves that the factor before $[UO_2^{++}]$ must

be equal to $$\frac{k_4}{k_2 + k_4 \,[\text{monochloracetic acid}]}.$$

With $k_4/k_2 = 99$ in 0.1M acid, the calculated value of this factor is 9.08, in agreement with the empirical value. This indicates approximate validity of the assumption $k_4 \simeq k_3$.

The explicit meaning of the empirical constant k_0 in (76) is $k_0 = k_4\,[\text{acid}]/Nh\nu\,(k_2 + k_4\,[\text{acid}])$.

2.4. *Hydroxy and Thio Acids*

Glycolic acid ($CH_2OH.COOH$). The uranyl-sensitized decomposition of glycolic acid was first observed by Baur (1913). A mixture 0.3M in glycolic acid and 0.016M in UO_2SO_4 was illuminated for 15 hr with a quartz lamp. The uranyl salt was found to be *reduced* without gas evolution and glycolic acid oxidized to an aldehyde (possibly glyoxalic acid, $CHO.COOH$, or formaldehyde, H_2CO). When potassium glycolate was substituted for free acid, no U(IV) was formed, but the illuminated solution nevertheless gave the aldehyde reaction, indicating the formation of an aldehyde by *sensitized decomposition* of glycolate, e.g.

$$CH_2OH.COOH \xrightarrow[\text{light}]{UO_2^{++}} HCOOH + H_2CO \qquad (79)$$

In a second paper (1919) Baur interpreted the formation of formaldehyde from glycolic acid and the effect of mercuric chloride on this reaction by an "electrochemical" scheme:

$$(U^{+6})_{--}^{++}\begin{cases} +CH_2OH.COO^- + OH^- \to \\ \qquad\qquad CO_2 + H_2O + H_2CO \\ +2HgCl_2 \to 2HgCl + 2Cl^- \end{cases} + U^{+6} \qquad (80)$$

This simultaneous reaction of a light-excited ion with an oxidant and a reductant can, of course, be replaced by two successive reactions, such as

$$U^{+6}* + CH_2OH.COO^- + OH^- \rightarrow$$
$$U^{+4} + CO_2 + H_2O + H_2CO \quad (81a)$$

$$U^{+4} + 2HgCl_2 \rightarrow 2HgCl + U^{+6} + 2Cl^- \quad (81b)$$

Courtois (1923) observed that in sunlight UO_2^{++} ions reacted with glycolic acid, in the presence as well as in absence of air, with reduction to U(IV) compounds and formation of a precipitate which first was yellow and then became green. The illuminated solution smelled of formaldehyde; gas (carbon dioxide) was evolved. Courtois suggested that the green precipitate was uranous formate. The reactions of uranyl ions and glycolic acid can thus be tentatively summarized as follows:

$$4CH_2OH.COOH \xrightarrow{UO_2^{++}*} 4H_2CO + 4HCOOH \text{ (sensitized}$$
$$\text{decomposition)} \quad (82a)$$

$$CH_2OH.COOH + UO_2^{++}* \rightarrow H_2CO + U^{+4} + CO_2 + 2OH^-$$
$$\text{(oxidoreduction)} \quad (82b)$$

$$4HCOOH + U^{+4} \rightarrow U(COOH)_4 + 4H^+ \text{ (precipitation)} \quad (82c)$$

$$5CH_2OH.COOH + UO_2^{++}* \xrightarrow{light}$$
$$5H_2CO + CO_2 + U(COOH)_4 + 2H_2O + 2H^+ \quad (82)$$

It is noteworthy that no simple sensitized decarboxylation

$$CH_2OH.COOH \xrightarrow[light]{UO_2^{++}} CH_3OH + CO_2 \quad (83)$$

(similar to those observed in the case of acetic, oxalic, and other non-substituted acids) has been reported; it looks as if the hydroxyl group is too easily oxidizable to survive the oxidation of the carboxyl group to free carbon dioxide without being itself oxidized to a carbonyl group.

More recently, Baur (1936) gave Fig. 4.14 for the time course of decomposition of glycolic acid and glycolate by uranyl sulfate in the presence of mercuric chloride as "depolarizer."

Determination of the amounts of Hg_2Cl_2 and H_2CO formed showed exact equivalency of the two products, indicating that in this case photochemical oxidation–reduction proceeded practically without interference by the sensitized decomposition.

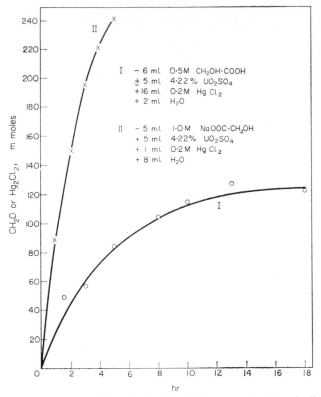

FIG. 4.14. Decomposition of glycolic acid by uranyl sulfate in light. Baur (1936).

It will be noted that the rate of reaction was much higher in sodium glycolate than in glycolic acid, indicating that the glycolate ion (rather than the glycolic acid molecule) may be the main reacting species.

Observations on the decomposition of *thioglycolic* acid by light in the presence of uranyl ions were made by Křepelka and Résö (1938); SO_2 and H_2S were found to be liberated in this reaction.

Lactic acid ($CH_3.CHOH.COOH$). The photodecomposition of lactic acid, sensitized by uranyl ions, was first noted by Bacon (1907). He said that it gives carbon dioxide and acetaldehyde, and that the products may also include formic acid ($CH_3.CHOH.COOH \rightarrow CH_3CHO + HCOOH$). Neuberg (1908) also noted that acetaldehyde is formed in UO_2^{++} solutions containing dil. L-lactic acid upon exposure to sunlight. Neuberg and Peterson (1914) found that 17 days of exposure to sunlight changed the reaction of a solution 1 per cent in sodium lactate and 0.1 per cent in uranyl sulfate from alkaline (0.2 ml $0.1N$ H_2SO_4 required for neutralization of 5 ml) to acid (1.2 ml $0.1N$ NaOH required for the same purpose).

Courtois (1914, 1923) stated that cold, saturated aqueous solutions of uranyl lactate are stable in darkness and diffuse light, but decompose in direct sunlight. If air is present, the solution becomes first green and then brownish, but no precipitate appears until after 4–5 days, when a violet hydroxide is formed, and the solution becomes almost colorless. In the absence of air the solution also becomes green, and some gas bubbles appear; basic U(IV) salt is precipitated in about 10 days. The gas evolution is small and consists of carbon dioxide, an aldehyde odor appears, and formic acid can be identified in the solution.

Bolin (1914) investigated the relation of oxidation–reduction to sensitized decomposition in the lactic acid photolysis by uranyl sulfate in light. To prevent the precipitation of basic uranium salts (carbonate, lactate, etc.) or U(VI) hydroxides, acid solutions were used (the natural acidity of uranyl sulfate was sufficient).

The aldehyde produced was titrated with sulfite and iodine, U(IV) with permanganate (after removal of lactic acid).

The rate of formation of U(IV) and aldehyde was found to be the same at 20°C and 30°C (0.87N lactic acid, 1.6 g UO_2^{++} sulfate, 60 min exposure to carbon arc light).

No direct photodecomposition of lactic acid occurred in arc light in the absence of uranyl ions, and no thermal decomposition could be detected in the dark in 2 days in the presence of uranyl sulfate.

In solutions of free lactic acid, the quantity of U(IV) formed was 2–3 times larger than that of aldehyde. In sodium lactate solutions, on the other hand, the two products were formed in approximately equivalent quantities.

Figure 4.15 shows dependence of the rate of decomposition on $[UO_2^{++}]$ (UO_2SO_4 in 0.87N sodium lactate). The curve approaches saturation, at > 10 per cent (complete absorption?).

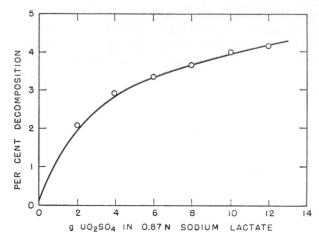

FIG. 4.15. Speed of decomposition of lactic acid by UO_2SO_4 in light in relation to $[UO_2^{++}]$. After Bolin (1914).

The equivalency of $\Delta U(IV)$ and ΔCH_3CHO indicates oxidation according to the equation

$$CH_3.CHOH.COOH + UO_2^{++*} + 2H^+$$
$$\rightarrow CH_3CHO + CO_2 + 2H_2O + U^{+4} \qquad (84)$$

As a check, the quantity of carbon dioxide also was determined and found to be about 5 per cent in excess of that calculated from Equation (84). In another experiment, in sunlight instead of arc light, the excess was 15 per cent.

The lactate concentration was without effect on the yield in the range 0.22–0.87M.

The time course of the reaction (initial composition: 0.8 g UO_2SO_4 in 40 ml 0.87N lactate) showed a gradual slowing down (at the end of 12 hr, to about 1/10 of the initial rate). At that time about 0.8 mole lactic acid was decomposed for 1 mole UO_2^{++} present. This result, too, indicates the practical absence of photocatalysis.

All these experiments were carried out in the absence of air. In the presence of oxygen, the U(IV) is reoxidized and the reaction is converted to sensitized autoxidation. The rate of the latter is approximately constant for 6 hr.

Müller (1926) measured the quantum yield of this reaction (0.1N NaOH neutralized lactic acid, 0.01M UO_2SO_4) in a glass vessel, in the total light of a quartz mercury lamp, assuming 402.5 mμ as average wavelength. In 95 min, 4.47×10^{19} quanta were absorbed and 4.24×10^{19} acetaldehyde molecules were formed, indicating a quantum yield of $\gamma = 0.95$. As a control, the measurement was repeated using an oxalate–uranyl sulfate mixture as actinometer; the comparison of the rate of the decomposition of the two systems (both in quartz vessels) led to a practical identity of the quantum yields. With Büchi's value (p. 278) of $\gamma \simeq 1.0$ for the uranyl–oxalate system, this appeared as confirmation of the above value of γ for lactate, but we recall (cf. p. 284) that subsequent investigations have given for the "actinometer" system a quantum yield of about 0.6 rather than 1.0.

Much later, Bhattacharyya and Gulvady (1952a) studied the photo-oxidation of lactic acid (pH 1.8–2.6, 25°C). The following equation was found to be accurate in control experiments:

$$CH_3CHCO + UO_2^{++} \rightarrow CH_3CHO + UO^{++} + H_2O + CO_2 \qquad (84a)$$
$$\underset{OH}{|} \quad \underset{OH}{|}$$

This stoichiometry was established in experiments in which mixtures containing 0.2M lactic acid and 0.002–0.010M uranyl nitrate were exposed to sunlight; the solutions were freed from dissolved O_2 and maintained under N_2. Subsequent bisulfite analyses for aldehyde showed a 1 : 1 ratio of [aldehyde formed] : [uranyl ions consumed] in every case.

Bhattacharyya and Gulvady used three wavelengths—366 mμ, 406 mμ, and 436 mμ. Quantum yields (based on aldehyde production) were about 1 for 436 mμ, about 4 for 406 mμ, and about 6 for 366 mμ. They increased with lactic acid concentration [L]. Although the authors did not quote a sufficient number of separate experiments to establish the dependence of quantum yield upon [L], they reported it to be $1/\gamma = C_1 + C_2/[L]$, with C_1 and C_2

independent of light intensity, or uranyl concentration, or pH, but dependent upon wavelength. From their plots of $1/\gamma$ vs. $1/[L]$, one reads $1/C_1$ (436 mμ) = 2.7, $1/C_1$ (406 mμ) = 9.5, $1/C_1$ (366 mμ) = 16. If the functional relationship given above is correct, these numbers signify quantum yields for infinite concentration of lactic acid. To explain the large quantum yields, Bhattacharyya and Gulvady speculated that a chain mechanism is involved, but did not guess what it might be. The situation is similar to that with tartaric acid.

The uranyl-sensitized photo-oxidations of lactic acid by potassium indigo tetrasulfonate (Bhattacharyya and Gulvady, 1952b) and by Meldola's blue (Gulvady and Bhattacharyya, 1952) also have been studied. The features observed are similar to those of the sensitized oxidations of ethanol and of mandelic acid (q.v.).

Tartaric acid (COOH.CHOH.CHOH.COOH). Tartaric acid was first observed to decompose in light in the presence of uranium compounds by Seekamp (1894). He noted that a 5 per cent solution of tartaric acid in which 1 per cent "uranium oxide" had been dissolved evolves gas and becomes green upon exposure to light. After prolonged exposure (several months), aldehyde could be distilled from the illuminated solution; the residue had a characteristic smell and was found to contain malic and succinic acid and an undetermined Cu^{++} reducing compound.

Fay (1896) also noted that when tartaric acid solution containing uranyl nitrate was exposed to sunlight it turned green, and after some time a light-green salt precipitated out. He observed no gas evolution. The formation of the precipitate was strongly accelerated by heat; it formed most readily in an equimolar mixture of $UO_2(NO_3)_2$ and tartaric acid. Upon standing the green precipitate redissolved to an amber solution. An attempted analysis of the precipitate was inconclusive.

Bacon (1907) said that carbon dioxide and *pyruvic acid*, CH_3.COCOOH, are among the products of uranyl-sensitized photo-decomposition of tartaric acid. The pyruvic acid was identified by the melting point of its phenylhydrazone.

Neuberg (1908) found that D-tartaric acid exposed to sunlight in the presence of uranyl ions gives *glyoxalic* acid and keto acids. The products reduced Fehling solution in the cold; they showed a very strong reaction with naphthoresorcin and had a mixed caramel and fruity odor.

Euler and Ryd (1913) noticed that the presence of uranyl ions accelerates the decomposition of tartaric acid by *ultraviolet light.*

Neuberg and Peterson (1914) measured the change in the alkaline titer of solutions of the salts of organic acids upon exposure to sunlight. A solution of 0.1 per cent uranyl sulfate, containing 1 per cent Na–K–tartrate, showed, after 17 days' exposure, a marked increase in alkalinity, probably because of the loss of CO_2 (1.4 ml 0.1N H_2SO_4 were required to neutralize 5 ml of the solution after exposure, in contrast to 0.05 ml before exposure; a sample left in the dark showed no appreciable change).

Courtois (1914, 1923) observed that the photochemical decomposition of tartrate by uranyl ions proceeds differently in the presence and in the absence of air. Without air the solution became turbid, acquired a yellowish-brown color, and formed, in 3–4 days, a yellowish precipitate of basic salt; later, gas evolution began. In air the basic salt transformed itself into a hydroxide, which was at first brown and then became violet (U_3O_8 hydrate).

According to Hatt (1918), *acid* solutions containing uranyl sulfate and tartaric acid become brown and develop gas in light; *alkaline* solutions also show reduction of UO_2^{++} to U(IV) (color change and precipitation!), but liberate no gas.

Hakomori (1927), who first found spectroscopic evidence for the formation of a uranyl tartrate complex, also noted that uranyl tartrate solutions are light-sensitive, darkening in color (apparently due to the formation of a colloid) and forming a white precipitate in light; the presence of U(IV) could be proved in the product. Complexing was also indicated by an increase of the specific rotatory power of a sodium tartrate solution (e.g. from 30° to 170°) by the addition of uranium sulfate. Rotatory power disappeared completely after prolonged exposure to light.

The uranyl tartrate complexing equilibrium was measured spectroscopically by Ghosh and Mitter (cf. Chapter 2). It was again confirmed by Rama Char (1942), who measured the optical rotation in uranyl nitrate–tartaric acid mixtures. Addition of uranyl nitrate hexahydrate to a solution of D- or L-tartaric acid enhanced the rotation; the maximum effect was reached at $[UO_2^{++}]$: [tartaric acid] = 4. Assuming that the observed average rotation, $\bar{R}$, is additive:

$$\bar{R} = R_{complex} \, [\text{complex}] + R_{tartrate} \, [\text{tartaric acid}]$$

the complexing constant K

$$K = \frac{[\text{complex}]}{[\text{UO}_2^{2+}]\,[\text{free acid}]} \tag{85}$$

can be calculated, e.g. from a set of $\overline{R}$ measurements at constant total tartrate concentration ([tartaric acid]$_0$ = [tartaric nitrate] + [complex]). An average value of $K = 10.2$ (individual values from 9.5 to 11.6) was derived from such measurements. This is not very different from $K = 20$, the spectroscopic value of Ghosh and Mitter (Table 2.7). (It must be kept in mind that K must depend on ionic strength, as well as on pH—the latter because of ionic dissociation equilibria of the acid and of the complex.)

In light, Rama Char found UO_2^{2+} to be reduced to U^{+4} and tartaric acid to be oxidized. He observed this reaction by U(IV) determination with permanganate. At all the wavelengths studied (313, 406, and 436 mμ) the rate was found to obey the equation

$$+\frac{d[\text{U(IV)}]}{dt} = 20.52 \times 10^{-8} \times \frac{I_a\,[\text{tartrate}]_0}{0.2 + [\text{tartrate}]_0} \tag{86}$$

where I_a is absorbed energy in ergs. The conditions were:

[UO_2^{2+}]$_0$: 0.125–0.500; [tartaric acid] : 0.063–0.500; $t = 28°\text{C}$; pH $\simeq 1$.

No difference was found between R-, L- and D-acids; there was no effect of circular polarization (D or L) of the light.

The quantum efficiencies, γ, are shown in Table 4.22. The form of Equation (86) indicates a simple competition between mono-molecular deactivation of excited UO_2^{2+} ions (or rather $\text{UO}_2^{2+}\text{A}^-$ complexes) and an oxidation–reduction reaction, with a ratio of 0.2 between the two rate constants. The absolute quantum yields found (up to ~ 5) seem to indicate a chain reaction (it is assumed that complexing is complete which should not be correct for the lower A values, and that the reaction requires the encounter of an excited complex with a second acid molecule). The effect of wavelength (decreasing yield with increasing wavelength) is in the direction explicable by the "cage effect" (greater probability of escape from primary back-reaction within the "cage" when the excess energy of the photochemical products is higher). Similar oxidations of citric acid, mandelic acid, and ethanol, mentioned in other sections of this book, seem to have the same general features.

TABLE 4.22. QUANTUM YIELD OF THE URANYL–TARTRATE REACTION
After Rama Char (1942)

Conc. (moles/liter)		γ of U(IV) formation at λ		
[tartaric acid]	[UO$_2^{++}$]	313 mμ	406 mμ	436 mμ
0.50	0.50	4.7	3.6	3.4
0.25	0.25	3.6	2.8	2.6
0.125	0.125	2.5	2.1	1.8

28°C, pH = 0.9–1.2

Malic acid (COOH.CH$_2$.CHOH.COOH). Bacon (1907) said that uranyl-induced photodecomposition of malic acid yields carbon dioxide and acetaldehyde, together with unknown products; he suggested that the first reaction step is the decarboxylation of malic acid to lactic acid, followed by the decomposition of the latter into acetaldehyde and (perhaps) formic acid.

Neuberg (1908) observed that, in sunlight, a mixture of uranyl sulfate and malic acid gave a product which reduced Fehling's solution in the cold. The reaction with naphthoresorcin was first positive, later negative. Phenylhydrazine gave a small amount of osazone of hydroxy pyruvic acid (or of the half-aldehyde of mesoxalic acid).

The same reaction was also observed by Neuberg and Peterson (1914). A solution of 0.1 per cent uranyl sulfate and 1 per cent potassium lactate, which required for its neutralization 0.4 ml 0.1N H$_2$SO$_4$ per 5 ml, became more alkaline after 8 days' exposure to sun (1.9 ml H$_2$SO$_4$) and after 17 days required as much as 2.3 ml H$_2$SO$_4$ (CO$_2$ loss!). In the darkened control sample, the alkalinity was practically unchanged.

Citric acid (COOH.CH$_2$.COH.COOH.CH$_2$COOH). Seekamp (1894) found that citric acid behaves in the presence of uranyl similarly to tartaric acid. Gas evolution sets in in sunlight; the solution becomes green and acquires a peculiar odor. After several months, *acetone* can be obtained by distillation; the following decomposition equation

$$C_6H_8O_7 \xrightarrow[\text{light}]{[UO_2^{++}]} CH_3COCH_3 + HOOC.COOH + CO_2 \qquad (87)$$

was tentatively suggested.

Neuberg (1908) noted that citric acid solutions containing uranyl ions produce, in sunlight, a substance which reduces Fehling's solution and acquire a fruity odor. Neuberg and Peterson (1914) found that 17 days of exposure to sunlight increased somewhat the alkalinity of a solution, 0.1 per cent in potassium citrate and 0.01 per cent in uranyl sulfate, so that 2.2 ml 0.1N H_2SO_4 were required for neutralization of 5 ml instead of the initial 1.3 ml.

Courtois (1914, 1923) found that cold, saturated 20 per cent solutions of uranyl citrate are somewhat unstable even in the dark, giving, after some time, a yellow precipitate of basic salt. In sunlight, one observes first (in 2–3 days) a yellow precipitate; then the solution becomes brown, and the precipitate slowly transforms itself into violet U_3O_8 hydrate. After one day in the sun, considerable amounts of carbonic acid begin to be evolved.

Hatt (1918) noted that acid solutions of uranyl sulfate and citric acid become brown in light and develop a gas which is probably CO_2 (since no gas is evolved in alkaline solution). Concentrated alkaline solutions of UO_2^{++} and citric acid cannot be obtained because of insolubility of complex salts; dilute, almost colorless alkaline solutions are stable in the dark but form a white precipitate in light.

2.5. *Keto Acids*

Glyoxylic acid (CHO.COOH). Baur (1936) observed the photo-decomposition of glyoxylic acid sensitized by uranyl sulfate with mercuric chloride as "depolarizer" (ultimate oxidant) in sunlight and in incandescent light. He measured the progress of reaction for 10 hr in a system consisting of 10 ml 1.6 per cent Na glyoxylate, 5 ml 4.22 per cent UO_2SO_4, 8 ml 0.2M $HgCl_2$, and 5 ml water, by Hg_2Cl_2 determinations. The reaction showed initial inhibition, which could be represented by the equation $\Delta[Hg_2Cl_2] = A(1 - e^{-bt})$, where t is time and A ($= 108$) and b ($= 0.425$) are constants. The gas evolved was pure carbon dioxide, so that the net reaction appeared to be

$$CHO.COOH + 4HgCl_2 + H_2O \xrightarrow[\text{light}]{UO_2SO_4} 2CO_2 + HCl + 2Hg_2Cl_2 \quad (88)$$

No formaldehyde was found among the products.

Pyruvic acid ($CH_3COCOOH$). Bacon (1907) observed that solutions of uranyl acetate containing pyruvic acid decompose in light, evolving carbon dioxide and forming n-butyric and isobutyric acid.

2.6. *Aromatic Acids*

Very little work has been done on uranyl sensitized photodecomposition of aromatic acids, with the exception of *mandelic acid*.

Benzoic acid (C_6H_5COOH) *and Salicylic acid* ($C_6H_4(OH)COOH$). Courtois (1923) found that uranyl benzoate solutions are not decomposed by exposure to sunlight. A yellow basic salt precipitate is formed very slowly, both in light and in the dark.

Uranyl salicylate solutions, according to Courtois (1923), also are stable in sunlight. It will be recalled that, according to Křepelka and Résö (1938), *p*-bromobenzoic acid, too, is more stable against uranyl-sensitized photo-oxidation than the corresponding aliphatic acids.

Courtois found that uranyl benzoate can be decomposed by light if it is dissolved in ethanol. A violet precipitate of hydrated U_3O_8 is formed; it becomes yellow (i.e. is converted to $UO_3.2H_2O$) by washing with cold water. Uranyl salicylate, however, proved to be stable in sunlight even in alcoholic solution.

Mandelic acid (*phenylglycolic acid*) ($C_6H_5.CHOH.COOH$). Bacon (1907) found that mandelic acid decomposed rapidly when exposed to sunlight in the presence of uranyl acetate. Benzaldehyde and benzoic acid were produced in considerable amounts, the latter perhaps as a secondary product of photochemical oxidation of the former.

Ghosh and co-workers (1935, 1936) investigated the photo-oxidation of mandelic acid sensitized by uranyl sulfate in the presence of methylene blue (MB) or bromine as ultimate oxidant.

Ghosh, Narayanmurti and Roy (1935) used methylene blue. It was added to a mixture of uranyl nitrate and mandelic acid. Upon exposure of the mixture, without methylene blue, to monochromatic mercury arc light (λ 436, 366, 313 + 334, or 254 mμ, isolated by filters), uranous salt was formed and benzaldehyde odor appeared. Addition of methylene blue (MB) led to reoxidation of U(IV) to U(VI), leaving sensitized oxidation of mandelic acid by MB as the net result of irradiation. The bleaching of MB could be followed spectrophotometrically at 540 mμ without marked interference by uranyl.

No change of [MB] was observed upon irradiation of uranyl nitrate (0.1M) + MB (4×10^{-4}M) or mandelic acid (0.1M) + MB (4×10^{-4}M) or upon mixing all three ingredients in the dark. Upon illumination of the ternary system, no reaction was observed in six hours at 546 mμ (where MB alone absorbs); at the other wavelengths, the bleaching proceeded rapidly after an initial induction period. The rate of disappearance of MB continued increasing for several hours. This was found to be due not to autocatalytic effect of the product, benzaldehyde, but probably to the presence of oxygen; removal of oxygen made the rate uniform and shortened (but not entirely suppressed) the induction period.

The observed extinction coefficients are shown in Table 4.23.

TABLE 4.23. EXTINCTION COEFFICIENT* OF UO_2^{++} + MANDELIC
ACID MIXTURES
After Ghosh *et al.* (1935)

λ (mμ)	436	365	313 + 334	254
ϵ (UO_2^{++} nitrate)	6.5	6.6		high
ϵ (same + excess mandelic acid)	15	20	50	1200
ϵMB	very low	2500	9000	13,000

* Natural, not decadic extinction coefficients; whether or not these values, like those of Ghosh and Mitter, require the correction previously noted (p.126) is not clear.

In the calculations of the light absorbed by uranyl ions, the higher values found in the presence of excess mandelic acid were used; these values presumably correspond to complete complexing. The kinetic mechanism was discussed as if no complexing occurred.

The constancy of the rate with time ($-d\,[MB]/dt = 0.127 \times 10^{-5}$ in the first 44 min period, with $[MB]_0 = 37 \times 10^{-5}M$; $-d\,[MB]/dt = 0.135 \times 10^{-5}$ during the third 45 min with $[MB]_0 = 27 \times 10^{-5}$) was taken as implying that the absorption (at 365 mμ) was the same for MB and the leuco base (so that the amount of light apportioned to uranyl remains unchanged by the bleaching of the MB), a conclusion which disagrees with the actual relationships (cf. Epstein, Karush and Rabinowitch, 1941).

The rate was found to be independent of acidity (addition of 0.1N HNO_3 had no effect). The effect of mandelic acid concentration was therefore not a pH effect. The reciprocal rate constant was a linear function of reciprocal acid concentration (Fig. 4.16). The rate was proportional to light intensity. Its dependence on uranyl nitrate concentration could be expressed by the equation

$$\frac{d\,[MB]}{dt} = \frac{-k_0\,I_{abs}}{1 + 17\,[UO_2^{++}]} \qquad (89)$$

with k_0 values of $\sim 4.0 \times 10^{-3}$ at 436 and 366 mμ, 7.6×10^{-3} at $334 + 313$ mμ, and 2.36×10^{-3} at 254 mμ.

All these results were explained in terms of the following reaction sequence:

$$h\nu + UO_2^{++} \underset{k_2}{\overset{k_1}{\rightleftharpoons}} UO_2^{++*} \qquad (90a)$$

$$UO_2^{++*} + UO_2^{++} \overset{k_3}{\rightarrow} 2UO_2^{++} \text{ (self-quenching)} \qquad (90b)$$

$$UO_2^{++*} + \text{mandelic acid} \overset{k_4}{\rightarrow} U(IV) + \text{benzaldehyde} \qquad (90c)$$

$$U(IV) + MB \overset{k_5}{\rightarrow} UO_2^{++} + \text{leucobase} \qquad (90d)$$

This mechanism, which neglects complexing, leads to a rate equation

$$-\frac{d\,[MB]}{dt} = \frac{A_{UO_2^{++}}}{Nh\nu}\,\frac{k_4\,[\text{mandelic acid}]}{k_2 + k_3\,[UO_2^{++}] + k_4\,[\text{mandelic acid}]} \qquad (91)$$

where $A_{UO_2^{++}}$ is the light energy absorbed by UO_2^{++}. This equation agrees with the above-given empirical relationships between the rate and the concentrations of mandelic acid and uranyl ions.

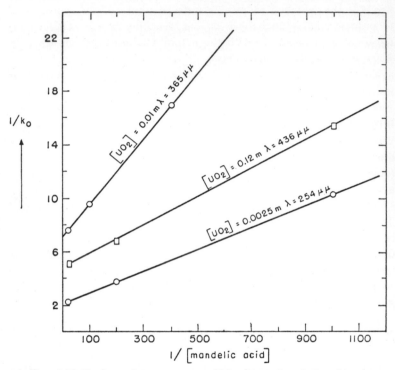

FIG. 4.16. Reciprocal rate constant of bleaching of methylene blue in mixture with uranyl salt and mandelic acid, as function of reciprocal concentration of mandelic acid. After Ghosh *et al.* (1935).

Fluorescence measurements give for the self-quenching (Vavilov's data) $k_3/k_2 = 99$. The values of k_4 and k_3 can be assumed to be equal (both reactions may occur by first encounter, cf. above) without contradicting the empirical value of the constant in Equation (91).

The quantum yield, extrapolated to excess mandelic acid and high concentration of uranyl ions, appears to approach 1 at 436, 366, and 254 mμ, where the equation

$$-\frac{d\,[\text{MB}]}{dt}(1+17\,[\text{UO}_2^{++}]) = A_{\text{UO}_2^{++}}/Nh\nu$$

is obeyed within ± 15 per cent, but to be much higher than 1 at 334 and 313 mμ.

A similar investigation was made by Ghosh and Ray (1936b) with bromine as ultimate oxidant; the advantage of the latter as compared to methylene blue is the absence of absorption < 300 mμ, so that experiments at 256 and 313 mμ can be made with practically all absorption accounted for by the uranyl salt. The rate of reduction was found to be independent of $[\text{Br}_2]$ between $[\text{Br}_2]_0 = 0.08$ and 0.16M (at [mandelic acid] $= [\text{UO}_2^{++}] = 0.02$M). The inverse rate was a linear function of inverse mandelic acid concentration. It appeared to be proportional to the *square root* of light intensity (comparison of rates at 829 and 1444 ergs/(sec cm²) at $[\text{UO}_2^{++}] = 0.02$ and 0.0566M). The rate was compared to light absorption by $\text{UO}_2^{++}+$mandelic acid, using a value of $\epsilon = 50$ (Ghosh and Mitter, Table 2.8). Between $[\text{UO}_2^{++}] = 0.01$ and 0.1M, at $I_0 = 829$ ergs/(sec cm²), the rate was found to be proportional to the square root of light energy absorbed by uranyl ions. The quantum yield appeared very high; e.g. at $[\text{Br}_2]_0 = 0.1263$M, $[\text{UO}_2^{++}] = 0.01$M, [mandelic acid] $= 0.0614$M, $A_{\text{UO}_2^{++}} = 183.4$ ergs/(sec cm²), and $\lambda = 313$ mμ, the average yield in 120 min was about 32.

The mechanism suggested to explain these results was based on a chain reaction initiated by Br atoms:

$$\text{UO}^{++}* + \text{Br}_2 \underset{k_1'}{\overset{k_1}{\rightleftharpoons}} \text{UO}_2^{++} + \text{Br} + \text{Br} \tag{92a}$$

$$\text{Br} + \text{Br} \overset{k_2}{\rightarrow} \text{Br}_2 \tag{92b}$$

$$\text{Br} + \text{Br}_2 \overset{k_3}{\rightarrow} \text{Br}_3 \tag{92c}$$

$$\text{Br}_3 + \text{mandelic acid} \overset{k_4}{\rightarrow} \text{oxidation product} + 2\text{HBr} + \text{Br} \tag{92d}$$

$$\text{Br}_3* \overset{k_5}{\rightarrow} \text{Br}_2 + \text{Br} \tag{92e}$$

giving the rate equation

$$-\frac{d\,[Br_2]}{dt} = [Br_2]\,k_3 \left(\frac{I}{k_2}\frac{^A UO_2^{++}}{Nh\nu}\right)^{\frac{1}{2}} \frac{k_4\,[\text{mandelic acid}]}{k_5 + k_4\,[\text{mandelic acid}]} \qquad (93)$$

This equation indicates first order reaction in respect to $[Br_2]$, proportionality to $\sqrt{I}$, and linear relation between inverse rate and inverse mandelic acid concentration.

The similar oxidations of mandelic acid by potassium indigo tetrasulfonate (PIT) and by Meldola's blue (MsB) were studied by Bhattacharyya (1952b) and Gulvady (1952). The (PIT) disappearance was followed by means of its absorption at 546 mμ. (No correction for the absorption of U(IV) at that wavelength was mentioned. However, if it is present as an intermediate, its concentration is sure to be very small.) The orders of magnitude of typical concentrations were $[\text{PIT}]_0 = 10^{-4}$M, $[UO_2^{++}] = 10^{-1}$M, $[\text{mandelic acid}]_0 = 0.01$–$1$M.

Our analysis of the results given by Bhattacharyya and Gulvady shows that Equation (91) can be fitted to the data. The inverse of the quantum yield (as referred to light absorbed by UO_2^{++} only) plotted against $[\text{mandelic acid}]^{-1}$ should yield a straight line with slope $(k_2 + k_3\,[UO_2^{++}])/k_4$, and intercept 1; the slope of $1/\gamma$ plot vs. $[UO_2^{++}]$ should be $[k_3/k_4] \times [\text{mandelic acid}]$ and the intercept, $1 + k_2/k_4\,[\text{mandelic acid}]$. Such plots can be made; however, the data given Bhattacharyya and Gulvady are not sufficiently accurate or precise to allow one to draw definite conclusions from these plots. It is possible to draw straight lines corresponding to the same value of k_3/k_2 for different photon energies (see Fig. 4.16a). However, these lines are not unique in fitting the data. One would require more experimental points to conclude that such an analysis is meaningful.

3. Photochemical Reactions of Uranyl Ions with Alcohols

3.1. *Carbohydrates*

Aqueous uranyl ion will photoreact with various carbohydrates. Heidt (1939) observed that the photoreaction between uranyl ion and sucrose produced some U(IV) and decreased the optical activity of the solution.

Heidt and Moon (1953) studied the same reaction in 2537 Å light. They worked with outgassed solutions under a CO_2 atmosphere.

Initial concentrations were about 0.01M UO_2^{++}, 0.5M ClO_4^- (or 0.2M acetate in an NaOAc–HOAc buffer), 0.1–0.4M Na^+, pH = 1–3.6.
Spectra of identical samples with and without irradiation, when

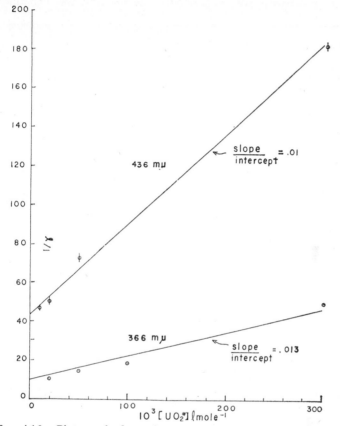

Fig. 4.16a. Plots made from data of Bhattacharyya and Gulvady (1952b) for photochemical UO_2^{++}-sensitized oxidation of mandelic acid by potassium indigo tetrasulfonate.

compared with typical uranyl and U(IV) spectra, proved the existence of U(IV) as a photolysis product (Fig. 4.17).

For the similar photolysis of glucose, D-gluconic acid, and methyl D-glucopyranoside, they observed that in acidic perchlorate mixtures (pH 1–2), the spectrophotometric concentration of U(IV) increased over a period of 15–30 min after illumination was stopped. This dark reaction is reminiscent of that observed in the uranyl–oxalate photoreaction (see Section 2.2). (It was assumed that no slow complexing reaction of U(IV), producing a species with higher molar absorbance, was occurring.) The reaction was explained as

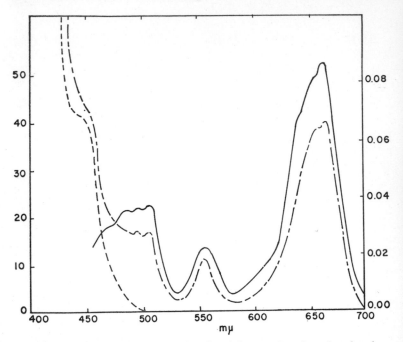

FIG. 4.17. Optical density of photolyzed (— · — ·) and unphotolyzed (— — —) aqueous sucrose solutions with uranyl sulfate. Also, molar absorbancy (based on U) of the original sucrose solution with added U(SO₄)₂ (———). All solutions were buffered with NaAc and HAc to pH 3.6. After Heidt and Moon (1953).

the thermal disproportionation of U(V), produced as the product of the primary photochemical uranyl–organic substrate electron transfer:

$$UO_2^{++} + S,\ \text{substrate} \rightleftharpoons UO_2S^{++} \tag{94a}$$

$$UO_2^{++}S + h\nu \rightarrow UO_2S^{++*} \tag{94b}$$

$$UO_2^{++} + h\nu \rightarrow UO_2^{++*} \tag{94c}$$

$$UO_2^{+*}+M \rightarrow UO_2^{+}+M \qquad (94d)$$

$$UO_2S^{++*} \rightarrow UO_2^{+}+S^{+} \qquad (94e)$$

$$UO_2S^{++*}+M \rightarrow UO_2S^{++}+M \qquad (94f)$$

$$2UO_2^{+}+H^{+} \rightarrow UO_2^{++}+UO_2H^{+} \qquad (94g)$$

$$(UO_2H^{+}+2H^{+} \rightarrow UOH^{+++}+H_2O, \text{ rapid})$$

$$S^{+} \rightarrow \text{products} \qquad (94h)$$

If step *g* is observed, appearance of U(IV) after photolysis should follow:

$$\frac{d\,[UOH^{+++}]}{dt} = k_g\,[H^+]\,[UO_2^{+}]^2 \qquad (95)$$

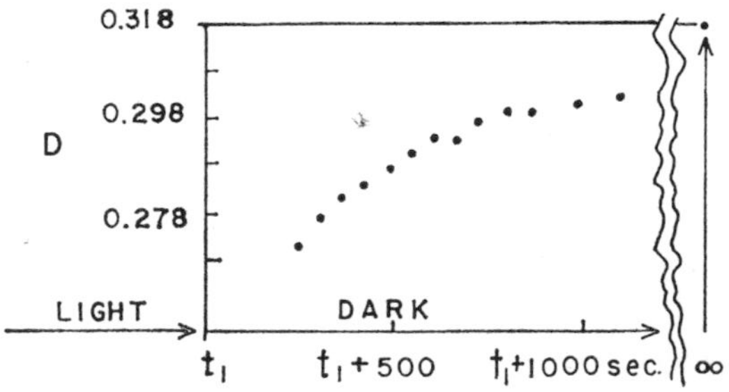

FIG. 4.18. Increase of optical density in UOH^{++} absorption region (650 mµ) in acid (pH 1.5) perchlorate solution of UO_2^{++} (0.010M)+ glucose (0.011M), which has been photolyzed to 7 per cent UO_2^{++} disappearance at time t_1. 25°C, 10 cm path.

Let observation begin at time t_1, when $[UOH^{+++}] = D_1/l\epsilon$, $[UO_2^{+}]$ $= 2(D_\infty - D_1)/\epsilon l$. (*D* and ϵ are optical density and molar extinction coefficient for U(IV), and *l* is cell length.)

$$\frac{dD}{dt} = \frac{4k_g\,[H^+]\,(D_\infty - D)^2}{\epsilon l}$$

or $\quad (D_\infty - D)^{-1} - (D_\infty - D_1)^{-1} = 4k_g\,[H^+]\,(t-t_1)/\epsilon l \qquad (96)$

A plot of $(D_\infty - D)^{-1}$ vs. $(t - t_1)$ is given in Fig. 4.19. Heidt and Moon gave the equation for a straight line drawn as shown, from the slope determining $k_g = 150 \; l^2 \; mol^{-2} \; sec^{-1}$, and from the intercept finding $[UO_2^+] = 5 \times 10^{-4} \; mol/l$.

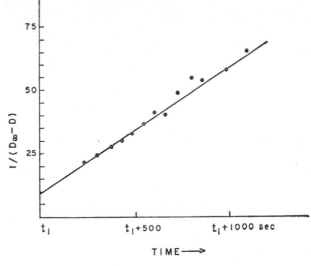

FIG. 4.19. Alternate plot of Fig. 4.18.

A consistency check was performed by Heidt and Moon. During the experiment described the light intensity was $I = 6.2 \times 10^{-6}$ einstein $l^{-1} \; sec^{-1}$. The measured quantum efficiency for U(IV) production was 0.135, and the corresponding efficiency for U(V) production should then be $\phi = 0.27$. The rate of production of U(V) is thus $1.65 \times 10^{-6} \; mol \; l^{-1} \; sec^{-1}$. The corresponding rate of destruction according to (94g) is

$$2k_g \, [H^+] \, [UO_2^+]^2 = 8.77 \; l \; mol^{-1} \; sec^{-1} \; [UO_2^+]^2$$

taken from the previous computation. Within the steady state approximation for the UO_2^+ intermediate during steady illumination,

$$[UO_2^+]_1 = (1.65 \times 10^{-6}/8.77)^{\frac{1}{2}} \; mol/l \qquad (97)$$

The value of (97), 4.3×10^{-4} mol/l, agrees as well as can be expected with the 5×10^{-4} obtained by the intercept method of the previous paragraphs.

Heidt and Moon (1953) suggested that the [probably U(V)] intermediate in carbohydrate photo-oxidation by uranyl occurs quite

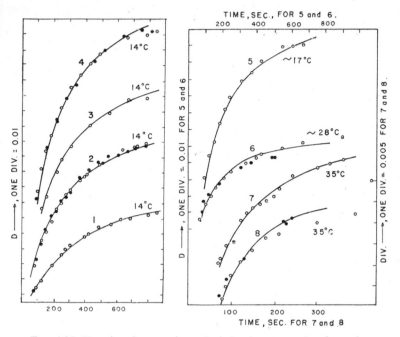

FIG. 4.20. Transient increase in optical density, D, at the absorption peak (~ 650 cm^{-1}) of U^{+4} following illumination (253.7 mμ) of aqueous solutions [0.01M UO$_2$(ClO$_4$)$_2$, 0.2M MeOH] buffered with HClO$_4$ to pH 1.03 ± 0.02 and brought to ionic strength of unity with NaClO$_4$. The absorption path was 10 cm. The time origin was the end of the actinic illumination. The points are experimental; the lines, theoretical. After Heidt (1954).

generally in uranyl photochemistry. Some of the data reported earlier in this chapter could be interpreted equally well by this hypothesis and steps similar to those of Equation (94).

Quantum yields on the carbohydrate oxidation were calculated as molecules U(IV) produced per quantum absorbed. Fluorescence and minor back-reactions were ignored. The yields ranged from

4 to 30 per cent. By Equation (94), the following set of relationships would apply:

$$[UO_2S^{++}] = K_a [UO_2^{++}] [S] \tag{98}$$

$$\frac{d[UO_2S^{++*}]}{dt} = \frac{IK_a [S]}{1 + K_a[S]} - k_e [UO_2S^{++*}] - k_f [UO_2S^{++*}] \tag{99}$$

Or, for a steady state with respect to UO_2S^{++*},

$$[UO_2S^{++*}] = IK_a [S]/(1 + K_a [S]) (k_e + k_f) \tag{100}$$

Then $$\frac{d [UO_2^+]}{dt} = k_e [UO_2S^{++*}] - 2k_g [UO_2^+]^2 [H^+] \tag{101}$$

For a steady state with respect to UO_2^+,

$$[UO_2^+]^2 = \{k_e IK_a [S]/2k_g [H^+] (1 + K_a [S]) (k_e + k_f)\} \tag{102}$$

Finally,

$$\frac{d[UOH^{++}]}{dt} = k_g [UO_2^+]^2 [H^+] = \frac{k_e IK_a [S]}{2(1 + K_a [S]) (k_e + k_f)} \tag{103}$$

The quantum yield, ϕ, is

$$\frac{1}{I} \frac{d[UOH^{++}]}{dt}$$

so $$\frac{1}{\phi} = \left(2 + \frac{2k_f}{k_e}\right) \left(1 + \frac{1}{K_a [S]}\right) \tag{104}$$

According to the preceding scheme, Heidt and Moon plotted $1/\phi$ vs. $1/[S]_0$ for several sugars. The data could be fitted reasonably well by straight lines, particularly for experiments run with (acetate) buffer. The intercept, according to this hypothesis, should be always greater than 2, the surplus over 2 being a measure of the rate of uneventful de-excitation of the photoactivated uranyl–sugar cluster as compared with that of electron transfer. Since the intercepts generally were about 3, the electron transfer process seemingly was highly efficient.

3.2. Methanol

The ideas of Heidt and Moon (see previous section) regarding a U(V) intermediate in photochemical reduction of uranyl were carried over into an attempt by Heidt (1954) to test the photostationary state hypothesis. He chose the oxidation of aqueous methanol by uranyl ion:

$$UO_2^{++} + 2H^+ + CH_3OH \xrightarrow{h\nu} H_2CO + U^{+4} + 2H_2O \qquad (105)$$

As in the carbohydrate oxidations, the concentration of U(IV) was observed to increase for some time after photolysis was stopped. The production of U(IV) during this dark period followed kinetics of apparent second order with respect to an intermediate, which was supposed to be U(V). Plots of several runs, together with Heidt's calculations based on Equation (96), are shown in Fig. 4.20.

The values of k_g (see Section 3.1) ranged from 43 l^2 mol^{-2} sec^{-1} at 14°C to 340 l^2 mol^{-2} sec^{-1} at 35°C, at pH = 1 and ionic strength = 1. An Arrhenius plot was made for the presumed U(V) disproportionation, and the corresponding activation parameters were evaluated for Equation (94g):

$$A = 6.5 \times 10^{14}, \; E_a = 17.3 \text{ kcal}, \; \Delta H\ddagger = 16.7 \text{ kcal}, \; \Delta S\ddagger = +8.3 \text{ e.u.}$$

According to Heidt's analysis of his experiments, the results gave a self-consistent set of data for all cases, which within a small margin of error could be interpreted by a steady-state hypothesis for an intermediate U(V) species. Rather than rely on the optical density of U(IV) species as an indirect measure of supposed U(V) intermediate concentration, one would like to have a direct measurement of U(V) concentration. There is some hope that this can be obtained from absorption spectra in the near-infrared.

A mechanism alternative to Heidt's can be suggested to explain the slow dark reaction which is second order in intermediate, and which produces U(IV):

$$UO_2^{++} + h\nu \rightarrow UO_2^{++*} \qquad (106a)$$

$$S + UO_2^{++*} \rightarrow S^+ + UO_2^+ \qquad (106b)$$

$$M + UO_2^{+*} \rightarrow UO_2^{+} + M \tag{106c}$$

$$S^{+} + UO_2^{+} + H^{+} \rightarrow U(IV) + products \tag{106d}$$

Since, in this series, $[UO_2^{+}] = [S^{+}]$, the process (106d) would appear to have the same effect as step (94g). With this mechanism one would have to explain why the rate constant k_d is essentially the same (as reported by Heidt) for several organic substrates and why the quantum efficiency at infinite substrate concentration approaches ~ 2–3 rather than 1. Neither of these difficulties can definitely rule out versions of Equation (106), however. More experiments are needed.

3.3. *Ethanol*

In a series of three papers Bhattacharyya (1952 a, b) and Gulvady (1952) reported kinetic studies of the photoreduction of ethanol to acetaldehyde by uranyl salts. Light frequencies of 22,940 cm^{-1}, 24,630 cm^{-1}, and 27,320 cm^{-1} were used. The overall stoichiometry was found by high light intensity, long-time experiments to be

$$CH_3CH_2OH + UO_2^{+} \overset{h\nu}{\rightarrow} UO^{++} + CH_3CHO + H_2O \tag{107}$$

when the alcohol was in excess at 0.2M in aqueous solution.

In the kinetic studies, the aldehyde concentration was studied as a function of time; the authors reported the rate of reaction to be independent of time but failed to explain the range of experimental conditions within which the independence held. Krishna and Ghosh (1953) commented upon this independence, pointing out that it should not hold for all experimental conditions within those reported by Bhattacharyya and Gulvady. In particular, the independence apparently was caused by the swamping ratio of substrate (alcohol) to oxidant (UO_2^{++}) which characterized the majority of Bhattacharyya and Gulvady's experiments. However, some of their experiments involved alcohol concentrations equal to or smaller than the UO_2^{++} concentrations, and it is not clear whether they noticed variations in rate with time for those cases and whether their reported rates are initial or average velocities.

In Fig. 4.21, Bhattacharyya and Gulvady's velocities are plotted vs. initial substrate concentration. They report that the inverse of the rate is linear in inverse substrate concentration for each wave-length; however, the linearity is not evident from replots of their data. More experimental points are needed to establish the true relationships.

If the ethanol photo-oxidation follows the mechanism of Heidt and Moon, as described by Equations (94–104), the rate of aldehyde formation would be given by (108):

$$\frac{d[\text{Prod}]}{dt} = k_h \, [\text{S}^+] = k_h k_e \, [\text{UO}_2\text{S}^{++*}]$$

$$= k_h k_e \, IK_a \, [\text{S}]/(k_e + k_f)(1 + K_a \, [\text{S}]) \qquad (108)$$

Thus a plot of $dt/(d\,[\text{Prod}])$ vs. $1/[\text{S}]$ would give a straight line whose intercept is $(1 + k_f/k_e)/Ik_h$ and whose slope is $1/K_a$ times the intercept. Calculated from the three wavelengths 366 mμ, 406 mμ, 436 mμ, $1/K_a$ would be ~ 0.045 mole l^{-1}; ~ 0.035 mole l^{-1}; ~ 0.029 mole l^{-1}. These values are not constant, as they should be unless either (*a*) Heidt's mechanism does not apply here or (*b*) there are different photosensitive complexes which are reactive to light of the different frequencies. That the mechanism is not the simple one is substantiated by the quantum yields for aldehyde production, calculated from the reports of Bhattacharyya and Gulvady. These were ~ 40 (366 mμ), ~ 28 (406 mμ), ~ 5 (436 mμ) in the limit of large alcohol concentration, as compared with $\sim \frac{1}{2}$ (as measured by U(IV) production) for the similar photo-oxidation of sugars carried out by Heidt and Moon. Bhattacharyya and Gulvady suggested that a chain mechanism is operative but did not attempt further theoretical work or speculation.

The uranyl-sensitized photo-oxidation of alcohols by organic dyes (Meldola's Blue [Gulvady and Bhattacharyya, 1952], potassium indigo tetrasulfonate [Bhattacharyya and Gulvady, 1952b]) has been studied. The rates of alcohol oxidation are much slower in the presence of these dyes, and the quantum yields (based on quanta absorbed by uranyl ions) are reduced by three or more orders of magnitude. It is likely that the dyes (in concentrations ~ 1 per cent of uranyl concentrations) promote deexcitation of the excited uranyl complexes at a rate much higher than that of the electron transfer or separation processes. The dye molecules studied have excited states in the same regions as do uranyl ions, with very large transition probabilities (e.g. ϵ [indigo, 366 mμ]/ϵ [UO_2^{++}, 366 mμ] = 617). Heidt followed only uranium species; Bhattacharyya and Gulvady only aldehyde formation. It is important to study all species in a photochemical reaction; this should be done for those reactions reported above.

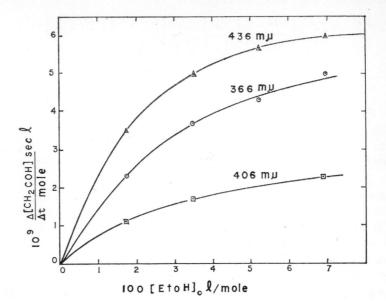

FIG. 4.21. Initial rates of aldehyde formation as function of ethanol concentration in photoreduction by UO_2^{++}. Plotted from data of Bhattacharyya and Gulvady (1952a).

CHAPTER 5

THEORY OF
ELECTRONIC STRUCTURE AND SPECTRA
OF THE URANYL ION

1. Electronic Structure of the Uranyl Ion

The bare U^{+6} ion has the configuration

$$K^2 L^8 M^{18} N^{32} 5s^2 5p^6 5d^{10} 6s^2 6p^6 \quad (16)$$

O^{--} ions have the configuration $K^2 2s^2 2p^6$. The isolated OUO^{++} ion is formed by a combination of ionic bonding and electron sharing. Coulombic repulsion between the two oxygens favor a linear structure. This configuration has been in fact found for the ion in several salts (cf. Chapter 1, Fig. 1.1).

The linear structure allows formation of several 2- or 3-atom molecular orbitals in which the 16 outer oxygen electrons may reside. Suppose we consider—partly following Eisenstein and Pryce (1955)—the empty $5f$, $6d$, and $7s$ U orbitals, and the occupied $2s$ and $2p$ oxygen orbitals. The latter will combine to yield a set as shown on the upper table on p. 336.

These will interact with uranium orbitals shown on the lower table on p. 336 (if we consider the $sp(I)$ and $sp(II)$ too far away to bond with the central ion).

Twelve electrons (besides the oxygen lone pairs) must be accommodated; there are six bonding orbitals. It is not clear how strongly covalent each of the bonds can be or to what extent the oxygen electrons are shared by the central U atom. We can safely presume that in the uranyl ion the U atom has a somewhat higher charge than $+2$ and that the O atoms are negatively charged. The assumption seems safe because the cations of uranyl double salts are always found close to the uranyl oxygens. The accumulated experimental evidence that a uranyl U atom, where it can, will

Type	Description
sp (I) $\rbrace$ sp (II)	sp hybrid on either O atom, directed outward along the bond axis.
σ_g	sp hybrid on both O atoms, directed inward toward U. Symmetric.
σ_u	As above, but antisymmetric.
π_{+u} π_{-u}	p_{+1}(I)$+p_{+1}$(II) $\rbrace$ Double ring charge cloud, antisymmetric upon inversion through the p_{-1}(I)$+p_{-1}$(II) $\rbrace$ U atom.
π_{+g} π_{-g}	p_{+1}(I)$-p_{+1}$(II) $\rbrace$ As above, but symmetric upon p_{-1}(I)$-p_{-1}$(II) $\rbrace$ inversion.

Constituent orbitals	Molecular orbitals
s, d_0, σ_g	Three σ; 1 bonding, 1 antibonding
f_0, σ_u	1 bonding σ, 1 antibonding σ
d_{+1}, π_{+g}	1 bonding π, 1 antibonding π
d_{-1}, π_{-g}	1 bonding π, 1 antibonding π
f_{+1}, π_{+u}	1 bonding π, 1 antibonding π
f_{-1}, π_{-u}	1 bonding π, 1 antibonding π
sp (I), sp (II), $f_{+2}, f_{-2}, f_{+3}, f_{-3}, d_{+2}, d_{-2}$	Involved only in secondary bonds to other atoms

surround itself with 6 or more secondary ligands seems overwhelming. Yet, to do this, the ligands have to crowd quite close together. The U atom must carry sufficient positive charge to attract the many ions (or dipoles) in spite of their crowding. Most likely, the formal charge on the U atom is between $+3$ and $+6$; on each uranyl O, between $-\frac{1}{2}$ and -2.

Connick and Hugus (1952) showed how the observed ionic entropy (-17 e.u.) of aqueous uranyl ion can be accounted for on the basis of equivalent spherical $O^-U^{+4}O^-$ ions. Though this model is crude, the general picture of charge distribution is reasonable.

Our discussion implies that all uranyl electrons are in filled atomic or bond orbitals. This agrees with the fact that uranyl salts are diamagnetic, or only faintly paramagnetic. Eisenstein and Pryce (1955) argued that the weak paramagnetic contribution to the molar susceptibility of the uranyl group—*ca.* 57×10^{-6}—can be accounted for as due to an f-orbital motion. They felt that strong participation of $5f$ orbitals in the occupied molecular bonding orbitals was indicated. However, this particular interpretation is by no means the only one possible. If one makes somewhat different guesses about the parameters involved in the treatment, one can predict about the same value based on mostly d-orbital contribution (cf. Belford, 1961).

Elliott (1953), employing a collinear isolated-ion model for transuranyl groups, has obtained theoretical magnetic susceptibilities for neptunyl and plutonyl salts, which are isomorphous and strikingly similar in behavior to uranyl salts. His model gives results very close to the measurements of Hutchison (1951) on the susceptibility of $NaNpO_2(CH_3COO)_3$, if the extra Np electron is taken to be in the f_3 atomic orbital. The remainder of the electrons would most likely have a uranyl configuration. Elliott assumed a spin-orbit coupling factor of *ca.* 500 cm^{-1}. His calculated points are compared with Hutchison's experiments in Fig. 5.1. If this result is correct, similar results are likely to be obtained for OUO^+ salts.

Eisenstein and Pryce (1955) presented a more extensive treatment of these ideas, and considered electron paramagnetic resonance. The spin-orbit coupling parameter is probably $> 1000 \text{ cm}^{-1}$.

Plutonyl salts have a paramagnetism which is in excellent agreement with the spin-only value for two electrons. The apparent lack of an orbital contribution would argue for continuation of the f-shell filling, in the UO_2^{++}, NpO_2^{++}, PuO_2^{++} series, by addition in each step of an electron to the f_{-3} orbital; a $^3\Sigma$ ground state would result from this process. Evidence from the aforementioned and other experiments generally supports the viewpoint that in uranyl ions the $5f$ shell contains the lowest-energy empty orbitals and that these are split rather widely into components by the strong axial electric field of the two nearby oxygen atoms. In contrast, the apparent existence of $m = 3$ as a "good" quantum number for a $5f$ electron in $NaNp(CH_3COO)_3$ would argue against a wide splitting of the $5f$ orbitals by the secondary ligands. This would mean that

5*f* orbitals are not significantly involved in bonding of the secondary ligands.

Coulson and Lester (1956) calculated some hypothetical ligand-to-uranium overlap integrals in an attempt to discover whether 5*f* orbitals on U contribute much to covalent bonding. They did not

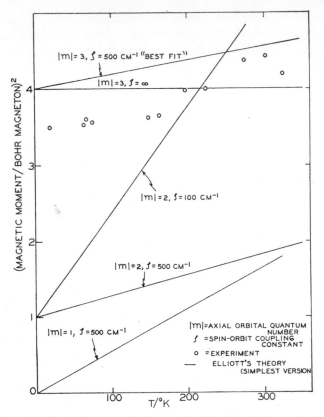

FIG. 5.1. Magnetic susceptibility of $NaUO_2(CH_3COO)_3$ containing NpO_2^{++}.

find appreciable overlapping between 5*f* Slater-type U^{+6} orbitals and H 1*s* stand-ins for ligands placed 1.76 Å away.

Plots of their Slater 6*d* and 5*f*, and Hartree 6*d* and 5*f* radial functions for U^{+6}, are shown in Fig. 5.2. A Thomas–Fermi 5*f* function, not shown, is similar to the Hartree 5*f*. The Slater function used by Coulson and Lester is in fairly good agreement with the others. Their results are therefore not likely to be much invalidated by their crude uranium wave-functions.

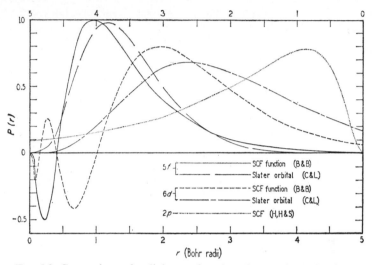

FIG. 5.2. Comparison of radial wave functions for uranium $5f$ and $6d$, and oxygen $2p$ orbitals. Functions plotted are $rR(r) = P(r)$. (B & B) = Belford and Belford. (C & L) = Coulson and Lester. (H H & S) = Hartree, Hartree, and Swirles. For oxygen, read upper scale. After Belford and Belford (1961).

Belford and Belford (1961) calculated some overlap integrals between hypothetical uranium and uranyl oxygen functions. Their results (see Fig. 5.2a and Table 5.1) indicated the possibility of strong σd and πd bonding and weak πf bonding, but were inconclusive on σf bonding.

Many workers have stated that $5f$ orbitals must be strongly involved in uranyl covalent bonding. However, there is as yet no firmly convincing evidence of this. The arguments used were based on observations of the following kind:

1. The U^{+6} $5f$ orbitals are stable compared with the $7s$ and $6d$ orbitals. This argument has been cited by Connick and Hugus (1952). The observation is well founded, experimentally and theoretically. Experimental proof is contained in the X-ray absorption data of Borovskii and Barinskii (1951) and the magnetic

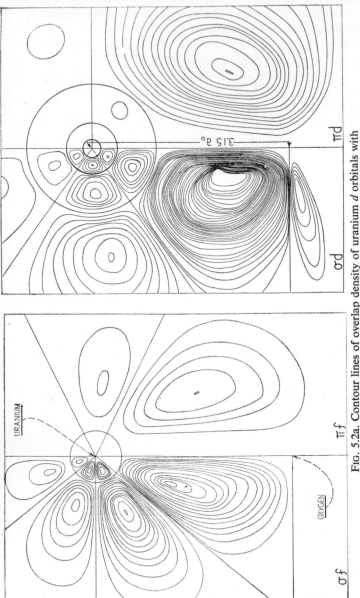

Fig. 5.2a. Contour lines of overlap density of uranium d orbitals with oxygen p orbitals are on right. The vertical coordinate is z and the horizontal coordinate ρ in cylindrical coordinates, both to the same scale. The function plotted is $\int \psi(U).\psi(O).\rho d\phi$, i.e. $2\pi\psi(U).\psi(O).\rho$. The interval of density is 0.00484. The perfect circles are radial nodes; the straight lines are angular nodes. The sign of the overlap function always changes when a node is crossed. Contour lines of overlap density of uranium f orbitals with oxygen p orbitals are on left. The interval of density

susceptibility data of neptunyl, as interpreted by Elliott (cf. above). The X-ray absorption work on UO_3 showed three bands in the L_{III}, M_{III}, and M_V edges. The relative intensities of the three bands differed from edge to edge. The M_{III} edge (loss of a $3p$ electron) had two strong bands, consistent with $3p \rightarrow 6d$ and $3p \rightarrow 7s$ transitions which obey the usual dipole selection rules, and a third, weaker band *of lower energy*, attributable to a "forbidden" $3p \rightarrow 5f$ transition.

The M_V edge (jump of a $3d$ electron) showed one band containing about 70 per cent of the intensity, and corresponding to the allowed $3d \rightarrow 5f$ transition, with weaker bands at higher frequencies, corresponding to the $3d \rightarrow 6d$ and $3d \rightarrow 7s$ transitions. The results are shown in Fig. 5.3. The bands are broad (3–7 eV) with the mean (peak-to-peak) spacings $6d$–$5f \simeq 6$ eV; $7s$–$5f \simeq 11$ eV (very uncertain!).

TABLE 5.1. OVERLAPS

U—O distance	σd	πd	σf	πf
$3.15a_0 = 1.67$ Å U—O	0.175	0.269	0.066	0.075
(O—U—O)	(0.32)	(0.38)	(0.093)	(0.105)
$3.62a_0 = 1.92$ Å U—O	0.193	0.192	0.052	0.047
(O—U—O)	(0.27)	(0.27)	(0.073)	(0.069)

The rough calculations of Belford and Muirhead (1960) involved integration of the central-field one-electron Schrödinger equation for a $5f$, $6d$, or $7s$ electron outside the fixed core of the U^{+6} ion (obtained by Ridley). The associated eigen values were $5f = -63.4$ eV, $6d = -49.1$ eV, $7s = -40.4$ eV. These and other evidences point to the general order of energies $5f$, $6d$, $7s$ in ionized uranium. The existence of low-lying f levels does not prove, however, that they are involved in covalent bonding. For this, the overlapping with ligand orbitals must also be favorable. As Coulson and Lester's calculations indicate, $6d$ and $7s$ orbitals are more favorable in that respect, particularly in the case of secondary bonds.

2. Specific characteristics of the secondary bonds imply a special kind of directed valence.

These statements often have been based on inadequate knowledge of the variety of uranyl compound structure. Several—often six—

ligands are usually found attached to the uranyl ion near its equator. Actually, only a few reliable X-ray diffraction structures of uranyl compounds are available, and many complex ion structures have been assumed to be similar simply by analogy. The assumption is

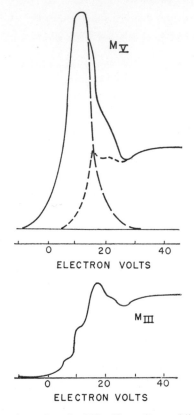

FIG. 5.3. Absorption edges in UO_3 (from Borovskii and Barinskii, 1951). The solid curves are experimental. The dashed curve is the part of the M_V edge which B. and B. attributed to the $5f \leftarrow 3d$ transition. The dotted curve is a remainder, containing two humps attributed to $6d \leftarrow 3d$ and $7s \leftarrow 3d$.

at best dangerous; at worst, disastrous. One could argue that the high charge on the central ion causes ionic or dipolar ligands to be bound very strongly, that they take up positions of least steric repulsion, and that the steric hindrance prevents them from getting very far from the equatorial plane (because of interference with the axial oxygens). The argument that six ligands must remain bound in a (distorted) hexagonal arrangement around the equator in order to satisfy sixfold directional hybrids using the uranium $5f_{\pm 3}$ orbitals cannot yet be backed up with any proof.

2. Near-visible Spectrum—Interpretational Attempts

McGlynn and Smith (1960) have given an interesting interpretation of the prominent features of the uranyl ion spectra. Observing the fluorescence and absorption spectra of uranyl ions in solution (cf. Figs. 2.1, 2.3, 2.4), they noted that the fluorescence spectrum appears to contain a single series, and can be looked upon (approximately) as the mirror image of the series corresponding to a certain electronic transition in the absorption spectrum. Subtracting the absorption series corresponding to this mirror image from the total absorption spectrum they were left with absorption bands which appear to form several series. This remainder was broken (rather arbitrarily but reasonably) into four series, i.e. assigned to four more electronic transitions. This is shown in Figs. 5.4 and 5.5. The regions are labeled Nos. 1, 2, 3, 4, and 5, and appear to correspond to the F, M, D, UV, and far UV series respectively, as labeled by Dieke and Duncan in their analysis of the spectra of single crystals of uranyl salts.

Next, the supposed molecular orbital bonding scheme of the isolated, linear OUO^{++} ion is invoked. The ligands are considered as minor perturbations upon the $D_{\infty h}$ OUO^{++} core. The bonding is considered to be essentially the same as that assumed by Eisenstein and Pryce (1955), Belford (1961), and others (see also the beginning of this Section). The lowest-energy transition would put one electron from a pi bond into a "non-bonding" uranium orbital—$5f$ or $6d$. The orbitals which might be occupied on excitation are $\delta_g(6d)$, $\delta_u(5f)$, or $\phi_u(5f)$. Among these, the $\phi_u(5f)$ is quite likely to be lowest, on account of the greater repulsion between the electrons of the polar oxygen atoms and the $\delta_u(5f)$ orbital. However, because of its lower angular momentum, the $\delta_u(5f)$ orbital has some intrinsic advantage over the $\phi_u(5f)$, and in some cases the perturbation effects of strictly equatorial ligands might actually cause the δ_u to be lowest. Because of its higher intrinsic energy in the uranium ion, the $\delta_g(6d)$ orbital would not seem so favorable (see below). The energy level scheme would be roughly as follows:

$$(\sigma_u)^2 (\sigma_g)^2 (\pi_u)^4 (\pi_g)^4 < (\sigma_u)^2 (\sigma_g)^2 (\pi_u)^4 (\pi_g)^3 (\phi_u)^1$$

$$\sim (\sigma_u)^2 (\sigma_g)^2 (\pi_u)^4 (\pi_g)^3 (\delta_u)^1 < (\sigma_u)^2 (\sigma_g)^2 (\pi_u)^4 (\pi_g)^3 (\delta_g)^1$$

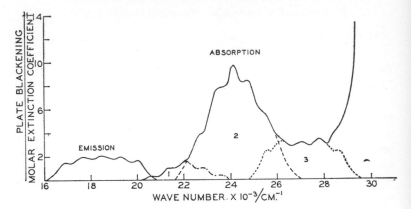

FIG. 5.4. The emission spectrum and low-energy absorption spectrum of UO_2^{++}. The scale on the left refers to molar extinction coefficient. The regions 1, 2, and 3 are somewhat arbitrarily defined. The height of the emission spectrum and the boundary of region 1 are drawn to emphasize a mirror image relationship. Regions 2 and 3 are drawn in the manner indicated to show their relationship to the M and D series of Duncan and Dieke. The arbitrariness in drawing in these boundaries does not appreciably affect the results of Table 5.2. There may be more than three transitions in the absorption region indicated, but complete resolution awaits further work. After McGlynn and Smith (1960).

Interchange of π_g and π_u produces three excited configurations whose energies would be ordered as those above, but their position with respect to the above set is, at first, unknown. The antibonding orbitals are not considered, as they are supposed to be high in energy relative to the nonbonding orbitals.

The ground state is $^1\Sigma^+{}_g$. The other configurations give rise to spectroscopic terms as follows:

$$(\pi_g)^3 (\phi_u)^1 : {}^3\Gamma_{(5,4,3)u}, \ {}^1\Gamma_{4u}, \ {}^3\Delta_{(3,2,1)u}, \ {}^1\Delta_{2u}$$

$$(\pi_g)^3 (\delta_u)^1 : {}^3\Phi_{(4,3,2)u}, \ {}^1\Phi_{3u}, \ {}^3\Pi_{(2,1,0)u}, \ {}^1\Pi_{1u} \ \text{etc.}$$

McGlynn and Smith, observing the Regions 1, 2, 3 in their analysis of the absorption spectrum, with very low intensities (maximum molar extinction coefficient = 10), attribute them to the three components of an excited spin triplet, $^3? \leftarrow {}^1\Sigma_g{}^+$. The spin–orbit coupling mechanism is the device suggested by them for injecting some

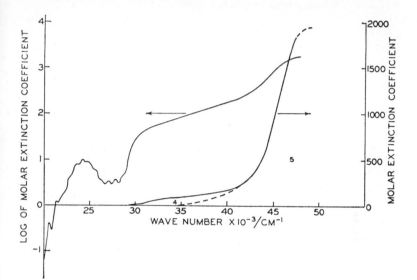

FIG. 5.5. The absorption spectrum of $UO_2{}^{++}$ with the high-energy regions 4 and 5 defined. Arrows refer curve to appropriate scale. Region 4 probably corresponds to the UV series of Dieke and Duncan (1949). The dotted line has been drawn in by exponentially extrapolating the boundary of region 5. The f-number of region 5 quoted in the text has been obtained by doubling the area under the depicted boundary of this region and is subject to some error, since the maximum observed may be spurious and due to the large amount of scattered light coming through a wide slit. After McGlynn and Smith (1960).

singlet character into the triplet states, to break down the usual prohibition of triplet ← singlet transitions.

The intensities of the spectral Regions 1, 2, 3, 4, 5 give computed oscillator strengths and their "natural lifetimes" as listed in Table 5.2.

Possible identification of the Regions 1, 2, 3 triplet and the Regions 4, 5 singlets depends, according to McGlynn and Smith, on the following assumptions and arguments:

1. Either the $^3\Delta_u$ or the $^3\Pi_u$ states are lowest.

2. The singlet states seen in Regions 4, 5 must be responsible for the intensity of Regions 1, 2, 3.

3. Spin–orbit coupling provides the mechanism for mixing of the Regions 4, 5 states with the lower triplet.

TABLE 5.2. QUANTITIES CALCULATED FROM FIGS. 5.5, 5.4
After McGlynn and Smith (1960)

Region	Oscillator* strength (f)	Frequency of most intense line ($\bar{\nu}_{max}$)	Calculated lifetime (τ)†
1	0.0000129	22,050 cm^{-1}	0.476 msec
2	0.0001800	24,125 cm^{-1}	0.0439 msec
3	0.0000345	27,000 cm^{-1}	0.121 msec
1+2+3	0.000141	25,000 cm^{-1}	0.0343 msec
4	0.0771	34,000 cm^{-1}	0.00098 msec
5‡	(0.00265)	(48,000 cm^{-1})	(0.0000169 msec)
4+5	(0.0798)	(48,000 cm^{-1})	(0.0000163 msec)

* Calculated as $f = 4.32 \times 10^{-9} \int \epsilon \, d\bar{\nu}$.
† τ is the mean intrinsic lifetime, calculated from the intensity of the absorption bands by means of the equation

$$\tau = 1.50 \, (g_u/g_l)/(\bar{\nu}_{max})^2 f$$

where g_u and g_l are the degeneracies of the assumed upper and lower states (*i.e.* $g = 1$ for $^1\Sigma_0$, $g = 2$ for other states).
‡ Band 5 is uncertain in position and intensity. Quantities calculated from it are given in parentheses.

4. States (with inclusion of spin–orbit coupling) of the same overall symmetry can perturb one another. More precisely, we say that two wave functions which form bases for the same irreducible representation of the group ($D_{\infty h}$) can interact. Table 5.3 gives representations of the group $D_{\infty h}$, together with the spectroscopic term symbols for molecular states which have the symmetry of each representation.

5. Region 2 is much stronger than Regions 1 and 3, which have similar intensities. Of the two singlet–singlet bands, Region 5 has much the highest intensity and its upper state is therefore most

likely the one which perturbs the upper state of band 2. Then Region 4 would perturb Regions 1 and 3.

6. By the symmetry arguments of (4) and of Table 5.3, and by statements (1) and (5), the following alternate assignments would be possible:

TABLE 5.3. CLASSIFICATION OF MOLECULAR TERMS FOR A MOLECULE OF SYMMETRY $D_{\infty h}$

Representation		States appropriate to representation			
A_{1g}		$^1\Sigma^+_g$		$^3\Pi^+_{0,\,2\,g}$	
A_{1u}	z	$^1\Sigma^-_u$		$^3\Pi^-_{0,\,2\,u}$	
A_{2g}		$^1\Sigma^-_g$		$^3\Pi^-_{0,\,2\,g}$	$^3\Sigma^-_0$
A_{2u}		$^1\Sigma^+_u$		$^3\Pi^+_{0,\,2\,u}$	
E_{1g}		$^1\Pi_g$	$^3\Delta_{1,\,3\,g}$	$^3\Pi_{1g}$	$^3\Sigma_1$
E_{1u}	$x,\,y$	$^1\Pi_u$	$^3\Delta_{1,\,3\,u}$	$^3\Pi_{1u}$	
E_{2g}		$^1\Delta_g$	$^3\Delta_{2g}$	$^3\Pi_{2,\,0\,g}$	$^3\Phi_{2,\,4\,g}$
E_{2u}		$^1\Delta_u$	$^3\Delta_{2u}$	$^3\Pi_{2,\,0\,u}$	$^3\Phi_{2,\,4\,u}$
E_{3g}		$^1\Phi_g$	$^3\Delta_{3,\,1\,g}$		$^3\Phi_{3g}$	$^3\Gamma_{3,\,5\,g}$
E_{3u}		$^1\Phi_u$	$^3\Delta_{3,\,1\,u}$		$^3\Phi_{3u}$	$^3\Gamma_{3,\,5\,u}$
E_{4g}		$^1\Gamma_g$			$^3\Phi_{4,\,2\,g}$	$^3\Gamma_{4g}$
E_{4u}		$^1\Gamma_u$			$^3\Phi_{4,\,2\,u}$	$^3\Gamma_{4u}$
E_{5g}		^1H_g				$^3\Gamma_{5,\,3\,g}$
E_{5u}		^1H_u				$^3\Gamma_{5,\,3\,u}$

TABLE 5.4

Region	Assignments possible		
1	$^3\Delta_{1u}$		$^3\Pi_{0u}$
2	$^3\Delta_{2u}$		$^3\Pi_{1u}$
3	$^3\Delta_{3u}$		$^3\Pi_{2u}$
4	$^1\Pi_u$ or $^1\Phi_u$		$^1\Delta_u$ (or $^1\Sigma_u^-$)
5	$^1\Delta_u$		$^1\Pi_u$

7. The only one of the listed upper states fully allowed in transition from a $^1\Sigma^+_g$ ground state is $^1\Pi_u$. Region 5 has the intensity expected for a "fully allowed" transition. Thus it seems reasonable to accept the second set of assignments mentioned above.

Zeeman effect. An *isolated* uranyl ion, having either of the above designations of states, should show characteristic band splittings when subjected to a magnetic field along the molecular axis. Specifically, the splitting to be expected is proportional to $2|\Lambda + 2\Sigma|\beta_0 H_z$, where β_0 is the Bohr Magneton, H_z the applied magnetic field, Λ the orbital quantum number, and Σ the spin quantum number for the state. In Table 5.5 we list the values of $|\Lambda + 2\Sigma|$ for the various possible states.

TABLE 5.5. EXPECTED ZEEMAN EFFECT FOR THE ENERGY LEVEL
SCHEMES OF TABLE 5.3

Region	Level	$|\Lambda + 2\Sigma|$	Level	$|\Lambda + 2\Sigma|$
1	$^3\Delta_{1u}$	0	$^3\Pi_{0u}$	1
2	$^3\Delta_{2u}$	2	$^3\Pi_{1u}$	1
3	$^3\Delta_{3u}$	4	$^3\Pi_{2u}$	3
4	$^1\Phi_u$	3	$^1\Delta_u$	2
	$^1\Pi_u$	1	$^1\Sigma^-_u$	0
5	$^1\Delta_u$	2	$^1\Pi_u$	1

In order to observe the Zeeman effect one must examine a single crystal at very low temperature, where the bands are sharp. Furthermore, the crystal field can split the degeneracy of some levels, and electronic–vibrational interaction (in this case, interaction with the ν_b modes and with lattice modes)—the Renner effect—can have the same consequences. If the applied magnetic field is not sufficiently strong to break down the interactions its effect will be negligible, and the Zeeman interaction will not be observed. The only identifiable Zeeman splitting so far observed in uranyl salts was found in Region 2 in the spectrum of some nitrates, $CsUO_2(NO_3)_3$ and $RbUO_2(NO_3)_3$ (which belong to D_{3h} in the crystal) and has been described in Section 4.5, Chapter 1. The splitting corresponded to $|2\Sigma + \Lambda| = 1$ and was first interpreted as indicating Region 2 to be $\Pi \leftarrow \Sigma$, while the others were presumed, by contrast, to be $\Sigma \leftarrow \Sigma$.

Looking at Table 5.5, one has difficulty finding an obvious interpretation for the Zeeman result. One might choose $^3\Pi_{1u}$ as Region 2, because it should have the experimental splitting whereas $^3\Delta_{2u}$ should be split twice as much. If, indeed, Regions 1, 2, 3 are the three components of the same triplet, then the fluorescence series, Region 1, should show the same splitting, while experimentally it shows none. On the other hand, the $^3\Delta_{1u}$ assignment is attractive for Region 1, since one expects no Zeeman splitting for it. Region

3 is expected to show a splitting, whether it be $^3\Delta_{3u}$ or $^3\Pi_{2u}$. These difficulties are not conclusive, since the $^3\Pi_{0u}$ may be split already into $^3\Pi_{0+u}$ and $^3\Pi_{0-u}$, each non-degenerate; the magnetic field might not be sufficiently strong to couple them. Similarly, ligand field and Renner effects may have removed the angular degeneracy of the $^3\Pi_{3u}$ states or of the $^3\Pi_{2u}$. There is much experimental work required before the Zeeman effects can be interpreted unambiguously.

Volod'ko, Sevchenko, and Umreiko (1960), at about the same time as McGlynn and Smith, reviewed some features of the infrared, Raman, fluorescence, and absorption spectra of uranyl nitrates in crystals and in solution. They independently pointed out the possibility of separating the absorption spectrum into at least four regions, but did not attempt to interpret them.

Other attempts have been made to understand bonding in uranyl compounds and to explain uranyl spectra on the basis of electronic structure. Though we have presented a scheme of McGlynn and Smith as a detailed example of such attempts, we point out that contradictory ideas, also worthy of serious consideration, have been put forth by Jørgensen (1959). Dr. J. B. Newman (1961) is working on a theoretical description of the uranyl ion and its compounds by means of a ligand field theory. Since the uranyl compounds involve far too many electrons and nuclei to be given detailed descriptions based purely on first principles, all of the theoretical treatments for some time are sure to be at best semi-empirical—whether explicitly or in a disguised manner. In fact, the task of description would be near-impossible were it not for the wealth of spectroscopic information which is on the record. We can look for future developments on two fronts:

1. Further arguments and evidence and refinements of theory are sure to be put forth by the theoreticians we have quoted above and by others.

2. Interacting with the conflicting theoretical predictions of various models, and using the great mass of past spectroscopic data on uranyl compounds as a guide, experimentalists can be expected to devise new spectroscopic experiments explicitly to serve as delicate tests of the various theoretical points. It is our hope that the review given in this book will serve as an aid to those engaged in such worthy efforts.

BIBLIOGRAPHY

References in the text are given in the order of name followed by date. The publication referred to may be found in this list by looking for the date first. All references in the list are in order of date first and alphabetical sequence of names.

1833. D. BREWSTER, *Trans. Roy. Soc. Edinburgh*, 12.
1842. L. L. BONAPARTE, *J. Chim. med.*, 8.
1842. J. J. EBELMEN, *Ann.*, **43**: 286, 294.
1843. L. L. BONAPARTE, *J. prakt. Chem.*, **30**: 308.
1852. G. G. STOKES, *Phil. Trans.*, **142**: 517.
1853. G. G. STOKES, *Phil. Trans.*, **143**: 385.
1860. NIÈPCE DE SAINT-VICTOR and L. CORVISART, *Ann.*, **113**: 112.
1862. W. SEEKAMP, *Ann.*, **122**: 113.
1865. W. SEEKAMP, *Ann.*, **133**: 253.
1866. C. BOLTON, *J. prakt. Chem.*, **99**: 269.
1872. E. BECQUEREL, *Compt. rend.*, **75**: 296.
1873. H. MORTON and H. C. BOLTON, *Chem. News*, **28**: 47, 113, 164, 233, 244, 257, 268.
1890. H. BREMER, Dissertation, Erlangen.
1891. O. KNOBLAUCH, *Wied. Ann.*, **43**: 738.
1891. G. WISBAR, *Ann.*, **262**: 232.
1892. H. BREMER, *Z. Anorg. Chem.*, **1**: 112.
1893. A. BACH, *Compt. rend.*, **116**: 1147.
1894. A. BACH, *Ber.*, **27**: 341.
1894. W. SEEKAMP, *Ann.*, **278**: 373.
1896. H. FAY, *Am. Chem. J.*, **18**: 265.
1898. A. BACH, *Arch. phys. nat.*, [4] **5**: 408.
1898. E. DUESSEN, *Wied. Ann.*, **66**: 428.
1899. C. DITTRICH, *Z. physik. Chem.*, **29**: 449.
1900. J. ALOY, *Bull. soc. chim. Paris*, [3] **23**: 368.
1900. J. ZEHENTER, *Montsh.*, **21**: 237.
1901. J. ALOY, *Ann. chim. et phys.*, [7] **24**: 418.
1903. W. N. HARTLEY, *J. Chem. Soc. (London)*, **83**: 221.
1904. A. BACH, *Ber.*, **37**: 3985.
1904. H. EULER, *Ber.*, **37**: 3411.
1905. H. KAYSER, *Handbuch der Spektroskopie*, **3**, S. Hirzel, Leipzig.
1906. A. BACH, *Ber.*, **39**: 1673.
1907. R. F. BACON, *Philipp. J. Sci.*, **2**: 129.
1908. E. BAUR, *Z. physik. Chem.*, **73**: 683.
1908. R. LUTHER and A. C. MICHIE, *Z. Elektrochem.*, **14**: 826.
1908. C. NEUBERG, *Biochem. Z.*, **13**: 305.
1909. H. BECQUEREL, J. BECQUEREL, and H. KAMERLINGH ONNES, *Verslag Akad. Wetenschap. Amsterdam*, **17**: 1045.
1909. H. N. McCOY and H. H. BUNZEL, *J. Am. Chem. Soc.*, **31**: 367.

1910. R. F. BACON, *Philipp. J. Sci.*, **5**: 281.
1910. E. BAUR, *Z. physik. Chem.*, **72**: 232.
1910. H. BECQUEREL, J. BECQUEREL, and H. KAMERLINGH ONNES, *Compt. rend.*, **150**: 647; *Ann. chim. phys.* 8, **20**: 145.
1910a. H. C. JONES and W. W. STRONG, *Carnegie Inst. Wash. Pub.*, 130.
1910b. H. C. JONES and W. W. STRONG, *Am. Chem. J.*, **43**: 37, 97.
1911. L. BRUNER and J. KOZAK, *Z. Elektrochem.*, **17**: 354.
1911a. H. C. JONES and W. W. STRONG, *Am. Chem. J.*, **45**: 1, 113.
1911b. H. C. JONES and W. W. STRONG, *Carnegie Inst. Wash. Pub.*, 160.
1912. H. C. JONES and W. W. STRONG, *Am. Chem. J.*, **47**: 27, 126.
1912. H. SCHILLER, *Z. physik. Chem.*, **80**: 641.
1913. E. BAUR, *Ber.*, **46**: 852.
1913. D. BERTHELOT and H. GAUDECHON, *Compt. rend.*, **157**: 333.
1913. M. BOLL, *Compt. rend.*, **156**: 1891.
1913. G. COURTOIS, *Bull. soc. chim.*, **13**: 449.
1913. H. EULER and S. RYD, *Biochem. Z.*, **51**: 97.
1913a. H. C. JONES, *J. Franklin Inst.*, **176**: 479, 677.
1913b. H. C. JONES and J. S. GUY, *Am. Chem. J.*, **49**: 1.
1913. J. H. MATHEWS and L. H. DEWEY, *J. Phys. Chem.*, **17**: 211.
1914. I. BOLIN, *Z. physik. Chem.*, **87**: 490.
1914. G. COURTOIS, *Compt. rend.*, **158**: 1511, 1688.
1914. V. HENRI and M. LANDAU, *Compt. rend.*, **158**: 181.
1914. C. NEUBERG and W. H. PETERSON, *Biochem. Z.*, **67**: 69.
1914. E. L. NICHOLS and E. MERRITT, *Phys. Rev.*, **3**: 457.
1915. H. L. HOWES, *Phys. Rev.*, **6**: 193.
1915. A. MÜLLER, *Z. anorg. Chem.*, **93**: 267.
1915. G. TRUMPLER, *Z. physik. Chem.*, **90**: 385.
1916. K. A. HOFMANN and K. SCHUMPELT, *Ber.*, **49**: 303.
1916. H. L. HOWES and D. T. WILBER, *Phys. Rev.*, **7**: 394.
1917. H. L. HOWES and D. T. WILBER, *Phys. Rev.*, **10**: 348.
1918. E. BAUR, *Helv. Chim. Acta*, **1**: 186.
1918. W. W. COBLENTZ, Nat. Bur. Standards (U.S.), Sci. Paper No. 325.
1918. E. C. HATT, *Z. physik. Chem.*, **92**: 513.
1918. H. L. HOWES, *Phys. Rev.*, **11**: 66.
1919. E. BAUR, *Z. Electrochem.*, **25**: 102.
1919. E. L. NICHOLS and H. L. HOWES, *Fluorescence of the Uranyl Salts*, Carnegie Inst. Wash. Pub., 298.
1919. E. L. NICHOLS, H. L. HOWES and F. G. WICK, *Phys. Rev.*, **14**: 201.
1920. J. ALOY and E. RODIER, *Bull. soc. chim. France*, **27**: 101.
1922. J. ALOY and E. RODIER, *Bull. soc. chim. France*, **31**: 246.
1922. E. BAUR, *Z. physik. Chem.*, **100**: 36.
1922. E. BAUR and A. REBMANN, *Helv. Chim. Acta*, **5**: 221.
1922. L. J. BOARDMAN, *Phys. Rev.*, **20**: 552.
1922. F. E. E. GERMANN, *J. Am. Chem. Soc.*, **44**: 1468.
1922. A. ROSENHEIM and G. TREWENDT, *Ber.*, **55B**: 1957.
1923. J. ALOY and A. VALDIGUIÉ, *Bull. soc. chim.*, **33**: 572; *Compt. rend.*, **176**: 1229.
1923. G. COURTOIS, *Bull. soc. chim.*, **33**: 1761, 1773.
1924. E. BAUR, *Z. physik. Chem.*, **111**: 315.
1924. P. F. BÜCHI, *Z. physik. Chem.*, **111**: 269.
1925. J. ALOY and A. VALDIGUIÉ, *Bull. soc. chim.*, **37**: 1135.
1925. W. T. ANDERSON and F. W. ROBINSON, *J. Am. Chem. Soc.*, **47**: 718.
1925. G. BERGER, *Rec. trav. chim.*, **44**: 47.

1925. G. H. DIEKE and A. C. S. VAN HEEL, *Verslag Akad. Wetenschap. Amsterdam*, **34**: 652; *Proc. Acad. Sci. Amsterdam*, **28**: 953; *Communs. Kamerlingh Onnes Lab. Univ. Leiden, Suppl.* 55a.
1925. A. C. S. VAN HEEL, *Verslag Akad. Wetenschap, Amsterdam*, **34**: 654; *Proc. Acad. Sci. Amsterdam*, **28**: 955.
1926. E. J. BOWEN and H. G. WATTS, *J. Chem. Soc.*, **1926**: 1607.
1926. R. H. MÜLLER, *Biochem. Z.*, **178**: 77.
1926. F. PERRIN, *Compt. rend.*, **182**: 929.
1927. T. DREISCH, *Z. Physik.*, **40**: 714.
1927. E. GAVIOLA, *Z. Physik*, **42**: 853, 862.
1927. E. GAVIOLA and P. PRINGSHEIM, *Z. Physik*, **43**: 384.
1927. S. HAKOMORI, *Sci. Repts. Tohoku Imp. Univ.*, I, **16**: 841.
1927. V. R. VON KURELEC, *Biochem. Z.*, **180**: 65.
1927. S. I. VAVILOV and V. L. LEVSHIN, *Naturwissenschaften*, **15**: 899.
1928. W. T. ANDERSON and L. F. BIRD, *Phys. Rev.*, **32**: 293.
1928. J. C. GHOSH and B. N. MITTER, *Quart. J. Indian Chem. Soc.*, **4**: 353.
1928. F. HEIN and W. RETTER, *Z. prakt. Chem.*, **119**: 368.
1928. R. H. MÜLLER, *Proc. Roy. Soc. London*, **A121**: 313.
1928. F. PERRIN and R. DELORME, *Compt. rend.*, **186**: 428.
1928. S. I. VAVILOV, *Z. Physik*, **50**: 52.
1928. S. I. VAVILOV and V. L. LEVSHIN, *Z. Physik*, **48**: 397.
1928. Y. VOLMAR, *Arch. phys. biol.*, **6**: 61.
1928. W. WEST, R. H. MÜLLER and E. JETTE, *Proc. Roy. Soc. London*, **A121**: 294; E. JETTE and W. WEST, *ibid.*, 299.
1929. E. BAUR, *Helv. Chim. Acta*, **12**: 793.
1929. R. DELORME and F. PERRIN, *J. Phys. radium*, **10**: 177.
1929. W. C. PIERCE, *J. Am. Chem. Soc.*, **51**: 2731.
1929. W. C. PIERCE, A. LEVITON, and W. A. NOYES, *J. Am. Chem. Soc.*, **51**: 80.
1929. P. PRINGSHEIM and M. YOST, *Z. Physik*, **58**: 1.
1930. W. G. LEIGHTON and G. S. FORBES, *J. Am. Chem. Soc.*, **52**: 3139.
1931. C. OUELLET, *Helv. Chim. Acta*, **14**: 936.
1932. E. BAUR, *Z. physik. Chem.*, **B16**: 465.
1932. L. J. HEIDT and F. DANIELS, *J. Am. Chem. Soc.*, **54**: 2384.
1933. F. P. BRACKETT, JR., and G. S. FORBES, *J. Am. Chem. Soc.*, **55**: 4459.
1933. F. EPHRAIM and M. MEZENER, *Helv. Chim. Acta*, **16**: 1257.
1933. Y. VOLMAR and MATHIS, *Bull. soc. chim.*, **53**: 385.
1934. F. DIÉNERT and F. VILLEMAINE, *Compt. rend.*, **199**: 1113.
1934. G. S. FORBES and L. J. HEIDT, *J. Am. Chem. Soc.*, **56**: 2363.
1935. I. FANKUCHEN, *Z. Krystallogr.*, **91**: 473.
1935. J. C. GHOSH, D. S. NARAYANMURTI, and N. K. ROY, *Z. physik. Chem.*, **B29**: 236.
1935. E. SCHNEIDER, *Z. physik. Chem.*, **B28**: 311.
1936. E. BAUR, *Helv. Chim. Acta*, **19**: 234.
1936. J. C. GHOSH, T. BANERJEE and B. BHATTA, *Z. physik. Chem.*, **B32**: 163.
1936a. J. C. GHOSH and B. B. RAY, *J. Indian Chem. Soc.*, **13**: 1.
1936b. J. C. GHOSH and B. B. RAY, *Z. physik. Chem.*, **B32**: 158.
1936. M. M. GUREVICH and L. CHAKHROV, *Bull. acad. sci. U.S.S.R.*, *Classe math. nat.*, *Ser. phys.*, **1936**: 509.
1936. E. C. PITZER, N. E. GORDON, and D. A. WILSON, *J. Am. Chem. Soc.* **58**: 67.
1937. P. PRINGSHEIM, *Physica*, **4**: 733.
1938. G. K. T. CONN and C. K. WU, *Trans. Faraday Soc.*, **34**: 1483.

1938. J. H. KŘEPELKA and Z. RÉSÖ, *Collection Czechoslov. Chem. Commun.*, **10**: 559.

1938. E. MONTIGNIE, *Bull. soc. chim. France*, **5**: 564.

1938. J. WEISS, *Trans. Faraday Soc.*, **34**: 451.

1939. L. J. HEIDT, *J. Am. Chem. Soc.*, **61**: 3223.

1939. N. F. MOERMAN and H. H. KRAAK, *Rec. trav. chim.*, **58**: 34.

1940. A. H. CARTER and J. WEISS, *Proc. Roy. Soc. London*, **A174**: 351.

1940. A. MÜLLER, *Ber.*, **73B**: 1353.

1941. L. F. EPSTEIN, F. KARUSH, and E. RABINOWITCH, *J. Optical Soc. Am.*, **31**: 77.

1941. J. LECOMTE and R. FREYMANN, *Bull. soc. chim.*, **8**: 622.

1942a. A. VON KISS, P. CSOKAN and G. NYIRI, *Z. phys. Chem.*, **A190**: 65.

1942b. A. VON KISS and G. NYIRI, *Z. anorg. Chem.*, **249**: 340.

1942. D. LIPKIN and S. I. WEISSMAN, Columbia Report A-520, 17 Dec. 1942.

1942. D. A. MACINNES and L. G. LONGWORTH, Report MDDC-911.

1942. T. L. RAMA CHAR, *J. Indian Chem. Soc.*, **19**: 369.

1942. B. S. SATYANARAYANA, *Proc. Indian Acad. Sci.*, **15A**: 414.

1942. G. M. SCHWAB and A. ISSIDORIDIS, *Ber.*, **75B**: 1048.

1944. D. D. PANT and N. D. SAKHWALKAR, *Proc. Indian Acad. Sci.*, **A19**: 135.

1944. A. N. SEVCHENKO, *J. Phys. (U.S.S.R.)*, **8**: 163.

1945. D. D. PANT, *Proc. Indian Acad. Sci.*, **A22**: 95, 110.

1945. J. T. RANDALL and M. H. F. WILKINS, *Proc. Roy. Soc. London*, **A184**: 347.

1946. M. FREYMANN, T. GUILMART and R. FREYMANN, *Compt. rend.*, **223**: 545, 573.

1946. J. J. MCBRADY and R. LIVINGSTON, *J. Phys. Chem.*, **50**: 176.

1947. H. W. CRANDALL, Report MDDC-1294.

1947. M. FREYMANN, *Compt. rend.*, **225**: 529.

1947. V. L. LEVSHIN and G. D. SHEREMETJEV, *Zhur. Eksptl. Teoret. Fiz.*, **17**: 209.

1947. S. SAMSON and L. G. SILLÉN, *Ark. Kemi. Min. Geol.*, **25**: No. 21.

1947. J. SUTTON, Report CRC-325; unpublished work.

1948. M. FREYMANN, *Compt. rend.*, **226**: 332; M. FREYMANN and R. FREYMANN, *Compt. rend.*, **227**: 1096; M. FREYMANN and H. CHANTREL, *ibid.*: 1029.

1948. W. F. NEUMAN and R. HAVILL, JR., Report AECD-1801.

1948. J. RODGERS and W. F. NEUMAN, Report AECD-2216.

1948. B. N. SAMOJLOV, *Zhur. Eksptl. Teoret. Fiz.*, **18**: 1030.

1948a. W. H. ZACHARIASEN, *Acta Cryst.*, **1**: 277.

1948b. W. H. ZACHARIASEN, *Acta Cryst.*, **1**: 281.

1948c. W. H. ZACHARIASEN, *Phys. Rev.*, **73**: 1104.

1949a. S. AHRLAND, *Acta Chem. Scand.*, **3**: 374.

1949b. S. AHRLAND, *Acta Chem. Scand.*, **3**: 783.

1949c. S. AHRLAND, *Acta Chem. Scand.*, **3**: 1067.

1949. T. V. ARDEN, *J. Chem. Soc. (London)*, **1949**: S299.

1949. R. H. BETTS and R. K. MICHELS, *J. Chem. Soc. (London)*, **1949**: S286.

1949. G. H. DIEKE and A. B. F. DUNCAN, *Spectroscopic Properties of Uranium Compounds*, National Nuclear Energy Series, Div. III, **2**, McGraw-Hill, New York.

1949. A. L. DOUNCE, J. F. FLAGG, P. FANTA, G. H. TISHKOFF and TIEN HO LAN, Chap. 1 of *Pharmacology and Toxicology of Uranium Compounds*, National Nuclear Energy Series, Div. VI, **1**, McGraw-Hill, New York.

1949. I. FELDMAN, W. F. NEUMAN and J. R. HAVILL, Report UR-85.

1949.   R. T. FOLEY and R. C. ANDERSON, *J. Am. Chem. Soc.*, **71**: 909.
1949.   J. L. HOARDE and J. D. STROUPE, *Spectroscopic Properties of Uranium Compounds*, National Nuclear Energy Series, Division III, **2**, McGraw-Hill, New York.
1949.   M. KASHA, *J. Chem. Phys.*, **17**: 349.
1949.   A. R. MATHIESON, *J. Chem. Soc. (London)*, **1949**: S294.
1949.   W. F. NEUMAN, J. HAVILL and I. FELDMAN, Report AECD-2728.
1949.   P. PRINGSHEIM, *Fluorescence and Phosphorescence*, Interscience, New York.
1949.   A. N. SEVCHENKO, *Bull. Acad. Sci. U.S.S.R.*, *Ser. phys.*, **13**: 188.
1949.   A. N. SEVCHENKO and B. I. STEPANOV, *Zhur. Eksptl. Teoret. Fiz.*, **19**: 1113.
1949.   J. SUTTON, *J. Chem. Soc. (London)*, **1949**: S275.
1950.   B. E. GORDON, *Doklady Akad. Nauk S.S.S.R.*, **74**: 913.
1950a. L. KAPLAN, R. A. HILDEBRANDT and M. ADER, Report ANL-4520.
1950b. L. KAPLAN, R. A. HILDEBRANDT and M. ADER, Report ANL-4521.
1951a. S. AHRLAND, *Acta Chem. Scand.*, **5**: 199.
1951b. S. AHRLAND, *Acta Chem. Scand.*, **5**: 1151.
1951c. S. AHRLAND, *Acta Chem. Scand.*, **5**: 1271.
1951.   M. N. ALENZEV, *Zhur. Eksptl. Teoret. Fiz.*, **21**: 133.
1951.   I. BOROVSKII and R. BARINSKII, *Izvest. Akad. Nauk S.S.S.R.*, **Ser. Fiz.**, **15**: 1225.
1951.   M. D. GALANIN, *Zhur. Eksptl. Teoret. Fiz.*, **21**: 126.
1951.   E. GLUECKAUF, H. A. C. McKAY and A. R. MATHIESON, *Trans. Faraday Soc.*, **47**: 437.
1951.   B. E. GORDON, *Izvest. Akad. Nauk*, *S.S.S.R.*, *Ser. Fiz.*, **15**: 624.
1951.   C. A. HUTCHISON, JR., O.N.R. Report.
1951.   J. J. KATZ and E. RABINOWITCH, *The Chemistry of Uranium*, National Nuclear Energy Series, Div. VII, **5**, McGraw-Hill, New York.
1951.   J. J. KATZ and G. GIBSON, *J. Am. Chem. Soc.*, **73**: 5436.
1951.   H. A. C. McKAY and A. R. MATHIESON, *Trans. Faraday Soc.*, **47**: 428.
1951.   D. D. PANT, *J. Sci. Research Benares Hindu Univ.*, **3**: 60.
1951.   R. A. ROBINSON and C. K. LIM, *J. Chem. Soc. (London)*, **1951**: 1841.
1951.   A. N. SEVCHENKO and B. I. STEPANOV, *Zhur. Eksptl. Teoret. Fiz.*, **21**: 212.
1951.   A. N. SEVCHENKO, V. M. VDOVENKO, and T. V. KOVALEVA, *Zhur. Eksptl. Teoret. Fiz.*, **21**: 204.
1951.   A.N. SEVCHENKO, *Izvest. Akad. Nauk. S.S.S.R.*, *Ser. Fiz.*, **15**: 613.
1951a. B. I. STEPANOV, *Zhur. Eksptl. Teoret. Fiz.*, **10**: 1153.
1951b. B. I. STEPANOV, *Zhur. Eksptl. Teoret. Fiz.*, **10**: 1158.
1952.   J. T. BARR and C. A. HORTON, *J. Am. Chem. Soc.*, **74**: 4430.
1952a. S. K. BHATTACHARYYA and S. GULVADY, *J. Indian Chem. Soc.*, **29**: 649.
1952b. S. K. BHATTACHARYYA and S. GULVADY, *J. Indian Chem. Soc.*, **29**: 659.
1952.   R. E. CONNICK and Z. Z. HUGUS JR., *J. Am. Chem. Soc.*, **74**: 6012.
1952.   A. W. GARDNER, H. A. C. McKAY, and D. T. WARREN, *Trans. Faraday Soc.*, **48**: 997.
1952.   A. W. GARDNER and H. A. C. McKAY, *Trans. Faraday Soc.*, **48**: 1099.
1952.   S. GULVADY and S. K. BHATTACHARYYA, *J. Indian Chem. Soc.*, **29**: 731.
1952.   J. S. JOHNSON and K. A. KRAUS, *J. Am. Chem. Soc.*, **74**: 4436.
1952   H. A. C. McKAY, *Trans. Faraday Soc.*, **48**: 1103.
1952a. D. D. PANT, *J. Sci. Research Benares Hindu Univ.*, **3**: 19.
1952b. D. D. PANT, *J. Sci. Research Benares Hindu Univ.*, **3**: 27.
1952.   E. STARITZKY and J. SINGER, *Acta Cryst.*, **5**: 536.

1952. J. SUTTON, *Nature*, **169**: 235.
1952. N. D. ZHEVANDROV, *Doklady Akad. Nauk S.S.S.R.*, **83**: 677.
1953. S. AHRLAND, *Acta Chem. Scand.*, **7**: 485.
1953. R. J. ELLIOTT, *Phys. Rev.*, **89**: 659.
1953. I. GAL, *Revueil de Travaux de l'Inst. Res. sur la Struct. di la Materiere*, Belgrade, No. **24**: 61.
1953. L. J. HEIDT and K. A. MOON, *J. Am. Chem. Soc.*, **75**: 5803.
1953. L. H. JONES and R. A. PENNEMAN, *J. Chem. Phys.*, **21**: 542.
1953. B. KRISHNA and S. GHOSH, *J. Indian Chem. Soc.*, **30**: 231.
1954. S. AHRLAND, S. HIETAN, and L. G. SILLEN, *Acta Chem. Scand.*, **8**: 1907.
1954. S. AHRLAND and R. LARSSON, *Acta Chem. Scand.*, **8**: 137, 354.
1954. F. H. ELLINGER, Los Alamos, unpublished. (Cited by Jones, 1955.)
1954. H. GOBRECHT, D. HAHN, and B. GRETZINGER, *Z. Physik*, **139**: 309.
1954. L. J. HEIDT, *J. Am. Chem. Soc.*, **76**: 5962.
1954. I. L. JENKINS and H. A. C. McKAY, *Trans. Faraday Soc.*, **50**: 107.
1954. J. S. JOHNSON, K. A. KRAUS, T. F. YOUNG, *J. Am. Chem. Soc.*, **76**: 1436.
1954. I. I. LIPILINA and O. YA. SAMOJLOV, *Doklady Akad. Nauk S.S.S.R.*, **98**: 99.
1954. T. MOELLER and M. V. RAMANIAH, *J. Am. Chem. Soc.*, **76**: 5251.
1954. T. NAKAI, *Bunko Kenyu*, **3**: 25.
1954 L. SACCONI and G. GIANNONI, *J. Chem. Soc.*, **1954**: 2751, 2368.
1954a. W. H. ZACHARIASEN, *Acta Cryst.*, **7**: 783.
1954b. W. H. ZACHARIASEN, *Acta Cryst.*, **7**: 788.
1954c. W. H. ZACHARIASEN, *Acta Cryst.*, **7**: 795.
1955. M. BACHELET, R. CLAUDE, and M. LEDERER, *Compt. rend.*, **240**: 419.
1955. C. L. CHRIST, J. R. CLARK, and H. T. EVANS, *Science*, **121**: 472.
1955. D. T. CROMER and P. E. HARPER, *Acta Cryst.*, **8**: 847.
1955. J. C. EISENSTEIN and M. H. L. PRYCE, *Proc. Roy. Soc.*, **A229**: 20.
1955. L. H. JONES, *J. Chem. Phys.*, **23**: 2105.
1955. D. D. PANT and D. P. KHANDELWAL, *Current Science*, **24**: 376.
1955. G. TRIDOT, *Ann. chim. (Paris)*, **10**: 225.
1955. K. S. VENKATESWARLU and BH. S. V. RHAGAVA RAO, *Anal. Chim. Acta*, **12**: 554.
1956. S. AHRLAND, *Acta Chem. Scand.*, **10**: 705.
1956. R. L. BELFORD, A. E. MARTELL, and M. CALVIN, *J. Inorg. Nucl. Chem.*, **2**: 11.
1956. C. A. BLAKE, C. F. COLEMAN, K. B. BROWN, D. G. HILL, R. S. LOWRIE, and J. M. SCHMITT, *J. Am. Chem. Soc.*, **78**: 5978.
1956. C. A. COULSON and G. R. LESTER, *J. Chem. Soc.*, **1956**: 3650.
1956. J. C. EISENSTEIN, *J. Chem. Phys.*, **25**: 142.
1956. A. F. KAPUSTINSKII, *Kristallografya*, **1**: 382.
1956. V. K. RAO and K. V. NARASIMHAM, *Indian J. Physics*, **30**: 334.
1956. A. N. SEVCHENKO and L. V. VOLOD'KO, *Izvest. Akad. Nauk S.S.S.R.*, Ser. Fiz., **20**: 464.
1957. E. W. DAVIES and C. B. MONK, *Trans. Faraday Soc.*, **53**: 442.
1957. L. A. HALL and G. H. DIEKE, *J. Opt. Soc. America*, **47**: 1092.
1957. M. ISHIDATE and Y. YAMANE, *Yokugaku Zasshi*, **77**: 386.
1957. D. D. PANT and B. C. PANDEY, *J. Sci. Ind. Research*, **16B**: 280.
1957. D. D. PANT and D. P. KHANDELWAL, *Current Science*, **26**: 282.
1957. V. M. VDOVENKO, A. A. PILOVSKII, and M. G. KUZINA, *Zhur. Neorg. Khim.* **2**: 970; 975.

1957.   V. M. VDOVENKO, M. P. KOVAL'SKAYA, and T. V. KOVALEVA, *Zhur. Neorg. Khim.* **2**: 1677.

1957.   Y. YAMANE, *Yokugaku Zasshi*, **77**: 389–403.

1958.   A. E. COMYNS, B. M. GATEHOUSE, and E. WAIT, *J. Chem. Soc.*, **1958**: 4655.

1958.   C. FRONDEL and I. BARNES, *Acta Cryst.*, **11**: 562.

1958.   B. M. GATEHOUSE, S. E. LIVINGSTONE, and R. S. NYHOLM, *J. Inorg. Nucl. Chem.*, **8**: 75.

1958.   B. M. GATEHOUSE, and A. E. COMYNS, *J. Chem. Soc.*, **1958**: 3965.

1958.   B. JEZOWSKA-TRZEBIATOWSKA and A. BARTECKI, *Bull. Acad. Polonaise Sci., ser. chim.*, **6**: 567.

1958.   G. I. KOBYSHEV and D. N. SUGLOBOV, *Doklady Akad. Nauk, S.S.S.R.*, **120**: (p. 35 in the American translation).

1958.   K. PAN, T. M. TSEU, and T. L. CHANG, *J. Chinese Chem. Soc.* (*Formosa*), **4**: 1.

1958.   D. D. PANT and D. P. KHANDELWAL, *Current Science*, **27**: 242.

1958.   E. C. RIDLEY, *Proc. Roy. Soc.* (*London*), **1247**: 422.

1958.   L. SACCONI, G. CAROLI and P. PAOLETTI, *J. Chem. Soc.*, **1958**: 4257.

1958.   L. V. VOLOD'KO and A. N. SEVCHENKO, *Optics and Spectroscopy*, **4**: 40.

1959.   S. COHEN, Relativistic S.C. Calculation for U Atom, Report UCRL-8633.

1959.   A. M. GUREVICH and E. V. KOMAROV, *Russian Journal of Inorganic Chemistry*, **4**: 590 (in the English translation).

1959.   S. HAYAKAWA and M. HIRATA, *J. Chem. Phys.*, **30**: 330.

1959.   L. H. JONES, *Spectrochim. Acta.*, **1959**: 409.

1959.   C. K. JØRGENSON, *Mol. Phys.*, **2**: 96. Also private communication.

1959.   E. V. KOMAROV, *Russian Journal of Inorganic Chemistry*, **4**: 591 (in the English translation).

1959a. D. D. PANT and D. P. KHANDELWAL, *J. Sci. Industr. Res.*, **18B**: 126.

1959b. D. D. PANT and D. P. KHANDELWAL, *Proc. Ind. Acad. Sci.*, **50A**: 323.

1959.   M. N. RAO and Bh. S. V. RAO, *Z. phys. Chem.*, **21**: 388.

1960.   R. L. BELFORD and J. S. MUIRHEAD, unpublished calculations.

1960.   R. L. BELFORD, A. E. MARTELL, and M. CALVIN, *J. Inorg. Nucl. Chem.*, **14**: 169.

1960.   G. L. CALDOW, A. B. VAN CLEAVE, and R. L. EAGER, *Can. J. Chem.*, **38**: 772.

1960.   S. P. McGLYNN and J. K. SMITH, Symposium on Molecular Electronic Spectroscopy, American Chem. Society Meeting at Cleveland, Ohio, 11th April 1960, published in *J. Mol. Spectroscopy*, **6**: 164, 188 (1961).

1960.   L. V. VOLOD'KO, A. N. SEVCHENKO, and D. S. UMREIKO, (a) *Doklady Akad. Nauk, S.S.S.R.*, **135**: 560; (b) *Izv. Akad. Nauk, S.S.S.R., Ser. Fiz.*, **24**: 749.

1961.   R. L. BELFORD, *J. Chem. Phys.*, **34**: 318.

1961.   R. L. BELFORD and G. BELFORD, *J. Chem. Phys.*, **34**: 1330.

1961.   S. P. McGLYNN, J. K. SMITH, and W. C. NEELY, *J. Chem. Phys.*, **35**: 105.

1961.   J. B. NEWMAN, Private communication and a paper presented at the Spectroscopy Symposium, Columbus, Ohio, June, 1963.

ADDITIONAL REFERENCES

The list of papers below provides a selected guide to some pertinent work whose appearance in the literature was noticed too late for comment in the text.

1963

"Infrared Spectra of Uranyl Nitrate and its Complexes with Neutral Ligands", V. M. VDOVENKO, D. N. SUGLOBOV, and V. A. KRASIL'NIKOV, *Radiokhimiya*, 5: 311.

"Luminescence and Intracomplex Energy Transfer in Uranyl Phthalocyanine", G. N. LIALIN and G. I. KOBYSHEV, *Opt. i. Spektroskopiya*, 15: 253.

"Luminescence of Uranyl Phthalocyanine", G. N. LIALIN and G. I. KOBYSHEV, *Doklady Akad. Nauk S.S.S.R.*, 148: 1053.

"Energy Transmission from a Uranyl Cation to Phthalocyanine", G. I. KOBYSHEV, G. N. LIALIN, and A. N. TERENIN, *Doklady Akad. Nauk S.S.S.R.*, 148: 1294.

"Effect of Secondary Processes on Luminescence Attenuation in Uranyl", D. S. UMREIKO, *Doklady Akad. Nauk Belorussk. S.S.S.R.*, 1: 237.

"Temperature Dependence and Nature of Electronic Uranyl Absorption", L. V. VOLOD'DO, A. N. SEVCHENKO, and D. S. UMREIKO, *Izv. Akad. Nauk S.S.S.R.*, *Ser. Fiz.*, 27: 651.

"Electronic Absorption Spectra of Uranyl Phosphate and Oxalate", K. V. NARASIMHAM, *J. Mol. Spectr.*, 11: 128.

"Bond Lengths in Uranyl Salts", H. R. HOEKSTRA, *Inorg. Chem.*, 2: 492.

"Determination of the U—O Force Constant in Uranyl Ion", U. Y. KHARITONOV and U. A. BUSLAYEV, *Opt. i. Spektroskopiya*, 14: 586.

"Hydrolysis of U(VI). Absorption Spectra of Chloride and Perchlorate Solutions", R. M. RUSH and J. S. JOHNSON, *J. Phys. Chem.*, 67: 821.

"Uranyl-Sensitized Photodecomposition of Organic Acids in Solution", G. E. HECKLER, A. E. TAYLOR, C. JENSEN, D. PERCIVAL, R. JENSEN, P. FUNG, *J. Phys. Chem.*, 67: 1.

1962

"Fine Structure of the Absorption Spectra of Uranyl Compounds", B. JEŻOWSKA-TRZEBIATOWSKA and A. BARTECKI, *Spectrochim. Acta*, 18: 799.

"Coordination Compounds of Uranyl Acetate with Organic Acids: Mandelic and Lactic", C. S. PANDE and S. K. MISRA, *J. Prakt, Chem.*, 17: 5.

"Fluorescence Spectra of Uranyl Phosphate and Oxalate", K. V. NARASIMHAM and V. R. RAO, *Spectrochim. Acta*, 18: 1055.

"Circular Dichroism and Optical Activity of Sodium Uranyl Acetate Single Crystals", M. S. BRODIN and Y. O. DOVGY, *Opt. i. Spektroskopiya*, 12: 285.

"Exciton Absorption Spectrum of Sodium Uranyl Acetate Single Crystal", M. S. Brodin and Y. O. Dovgy, *Ukrain. Fiz. Zhur.*, **7**: 31.

"Infrared Spectra of Intracomplex Uranyl Compounds with Schiff Bases and Determination of UO Bond Length", V. V. Zelentsov, *Doklady Akad. Nauk S.S.S.R.*, **146**: 97.

"Absorption Spectra of Uranyl Acetate and Nitrate", K. V. Narasimham, *J. Sci. Ind. Res. (India)*, **21B**: 468.

"Synthesis and Molecular Spectroscopy of Anhydrous Uranyl Nitrate", B. Jeżowska-Trzebiatowska and B. Kedzia, *Bull. Acad. Polon. Sci., Ser. Sci.-Chim.*, **10**: 213, 275.

"Spectroscopic Characteristics of Anhydrous and Hexahydrate Uranyl Nitrate", B. Jeżowska-Trzebiatowska, A. Bartecki, and B. Kedzia, *Bull Acad. Polon. Sci., Ser. Sci.-Chim.*, **10**: 433.

1961

"Effect of Secondary Processes on the Spectral-luminescent Characteristics of Uranyl Compounds", L. V. Volod'do, A. N. Sevchenko, and D. S. Umreiko, *Vest. Akad Nauk Belorussk. S.S.S.R., Ser Fiz.*, **1961**, No. **1**: 75 and No. **2**: 64.

"Kinetic Studies of the Photochemical Reduction of Uranyl Sulfate in the Presence of α-Hydroxy-isobutyric Acid", K. Pan and W. Wong, *J. Chinese Chem. Soc. (Taiwan)*, **8**: 1.

"Synthesis and X-ray data of Magnesium Uranyl Sulfate", N. S. Rocha, *Anais Acad. Brasil Cienc.*, **32**: 341.

"Luminescence of Crystals Surface-activated with Uranyl", G. I. Kobyshev, *Izvest. Akad. Nauk S.S.S.R., Ser. Fiz.*, **25**: 542.

"Luminescence of LiF Crystals activated with Uranyl Nitrate", E. P. Alexeeva, *Izvest. Akad. Nauk S.S.S.R., Ser Fiz.*, **25**: 545.

"Solvent Effect in Absorption Spectra of Uranyl Nitrate", B. Jeżowska-Trzebiatowska and A. Bartecki, *Bull. Acad. Polon. Sci., Ser. Sci.-Chim.*, **9**: 87.

"Vinyl Polymerization photosensitized by Uranyl Ions", V. Mahadevan and M. Santappa, *J. Polymer Sci.*, **50**: 361.

"Ligation Effects on the Infrared Spectrum of the Uranyl Ion", S. P. McGlynn, J. K. Smith, and W. C. Neely, *J. Chem. Phys.*, **35**: 105.

"The Electronic Structure of Uranyl", M. E. Dyatkina, V. P. Markov. I. V. Tsapkina, and Yu. N. Mikhailov, *Zhur. Neorg. Khim.*, **6**: 575.

1960

"Fluorescence Spectra of Solutions of Uranyl Nitrate at Liquid Air Temperature", D. D. Pant and D. P. Khandelwal, *Proc. Indian Acad. Sci.*, **51A**: 60.

"Infrared Absorption of Uranyl in Organic Solvents. Spectra of Coordination Bound Water in Hydrated Uranyl Nitrate in the Region of Valence Vibration Frequencies", V. M. Vdovenko and D. N. Suglobov, *Zhur. Fiz. Khim.*, **34**: 51.

AUTHOR INDEX

359

DIÉNART, F. 243
DITTRICH, C. 273, 281, 288
DOUNCE, A. L. 99, 136
DREISCH, T. 20
DUNCAN, A. B. F. 12, 13, 19, 30, 32, 37, 40, 41, 44, 47, 48, 49, 50, 55, 56, 57, 58, 62, 63, 64, 69, 70, 71, 72, 79, 90, 107, 207, 343, 344, 345

EAGER, R. L. 31, 34
EBELMEN, J. J. 264, 266
EISENSTEIN, J. C. 335, 337, 343
ELLINGER, F. H. 181
ELLIOTT, R. J. 337, 341
EPHRAIM, F. 85, 87
EPSTEIN, L. F. 321
EULER, H. 257, 315
EVANS, H. T. 5

FANKUCHEN, I. 2
FANTA, P. 99
FAY, H. 245, 257, 263, 265, 266, 300, 314
FELDMAN, I. 101, 136, 137
FLAGG, J. F. 99
FOLEY, R. T. 132, 133, 135
FORBES, G. S. 282, 284, 285, 286, 288, 293, 295, 297
FÖRSTER 255
FRANCK 8, 213, 237, 255
FREYMANN, M. 12, 18, 19
FREYMANN, R. 12, 18, 19, 21, 22
FRONDEL, C. 3

GALANIN, M. D. 227, 228
GATEHOUSE, B. M. 26, 29, 30, 31, 36, 38, 165, 168, 169, 183
GAUDECHON, H. 297
GAVIOLA, E. 195, 200, 201, 210
GERMANN, F. E. E. 84
GHOSH, J. C. 123, 125, 126, 127, 128, 129, 130, 262, 270, 281, 282, 298, 299, 300, 301, 302, 303, 304, 306, 307, 315, 319, 320, 322, 323
GHOSH, S. 332
GIANNONI, G. 165, 166
GOBRECHT, H. 198, 206
GORDON, B. E. 73, 76, 84
GORDON, N. E. 256, 286, 287

GRETZINGER, B. 198, 206
GUILMART, T. 18, 89
GULVADY, S. 313, 314, 324, 325, 332, 333, 334
GUREVICH, M. M. 201
GUY, J. S. 115

HABER 237
HAHN, D. 198, 206
HAKOMORI, S. 124, 315
HALL, L. A. 198, 207, 209
HARPER, P. E. 5
HARTLEY, W. N. 142
HAVILL, J. R. 101, 136, 137
HATT, E. C. 231, 235, 237, 239, 246, 247, 248, 249, 250, 253, 315, 318
HAYAKAWA, S. 84, 85, 87
HEIDT, L. J. 284, 286, 324, 325, 328, 329, 330, 331, 332, 333
HEIN, F. 200
HEISENBERG 208
HENRI, V. 120, 121, 122, 123, 126, 129, 262, 270, 274, 281
HILDEBRANDT, R. A. 143, 147
HIRATA, M. 84, 85, 87
HOARDE, J. L. 4
HOFMANN, K. A. 246
HOWES, H. L. 12, 14, 15, 16, 17, 19, 41, 43, 44, 45, 46, 56, 57, 60, 61, 62, 64, 66, 67, 68, 71, 73, 75, 76, 79, 80, 81, 82, 83, 84, 85, 86, 90, 191, 192, 193, 194, 195, 198, 199
HUGUS, Z. Z. 336, 339
HUTCHISON, C. A. 337

ISHIDATE, M. 162, 164, 165
ISSIDORIDIS, A. 243

JETTE, E. 224, 279
JEZOWSKA-TRZEBIATOWSKA, B. 160, 161, 170
JOHNSON, J. S. 132
JONES, L. H. 27, 28, 29, 112, 114, 115, 120, 140, 141, 142, 179, 180, 181
JØRGENSEN, C. K. 349

KAPLAN, L. 143, 145, 146, 147, 153, 155, 156, 178

SUBJECT INDEX*

* The symbol **A** denotes the Addendum.

363